Health Services Research
And R&D
In Perspective

Health Services Research
And R&D
In Perspective

Edited by
E. Evelyn Flook
and
Paul J. Sanazaro, M.D.

Health Administration Press

Contributors

Faye G. Abdellah, R.N., Ed.D.
Acting Deputy Director
National Center for Health Services Research
    and Development (NCHSRD)
Health Services and Mental Health Administration
Department of Health, Education, and Welfare
    Dr. Abdellah is also Chief Nurse Officer of the U. S. Public
Health Service. Prior to coming to the National Center, she
administered the research grants program of the Division of
Nursing, Bureau of Health Manpower Education, National
Institutes of Health. Dr. Abdellah is author and co-author of a
number of publications on nursing research, including *Better
Patient Care Through Nursing Research.*

Thomas W. Bice, Ph.D.
Associate Professor
Department of Social Relations, and
Senior Research Associate
Center for Metropolitan Planning and Research
The Johns Hopkins University
    Dr. Bice is an active health services research investigator,
with particular interest in research on local management bod-
ies in the health services field. He is currently a member of the
Health Services Developmental Grants Study Section.

Duncan W. Clark, M.D.
Professor and Chairman
Department of Environmental Medicine and Community
    Health
State University of New York
Downstate Medical Center
    Dr. Clark is a former member of the Health Services Research Study Section and former Chairman of the NCHSRD Health Services Research Training Committee. He is also Past President of the Association of Teachers of Preventive Medicine and co-editor and co-author of a textbook on preventive medicine.

Robert L. Eichhorn, Ph.D.
Professor
Department of Sociology
Purdue University
    Dr. Eichhorn is Director of the Department's Health Services Research and Training Program. He spent two years with the National Center for Health Services Research and Development, serving first as Director of its Social and Economics Analysis Division and later as Director of its Special R&D Projects Division. He is presently Chairman of the Health Services Research Study Section.

E. Evelyn Flook
Associate Director
National Center for Health Services Research and
    Development
Health Services and Mental Health Administration
Department of Health, Education, and Welfare
    Before joining the staff of the National Center at the time of its establishment, Miss Flook was Chief of the Research Grants Branch of the Divisions of Community Health Service and Medical Care Administration. Prior to coming to the Center, she participated in a wide range of intramural studies of health services administration.

Robert J. Haggerty, M.D.
Professor and Chairman
Department of Pediatrics
School of Medicine and Dentistry
The University of Rochester

Dr. Haggerty has long been an active investigator in the field of health services research, and has contributed importantly to the field. He is currently a member of the National Advisory Health Services Council. Formerly, he was a member and Chairman of the Health Services Research Study Section.

Elizabeth L. Ryan, M.S.P.H.
Liaison Officer
National Center for Health Services Research and
    Development
Health Services and Mental Health Administration
Department of Health, Education, and Welfare

Miss Ryan was formerly Executive Secretary of the Center's Research Scientist Awards and Fellowship Committee.

Paul J. Sanazaro, M.D.
Associate Deputy Administrator for Development
Health Services and Mental Health Administration
Department of Health, Education, and Welfare

Prior to becoming the first Director of the National Center for Health Services Research and Development, Dr. Sanazaro was on the faculty of the University of California (S.F.) and then the University of Illinois School of Medicine. He was a member, then Chairman, of the Health Services Research Study Section. He has conducted research on methods of evaluating the quality of medical care.

The several authors have worked as an editorial committee in the preparation of this book, critically reviewing and commenting on the individual chapters. However, responsibility for the views expressed in each chapter rests with the respective authors.

Acknowledgments

The authors are indebted to a number of consultants who provided personal briefings on significant events and their background during various periods in the evolution of health services research. Those who gave generously of their time and knowledge are: Odin W. Anderson, Ph.D., Lester Breslow, M.D., George Bugbee, J. Douglas Colman, Lester Evans, M.D., I. S. Falk, Ph.D., Herschel Griffin, M.D., Jack C. Haldeman, M.D., James Hamilton, Margaret Klem, Andrew Pattullo, George S. Perrott, Allen Pond, Louis Reed, Ph.D., Milton I. Roemer, M.D., William Schottstaedt, M.D., Cecil G. Sheps, M.D., and Myron Wegman, M.D. Their personal views and assessments have enriched greatly the perspectives of the authors.

Without the excellent assistance of Mrs. Alice Wallis and Mrs. Betty Wilmot, the task of the authors would have been much more difficult. For their unfailing support throughout the preparation of the book, the authors are deeply grateful.

Preface

Health services research and health services R&D as defined areas of investigation and innovation have evolved from the merging of many more limited streams of inquiry and experimentation. Some of these may be traced back for more than half a century. Others have emerged within the past two years. The purpose of this volume is to bring together these separate, but related, currents and to show how they have eventually converged to form the broader field of health services research and the new entity, health services R&D.

Other review books and articles have delineated the history and impact of selected segments of the total effort. By using a wider-angle lens, and describing the substantive transformation in health services research which has taken place over the years, the authors of this volume present an account of the development of the entire field.

Critical events at particular times have often revealed, occasionally created, major problems in the delivery of health services. This book shows how research has responded — in terms of the problems addressed, types of studies generated, and methods employed. Shifts in emphasis and sources of support, changes in research settings and in the kinds of investigators involved, and a gradual linking of independent lines of inquiry characterize the evolution of health services research as here portrayed. Clearly, this is a dynamic field whose continued growth and cumulative impact on health policy will determine the rational base for national efforts to achieve equity in health care.

E. Evelyn Flook and
Paul J. Sanazaro, M.D.

Contents

Introduction

The purpose of this summary volume is to orient new-comers to the field of health services research — whether students, faculty, established investigators in other fields or administrators — by providing a chronological bibliography of illustrative studies in the major areas of health services. It is not meant to be a definitive treatise on the subject nor a source book of information gleaned by research. Rather, its aim is to summarize and place in perspective the evolution of health services research and R&D as we know them today by looking retrospectively at their historical development and prospectively to the new directions being charted for the future.

Substantive findings of individual studies and conclusions of the investigators are not discussed unless they form a base for additional research. Citations are limited to publications in the 20th century, through early 1973.

The first two chapters of this book describe what has been done, by whom, and when, in the evolution of health services research in the United States. Beyond identifying the principals, they aim at conveying the sense of a succession of stages in the development of this research movement. Chapter III is a period piece, a narrative account of efforts to apply health services research as public policy at a critical time in the Nation's history. All references in these chapters are illustrative, and in no sense complete. The next three chapters examine the field from three different points of view: the academic community, the several disciplines involved in health services research, and the National Center for Health Services

Research and Development. Chapter VII is a brief overview of the international health services research effort.

Probably the most difficult task the authors faced was limiting the size of the volume and the scope of its coverage, in order that it serve its stated purpose. Certain decisions had to be made to guide the selection and the selective omission of material.

Within the limits we have imposed, health services research does not include the areas of clinical research or research on the education or training of members of the several health professions. Although highly relevant to health services research, they have almost always been separate. Manpower studies included here pertain only to supply, distribution, and utilization. The entire area of research in mental health services for the mentally ill has developed as a separate entity from general health services research and, regrettably, the two have never been integrated.

The historical picture presented in Chapter I is based on published books, reports, and articles deriving from research. Philosophical and exhortatory essays on issues and public policy of the day are not included. Neither are reports of proceedings of seminars, conferences, or symposia addressed to various aspects of the delivery of health care included unless new research methods or concepts are introduced, those in use are clarified or refined, or previous research of others is compiled and analyzed within a new framework.

Analytical articles and volumes that discuss a pertinent subject with insight are included, provided they are built upon data, either presented or documented by reference.

Routine, recurring compilations of statistics have been omitted. Although these reports provide valuable resource material, they are not the products of original research of the type covered by this volume. Reports of Congressional Committees, for which existing resource material has been assembled as documentary background, have not been included in our literature search.

Research publications cited in Chapter I have been classified according to 13 selected categories. They are:

Health Manpower
Health Facilities

Organization and Administration of Health Services
    Public programs
    The private sector
Evaluation and Quality of Health Services
Utilization of Health Services
Economics, Costs, and Financing of Health Care
Social-Behavioral Aspects of Health Care
Nursing Health Services Research
Dental Health Services Research
Pharmacy-Related Health Services Research
Health Services Technology
Research Methods
The Emerging Concept of Health Services Research

These categories are not mutually exclusive. Some represent a disciplinary approach, some a component of health care. Thus, a single research report might fit under several groupings. In such instances, the decision as to its placement was based on the stated or perceived primary aim of the research. The last two categories deal specifically with research methods and concepts and therefore may be cross-referenced to earlier categories.

The reference grid (Appendix) was constructed to relate the growth of health services research to the critical historical events in the delivery of health services which occurred within the same time frame. Some of the relationships of the research produced to this backdrop of issues and events are analyzed in a case study in Chapter III.

Subsequent chapters are essentially free standing, each developing the theme suggested by its title.

Chapter I
Health Services Research:
Origins and Milestones

E. Evelyn Flook and Paul J. Sanazaro*

Today, those newly entering the field of health services research—whether as students, teachers, investigators, or research administrators—are able to address an identified area of study and demonstration (1–8). Although no precise definition of health services research has been generally agreed upon, its broad purpose is to produce knowledge that will contribute to improvement of the delivery of health care.

Health services research is concerned with problems in the organization, staffing, financing, utilization, and evaluation of health services. This is in contrast to biomedical research, which is oriented to the etiology, diagnosis, and treatment of disease. Health services research subsumes both medical care and patient care research. It could well be termed "socio-medical" research.

Currently, there is nationwide attention to three major goals in the health care system: equity of access, moderation of costs, and assurance of quality. Health services research is being challenged to produce a body of knowledge which will provide sufficient predictability in health services to support major

* Assisted by Faye G. Abdellah and Elizabeth L. Ryan. Dr. Abdellah prepared the section, Nursing Health Services Research. Miss Ryan developed preliminary drafts of the sections, Dental Health Services Research and Pharmacy-Related Health Services Research.

1

policy and operating decisions at various levels of the health services structure. The relationship of health services research (HSR) to health services research and development (R&D) in meeting this challenge has been described by Sanazaro (9). Briefly, health services research addresses itself to an understanding of the underlying factors and processes of health services. Through such systematic research, new knowledge, theories, and methods are produced on which to base long-range plans and policies for continued improvement of the delivery of health care.

Health services R&D emerged as a distinctive activity in 1969 as part of the program of the National Center for Health Services Research and Development. It is directed to improving the organization, delivery, and financing of health care through the introduction and testing, in real community situations, of carefully designed innovations in specific aspects of health care delivery. Among these are health manpower, health care facilities, methods of financing health care, health care technology, methods for assuring the quality of care, and health services data systems. Health services R&D brings about practical desirable changes in health services in the short-run, within a limited time span. Chapter VI describes its evolution.

The conceptual framework of HSR has emerged gradually over the past 50 years, although its present definitive shape owes much to work of the past decade. The scope and content of the HSR concept, as we presently know it, have been determined largely by progressively combining previously disparate subject areas into more meaningful relationships. Some of the elements of health services have been studied for many years, but in isolated or unidimensional ways, unlike the more comprehensive, interrelated study they receive in HSR today.

To a person unfamiliar with the field, some knowledge of its history is essential for understanding the present. Acquiring this knowledge can be an overwhelming task. Even for the initiated, it is difficult to place in perspective the vast body of research literature that has been produced.

The purpose here is to trace research within each substantive category to its origin, thereby identifying the roots of health services research. By highlighting important milestones in the growth of each category, a cumulative perspective of the broader field will be provided. Health manpower research and health facilities research appear to be most deeply rooted in time.

HEALTH MANPOWER RESEARCH

Perhaps the most pervasive problems affecting the delivery of health care today are the shortage and maldistribution of physicians providing primary care and the explosive proliferation of new categories of health manpower. Because the former limit our ability to improve access to care, and the latter is compounding the problem of an already labor-intensive field, health services research today is especially concerned with rationalizing the use of old and new categories of health manpower in all settings.

Problems in manpower are not new. In the early years, the chief concern of studies was to determine the extent to which less qualified persons were practicing in the physician's stead. Anderson (10) credits the Chicago Medical Society with one of the earliest studies of the century in the health services field. In 1908, this organization, in collaboration with Hull House, sponsored a birth record survey of midwifery in Chicago (11). A second study, five years later, found that almost half of the 40,000 births in Chicago in 1913 were registered by midwives and the remainder by physicians (12).

The famed Flexner Report (13) was published in 1910. This study was concerned primarily with the quality of medical education. By strict definition, it does not fall within the boundaries of health services research set for this volume.[1] But the force of its impact on numbers and qualifications of physicians has so markedly influenced the delivery of health care that it must be mentioned.

In 1932, two reports of the Committee on the Costs of Medical Care addressed the use of nonmedical personnel in the provision of medical care. One reviewed the use of midwives, chiropodists, and optometrists (14). The other was a study of sectarian medical practice (15). All of these early studies were descriptive, fact-finding surveys.

---

[1] See p. 1.

SUPPLY AND DISTRIBUTION

During the 1940's, Mountin, Pennell, and associates made a series of studies of the location and movement of physicians in the United States during the 15-year period, 1923–1938 (16–20). The purpose of these studies was to acquire a better understanding of where physicians are likely to locate, how long they are apt to remain in the same place, the types of communities to which they tend to migrate, and other factors affecting the supply and distribution of medical manpower. Following these analyses, the same group developed an estimate of the number of physicians required to serve geographic areas of defined characteristics (21).

These were all very simple secondary analyses of data, in sharp contrast to the multidimensional schematic framework proposed by Butter for health manpower research some 20 years later (22). The limited data available for the early studies pointed up the need for more complete quantitative data on the supply and distribution of health manpower, not only for physicians, but for other professions as well. The Public Health Service responded to this need in 1952 by initiating the Health Manpower Source Book Series. In 1967, Theodore and Sutter reported the results of the first periodic survey of physicians by the American Medical Association (23).

Fein assessed the problem of physician shortage within the framework of economics (24). Fuchs and associates studied the surgical work loads of general surgeons, using a weighting system similar to "price weights" as in general economics studies (25). Schonfeld, Heston, and Falk (26) reported their estimates of the shortage of primary care physicians (pediatricians and internists). Their method, a modification of that used in the Lee-Jones report of 1933 (27), was based on clinical judgments of the content of good primary care and the frequency of conditions requiring it.

UTILIZATION

To cope with the short supply of dentists, experimental programs were established to expand the functions of dental assistants. These experiments were aimed at more effective utilization of the limited number of dentists available. A study reported by Klein (28) in 1944 demonstrated that the skilled use of dental assistants enabled the dentist to treat more patients. A few years later, Klein's findings were corroborated by Waterman and Knutson (29-31). Subsequent studies by the U. S. Public Health Service over the next two decades (32-34) and by the Royal Canadian Dental Corps (35-37), the General Dental Council of Great Britain (38), and the U. S. Navy Dental Corps (39) during the latter part of that period, brought refinements to the earlier work. By experimenting with various combinations of dentists, technicians, and arrangement of chairs, maximum productivity was achieved. This experience in the provision of dental services blazed the trail for similar experimentation by other health professions.

Efforts to expand the productivity of physicians through use of specially trained assistants were not initiated until the latter half of the 1960's when the effects of maldistribution of medical manpower in geography and specialty became acute. Since that time, there has been a steadily growing body of experience in the use of different types of physician extenders in a variety of settings. Two major types have emerged: the nurse practitioner (pediatric nurse practitioner, school nurse practitioner, family nurse practitioner—Primex, etc.) and the physician's assistant—predominantly retrained medical corpsmen discharged from military service (Medex) and their civilian counterparts. Physicians' extenders fill various roles, always under the supervision of a physician, in private doctors' offices, clinics, home, school, and hospital settings. These assisting personnel are trained specifically for their roles and functions. Specialty technical assistants such as x-ray technicians, urologic assistants, orthopedic assistants, etc., have been omitted from consideration here because both their training and scope of operation focus upon a particular expertise rather than the broader area of health services delivery.

The pediatric nurse practitioners are currently the most advanced prototypes of mid-level medical worker. Time-motion studies by Bergman, et al., in local areas suggested much of the practicing pediatrician's time was consumed by minor medical and many non-medical tasks (40). In 1967, the American Academy of Pediatrics conducted a nationwide survey of how practitioners of pediatrics utilize their time, what characteristics of practice are associated with task delegation, and how pediatricians view task delegation in ambulatory care. Yankauer, Connelly, and Feldman were responsible for the conduct and reporting of this survey (41–45).

One of the first pediatric nurse practitioner programs was developed by Silver and Ford at the University of Colorado. Preliminary evaluations of their performance in clinical settings have been reported (46–49). The use of nurses for ambulatory care of adults in a clinic-based project at the University of Kansas Medical Center was systematically evaluated by means of randomized controlled studies and reported by Lewis and Resnick in 1967 (50,51). Improved end results of care and lowering of per patient costs were demonstrated. Charney has also reported a controlled study of the pediatric nurse practitioner (52).

In 1969, Patterson reported a time and motion study of six pediatric office assistants and, with Bergman and Wedgewood, a study of parent reaction to the concept of pediatric assistants (53,54). Other studies of attitude toward the use of physicians' assistants were those of Coye and Hansen (55) and McCormack, Allen, and Livers (56).

Yankauer, et al., conducted a national mail survey of obstetrical and gynecological specialists to determine opinion and practice in delegation of patient services (57). They found that opinion favors delegation consistent with the nurse, not midwife, role. In practice, however, there was relatively little delegation of patient services in office practice. More delegation occurred in hospitals without house staff than in those with house staff.

Legal issues have arisen in the use of nurse obstetric assistants (58). In spite of favorable results in the experimental use of such personnel in a rural California county, the State Medical Association declined to endorse a change in the hospital licensing regulations to permit nurse obstetrical assistants to provide delivery services in selected hospitals of the State.

Estes (59) has reported on the experience of Duke University's physician's assistant training program and Yankauer, et al. (60), have assessed the outcomes and service impact of a pediatric nurse practitioner training program.

Unfortunately, many innovations in the use of health manpower have been introduced without provision being made for objective evaluation, and no comparative analyses of results have been reported. In order to remedy this deficiency and obtain objective evidence from which to judge the success of alternative models and uses of personnel, the National Center for Health Services Research and Development supported a number of physician extender projects that were to be evaluated by use of a uniform protocol (61).

Several investigators have studied the use of combinations of substitutive personnel rather than a single type. Rogers and associates (62,63) found that a team of nonphysician personnel, under supervision, could assume some of the duties usually performed by physicians. This increased the effectiveness of the physician and permitted expansion of the scope of services beyond that usually provided in a general practice. Riddick, Bryan, et al., examined the practices and attitudes of internists with respect to office use of a variety of allied health professionals (64). Gilpatrick and Corliss studied the occupational structure of New York Municipal Hospitals (65).

The effect of licensing and certification requirements upon the changing role and functioning of health professionals in the delivery of health care today is a matter of increasing importance. Shryock's historical study of medical licensing in America (66) and Roemer's review and analysis of current licensure laws (67) in relation to emerging patterns of health care delivery provide valuable baseline information. The resolution of legal questions surrounding the introduction of nurse practitioners and physician's assistants remains a pressing policy issue.

HEALTH FACILITIES RESEARCH

The American Medical Association gave early attention to obtaining, in a systematic fashion, information concerning the character and distribution of hospital facilities. Its first nationwide survey of hospitals was made in 1909. By the mid-1930's, however, there was a growing need for more comprehensive knowledge, not only of facilities and their use, but also of the financial and employment conditions within such institutions.

Through the Business Census of Hospitals—undertaken by the United States Public Health Service in connection with the National Health Survey in 1935—data were assembled con-

cerning the financial structure of hospitals and opportunities
for employment within them. This Census was a unit of the
Census of American Business for 1935, which was conducted
by the Department of Commerce (68). Between 1937 and
1942, Mountin and colleagues analyzed the data obtained and
released some dozen reports (69-80). As an outgrowth of this
work, Mountin, Pennell, and Hoge developed the concept of
health service areas for general hospitals and health centers
(81). This was a forerunner to the provision for areawide
planning for hospital care contained in the Hill-Burton Hospital Survey and Construction Act, enacted in 1946. During the
next five years, the service area concept was further refined by
Mountin and Greve, with emphasis on the coordination of
public health areas and hospital facilities (82).

In 1944, the American Hospital Association established a
Commission on Hospital Care as an independent body to
survey the Nation's hospital needs and advise on the part
hospitals should play in medical care of the future. The Commission's work was financed by the Commonwealth Fund, the
W. K. Kellogg Foundation, and the National Foundation for
Infantile Paralysis, with professional and technical staff assistance from the U. S. Public Health Service. The Commission's
study, directed by A. C. Bachmeyer, initiated the first complete
inventory of the Nation's hospitals as part of a broad study of
economic, geographic, and population factors.

The Commission was primarily concerned with an evaluation of the general hospital's function as a community institution and its role in the care of all types of illness. Literature searches were made on the historical development, legal
status, methods of finance, and administrative and operational
relationships of governmental and nongovernmental hospitals
and health agencies. The importance of individual State studies was emphasized by the Commission. A pilot study was
made in Michigan by Commission staff. Procedures and methods of study were developed and a basic plan outlined for that
State. These then served as a work pattern for study groups of
other States. The Commission's report, *Hospital Care in the
United States,* contains a series of conclusions, principles, and
recommendations which served as a guide for the provision of
more effective hospital care (83). Throughout the nation, the

Commission found hospitals distributed haphazardly, depending primarily upon the availability of local funds. Usually, people in rural areas were not receiving adequate care. The Commission concluded that more general hospital beds were needed, and that additional facilities should be built in areas of greatest need. It also recommended that Federal funds should be used to stimulate hospital construction. The Commission's report had a strong influence on the development and enactment of Federal legislation authorizing a nationwide hospital survey and construction program (the Hill-Burton program). Among individual State hospital studies, that of New York (84) is probably best known.

The Commission on Hospital Care did not address the problems of financing hospital care. Consequently, in 1951, a second commission (Commission on Financing of Hospital Care) was appointed by the American Hospital Association to make a detailed study of this area. (See section on Economics, Costs, and Financing of Health Care, p. 32 for report, *Financing of Medical Care,* issued in three volumes in 1954 and 1955.)

Corwin's book, *The American Hospital* (85), was one of a series of monographs prepared for the New York Academy of Medicine's Committee on Medicine and the Changing Order, established in the mid-'40's. Two books of importance to the hospital field appeared in 1956. Burling, Lentz, and Wilson reported a study of the organization and relationships of hospital personnel (86). Rosenfeld and Makover published a report on the experience of the Rochester Regional Hospital Council (87). Established as a demonstration by the Commonwealth Fund, this was one of the first regional hospital councils.

Several years later, Lembcke, Hermansen, and Poland proposed a standard method for measuring hospital capacity (88) and Thompson examined hospital recovery room usage as a basis for designing intensive care units (89). Subsequently, with Pelletier, he also developed an index for measuring design efficiency (90,91) and with Fetter studied the relationship between patients' waiting time and doctors' idle time in an outpatient setting (92).

The original Hill-Burton Hospital Survey and Construction Act of 1946 was amended in 1950 to provide for the support of research in hospital administration. An appropriation for this purpose, however, was not made until five years later. At that time, the Public Health Service initiated a research and demonstration grants program and established the Hospital Facilities Study Section. Stimulated in part by this program, the volume of health facilities research grew greatly during the 1960's.

More research has been reported since 1960 than in the prior three-score years. Examples of areas studied were: staff organization, administration, and functioning of hospitals (93-108); design of hospital nursing units (109,110); hospital information and communication systems (111-113); staff interrelationships, morale, and role perceptions (114,115);[2] demand for and use of hospital facilities (116-124); planning for hospitals (125-129); and hospital mergers and shared services (130-133).[3]

Unfortunately, the results of these many studies have not been well integrated and only recently has an assessment of this massive literature been attempted. A critical review and partial synthesis of recent social-psychological research on hospital organization is presented in the new volume edited by Georgopoulos (134).

During the late 1950's and early '60's, the intramural research effort of the Division of Hospital and Medical Facilities of the Public Health Service was concentrated on testing the concept of progressive patient care, a way of grouping patients by their common medical and nursing needs into intensive care, intermediate care, and self-care areas. A basic two-year study was conducted at the Memorial Hospital, Manchester, Connecticut. This led to several publications (135-139) which have been widely used.

The progressive patient care concept attracted widespread interest. During the summer of 1962, a research team of the Bureau of Hospital Administration, University of Michigan, began a three-year study at McPherson Community Health Center in Howell, Michigan, encompassing all the elements of progressive patient care. As part of this project, an anthology

---

[2] Additional references in section on Nursing Health Services Research, pp. 42-49.

[3] For the most part, reports on hospital mergers and shared services were retrospective accounts of individual community experiences, with no predetermined criteria or design for evaluation.

of pertinent articles was assembled and edited by Weeks and Griffith, and published by the University in 1964 (140). The full history of the experiment was published in 1967 (141).

In response to the growing public concern with the spiraling costs of health care, a number of economists were attracted to the broad field of health services research during the 1960's and early '70's. Since institutional care is the most expensive single element of total health service costs, this area offered a particular challenge to the theories and methods of economics research. During this period, economists were progressively refining general theories and methods to accommodate the unique differences between the field of health services and other "market places." Prominent during this period were the studies of hospital costs and production of services of the two Feldsteins—Martin (142,143) and Paul (144,145,147,152), of Berry (146), Carr (147,148), Cohen (149,150), Francisco (151), Long (152), Stevens (153), Muller and Worthington (154), and Mann and Yett (155).

Other modern hospital research of note was Hamilton's *Patterns of Hospital Ownership and Control* (156) and Klarman's application of microeconomic principles and techniques in his studies of hospital care in New York City (157,158). Flagle's operations research at Johns Hopkins Hospital (159) was aimed at the optimizing of staff, equipment, and procedures for a hospital nursing unit. Blumberg (160) also applied operations research principles to the operation of hospitals and determination of bed needs. Shuman, Wolfe, and Hardwick (161) developed an industrial engineering model which can be used to predict and evaluate hospital costs. Belknap and Steinle published *The Community and Its Hospitals—A Comparative Analysis* (162). The landmark study of McNerney, et al. (163) was not limited to health facilities research. It will be referred to again in later sections, but is mentioned here because of the important sections on hospitals and allied institutions and accounting and finance.[4]

Nursing homes and homes for the aged, as well as hospitals, have been the subject of occasional study since the mid- '50's (164-171). Studies have also been addressed to the problems of hospital-nursing home relationships (172,173).

---

[4] For additional pertinent references, see sections on Economics, Costs, and Financing of Health Care and Nursing Health Services Research.

Of the many factors contributing to the escalation of the costs of health care, several associated with the operation and management of hospitals proved amenable to modification by HSR&D and to prospective evaluation. These include shared services (174), mergers (175), and hospital discharge data (176–177a). These R&D projects are discussed in Chapter VI.

ORGANIZATION AND ADMINISTRATION OF HEALTH SERVICES

Because research on the organization and administration of publicly supported programs of health services followed an historical pattern almost directly opposite to that which evolved in the private sector, they will be discussed separately.

PUBLIC PROGRAMS

Public programs administered by State agencies, as well as those operated by units of local government—cities, counties, or some combination thereof—were the subject of early study. In 1914, at the request of the Council on Health and Public Instruction of the American Medical Association, Chapin began work on a survey of the activities, equipment, and accomplishments of the various State boards of health. The report of this study was published in 1915 by the American Medical Association (178). Six years later, Chapin followed his first study with a 50-year history of State and municipal control of disease (179).

In 1920, the American Public Health Association established a Committee on Municipal Health Department Practice. This Committee saw as its first need authentic information regarding the current procedures, practices, and expenditures of health departments serving American cities. With financial assistance from the Metropolitan Life Insurance Company, and assistance in data collection from the U. S. Public Health Service and American Red Cross, the Committee initiated a survey of health departments in 83 cities having a population of 100,000 or more. The report of this survey was published by the Public Health Service (180).

A second study, to update the information, was made in 1924. This time, instead of repeating the elaborate field surveys, authors closely associated with special activities, or who were recognized as authorities in their respective fields, prepared a series of monographs. The 1924 study included the 100 largest cities in the United States. This too was a cooperative endeavor of the APHA and the U. S. PHS (181).

At the request of the State and Provincial Health Authorities of North America, an exhaustive study of State health organizations was made by the International Health Division of the Rockefeller Foundation for use in connection with the third White House Conference on Child Health and Protection. Published in 1927, it was revised in 1932 (182,183). Both editions were published by the Public Health Service. In 1940 and again in 1950, the PHS had full responsibility for repeating this study in order that the data might be kept current. By that time, new fields of public health activity had developed both within the health department and within other official State agencies. Therefore, both the 1940 and 1950 studies were extended to include not only the functions of the main State health agency but also the health activities of all other official State agencies (184–186). These data were unique in this respect.

Prior to 1930, the Public Health Service, as well as several foundations, made a number of individual studies of health organization and administration in States and cities. These, however, were investigations made upon the request of the respective State and local health authorities because of specific problems. No extensive comparative studies were attempted.

Not until 1931, when the Office of Public Health Methods was established in the PHS under the direction of Dr. Joseph W. Mountin, was experimental work initiated in the development and testing of new administrative methods and procedures in health departments. Surveys of local health problems and community services during the 1930's included detailed analysis of selected operations in the programs of health agencies and experimental work in the development and testing of new administrative methods and procedures.

The studies conducted in Brunswick and Greensville Counties, Virginia; Forsyth County, North Carolina; Fairfax County, Virginia; and Montgomery County, Maryland, are examples of the work of this period in the field of local health administration (187,188). These studies were designed to relate the health needs of people living in rural areas to the manner in which county health departments operating under different plans of administration were meeting these problems. From studies of this type, it was possible to evaluate certain administrative methods and to adapt and reshape public health practices to meet changing requirements.

The requirements of public health organizations for meeting the special needs of children for health services were emphasized by the Report of the White House Conference on Child Health and Protection (189).

Both the Rockefeller Foundation and the Public Health Service regarded the county health department movement as the outstanding health service development for the rural population during the quarter century 1908–1933. Prior to that time, cities and towns had developed organized public health services, but very little had been done for the rural areas. A record of this development was compiled by Ferrell and Mead of the Rockefeller Foundation staff (190). This history did not address the variation in stability of these county health organizations, but a concurrent PHS analysis of the factors which influenced growth and survival (191) served as a companion study. Ten years later a similar study was made of joint city-county health units (192).

As part of the National Health Survey in 1935–36, information was collected on the activities of all types of health agencies in 94 selected counties. From this body of data, further analyses were made of the variations in form and services of public health organizations (193,194).

With passage of the Federal Social Security Act in 1935, establishment of local health departments gained considerable momentum. The early studies cited above contributed useful information for their guidance. It soon became clear, however, that development of a nationwide network of organized health services required a basic plan. The Committee on Administrative Practice of the APHA turned its attention to this problem. *Local Health Units for the Nation* (195), produced by Emerson and Luginbuhl serving as staff to the Committee, was one of the most provocative publications of its time. This report outlined a pattern for complete coverage of the continental United States with full-time local health units. It contained estimates of personnel required to staff these units and of the costs that would be involved in providing what were then known as the "basic 6" services. These were: vital statistics, communicable disease control, environmental sanitation, public health laboratory services, maternal and child health services, and public health education. This ambitious project, as well as other activities of the Committee on Administrative Practice, was supported by the Commonwealth Fund. Of particular note was the work of Walker and Randolph in the development of health department records (196). Mustard's *Government in Public Health* (197), prepared for the Committee on Medicine and the Changing Order of the New York Academy of Medicine, was also published by the Commonwealth Fund.

The device of Federal grants-in-aid, initiated in 1935, has served as a strong stimulus to expansion and improvement of State and local health services. During the 1940's, several investigations were made of the role and influence of Federal health grants (198,199) and of ways to improve the efficiency of their administration (200).

The several editions of *Community Health Organization* by Hiscock (201) and Hanlon's *Principles of Public Health Administration* (202) have been useful instruments for organizing and translating into plans for practical application selected findings from early research in administrative practice.

With the major shift toward disease-oriented categorical grants, there was a sharp decline in research directed to general organization and administration of publicly financed health programs. To some extent, concern with the latter was renewed by the National Commission on Community Health Services, established in 1962. However, since the Commission's interests and charter extended well beyond research directed to the organization and administration of the public sector of health services, its work will be considered in a later section, Chapter II, pp. 102–103.

Griffith (203) summarized the role of government in personal health care in his chapter of the study *Hospital and Medical Economics,* previously cited (163).

Reed's report of the Canadian hospital insurance program (204) discusses the role of that country's government in the provision of hospital care. Reed states, "One misreads the nature of these programs if he considers them merely as programs of hospital insurance. While they spread the risk of hospital costs, they go beyond insurance. Essentially they are programs for providing hospital care to the whole population."

THE PRIVATE SECTOR

With the exception of the pioneering study of *Dispensaries* by Davis and Warner in 1918 (205), and Davis' later *Clinics, Hospitals, and Health Centers*, (206), the Committee on the Costs of Medical Care was the only group until 1933 to engage in research directed to the organization and administration of the private sector of medical care. Although this Committee was basically concerned with the *costs* of medical care, it recognized that the need for care (sickness and disability), the receipt of care (utilization), and the costs of care were inextricably interrelated. Hence, the research program of CCMC was organized around three broad questions:

• What data are now available showing the incidence of disease and disability requiring medical services, and what are the established facilities[5] for dealing with them?

• What do existing services cost the people, and what return accrues to the physicians and other agents furnishing such services?

• What specifically organized facilities for medical care serving particular groups of the population may now be found, and how do they compare in adequacy and economy with unorganized services?

Because of the breadth of its work and its long-time influence, the initiative for and the conditions under which CCMC functioned warrant attention. This Committee, composed of 48 members, was a self-constituted voluntary body, financed by contributions from eight foundations. This pioneering group produced 28 reports between 1928 and 1933. Individual titles are distributed in this chapter among the categories of research which they address. Several dealt with a

---

[5] "Medical facilities" as defined by CCMC included the practitioners of medicine, dentistry, nursing, and pharmacy (health manpower), as well as health care institutions.

variety of organizational forms and methods for the delivery of medical services (207–213).

From 1933 until 1950 the primary subject of inquiry by those studying the organization of medical care was group medical practice. Investigators prominently identified with studies of this organizational entity were Rorem and Musser (214,215), Hunt and Goldstein (216–222), and the Bureau of Medical Economics of the American Medical Association (223,224).

During the next five years, the work of the Commission on Chronic Illness, which also dealt with organization of the private sector, held center stage. Established in 1949, the Commission was a successor to a Joint Committee on Chronic Disease formed in 1946 with representation from the American Hospital Association, American Medical Association, American Public Health Association, and American Public Welfare Association. All four organizations had experienced the pressure of the growing burden of chronic disease and disability. The National Health Assembly of 1948 recommended that the existing Joint Committee on Chronic Disease be continued and constituted as a national commission, and that its membership be expanded. The American Medical Association took the initiative to accomplish this. The Commission was in existence from 1949 until 1956. Its work was reported in four volumes, two of which (225,226) are particularly pertinent to the organization and administration of the private sector of health services. The other two encompass several interrelated categories of research, and have been classified under The Emerging Concept of HSR (see p. 76).

In addition to its four main volumes, the Commission, in collaboration with the Public Health Service, made a study of home care programs (227).

The following reports are illustrative of research published during the latter half of the 1950's on organization of the private sector for provision of health services: Hassinger *The Pattern of Medical Services for Incorporated Places of 500-or-more Population in Missouri, 1950* (228); Weinerman *An Appraisal of Medical Care in Group Health Centers* (229); Trussell *Hunterdon Medical Center* (230); Boulware *The Composition of Private Pediatric Practice in a Small Community in the South of the United States:*

A 25-Year Study (231); and Shortliffe, Hamilton, and Noroian *The Emergency Room and the Changing Pattern of Medical Care* (232).

Since 1960, investigators have studied a wider variety of problems associated with the organization and administration of medical care. Group practice has commanded major attention (233–240), especially prepaid group practice and its implications for public policy (241–245). Studies of the 1960's and 1970's were more diversified than the earlier group, and involved a new and enlarged list of investigators. Broader studies of the medical systems of other countries were made by Roemer, Odin Anderson, Stevens, Forsyth and Logan, and Field (246–250). McNerney and Riedel studied regionalization in rural health care (251), Freidson looked at the organization of medical practice in a sociological context (252), and Bailey examined the economies of scale in medical practice (253).

Littauer, Flance, and Wessen studied home care (254); Huntley described the epidemiology of family practice (255); and Hessel and Haggerty studied the practice of pediatrics in the mid-'60's (256). Finally, several experiments with new forms of ambulatory medical care, including the coordination of hospital services with those of neighborhood health centers and with the general practitioners of a community (257–259), have extended the boundaries of this category of research. Weinerman's review article of 1966 (260) provides a frame of reference within which to view the contributions of these several investigators.

EVALUATION AND QUALITY OF HEALTH SERVICES

Evaluation of health services has long been a prominent concern, judging by the volume of health services research devoted to it. Yet progress in developing standardized methods which are reliable, feasible, practical, and easily applied has been relatively slow. In part this is due to the complexities inherent in the variability of organization and delivery of health services themselves. Part of the explanation lies in the lack of clarity or agreement on the meaning of such concepts as "efficiency," "effectiveness," and "quality." Another factor limiting the rate of progress is the nature of the techniques required for various types of evaluation; they are generally cumbersome, costly, and time consuming.

Studies whose primary purpose has been the evaluation of health services can be classified in one of three broad categories:

(1) the evaluation of public health programs and the services provided through these programs;

(2) the development and application of methods for evaluating the quality, i.e., content and impact of medical care, regardless of its private or public auspices;

(3) the evaluation of special aspects of medical care by techniques of the social scientists, economists, systems analysts, and industrial engineers.

EVALUATION OF PUBLIC HEALTH PROGRAMS

Prior to 1935, the American Child Health Association and the Committee on Administrative Practice of the American Public Health Association were the two groups most actively involved in the development of tools and methods for evaluating publicly supported health services. The several editions of Appraisal Form for City Health Work, for Rural Health Work, and eventually, in 1938, for Local Health Work (City and Rural, combined) were the products of the APHA effort (261-268). Five years later, the Evaluation Schedule and Health Practice Indices of APHA were put into use (269,270).

Dr. George Palmer, Chief of the Division of Research of the American Child Health Association, directed two studies which were pioneering efforts (271). The first was a descriptive study of the health problems, programs, and administrative structure of 86 cities having 40,000 to 70,000 population with a proposal for a health program and plan of reorganization considered suitable to a city of 50,000 (272). The second, was an evaluation of the effectiveness of school health programs in a sampling of schools throughout the country, with more intensive follow-up research in the school system of New York City (273).

Palmer's early evaluation of school health services was followed by the more elaborate work of Nyswander and associates (274) sponsored by the Health Department and the Board of Education of New York City. Later, Yankauer produced a second generation of school health studies (275–279).

An important early work is Sydenstricker's 1926 report, *The Measurement of Results of Public Health Work* (280). A number of reports which evaluated various aspects of the country's health departments referred to in the previous section appeared during the period 1936–1940 (281–286). A similar study of illness and medical care in Puerto Rico was reported in 1937 (287).

Except for continued refinement of the APHA Evaluation Schedule in the early '40's, and the school health studies already mentioned, there was relatively little sustained research on the evaluation of public programs between 1940 and 1960. The few additional investigators who reported research during this period were Reed and Clark (288), Frost (289), Greenberg and associates (290), Sheps and Sheps (291), and Glasser (292).

Since 1960, considerably more investigators have turned their attention to problems of assessing public programs of health services. Outstanding contributions during this period have been James' formulation of evaluation in public health practice (293) and Densen's closely related work (294,295). Suchman's volume on evaluative research (296) was an important addition to the understanding of problems inherent in the evaluation of broad programs of general health services, a subject also discussed by Kelman and Elinson (297), Hopkins (298), and Borgatta (299).

With the emphasis on establishment of neighborhood health centers in the latter part of the 1960's, Morehead and associates (300) and Dreyfus, et al. (301) concentrated on this particular segment of a total community health services program. The Task Force on Medicaid and Related Programs (Chairman, Walter McNerney) critically examined the operation of those programs in 1970 (302) and recommended sweeping changes in order to improve their effectiveness.

EVALUATION OF THE QUALITY OF MEDICAL CARE

The first formal attempts to evaluate the quality of care related physician performance to end results and were reported by Cabot in 1912 (303) and by Codman in 1914 and 1916 (304,305). The next major contribution was the classic report by Lee and Jones *The Fundamentals of Good Medical Care* released in 1933 as one of the CCMC series (27). In 1947 Franz Goldmann published *The Adequacy of Medical Care* (306) and Odin Anderson reported his analysis of the medical-dental care program for the recipients of Old-Age Assistance in the State of Washington (307).

Statistical methods were applied in studies of the quality of care in group practices by Ciocco, et al. (308), and by Lembcke in comparing rates for specific operations among hospital service areas (309). Lembcke next proposed the development of explicit criteria and standards for diagnosis, treatment, hospital admission, and length of stay as the basis of medical auditing. He demonstrated the scientific and professional feasibility of this approach in major female pelvic surgery (310). This work drew attention to the importance of completeness, reliability, accuracy, and validity of information contained in the clinical record, if that is to be the basis for evaluating the quality of care. Makover had earlier used implicit criteria in assessing the quality of care provided by the medical groups associated with the Health Insurance Plan of New York (311).

The limitations of chart review based on judgments of individual reviewers were made clear by Rosenfeld who also described the conditions under which reliability can be increased (312). Daily and Morehead refined this technique in evaluating care in the Health Insurance Plan of New York City (313). This method of chart review was used in the classic "teamster studies" reported by Trussell and by Morehead and associates (314,315). A technical critique of the methods used in the Trussell study was published (316).

Lembcke's "Reports on Professional Activities" were taken up and modified by the Southwestern Michigan Hospital Council which subsequently developed the Professional Activity Study (PAS) (317,318). This in turn was taken over by the Commission on Professional and Hospital Activities when the latter was incorporated in Ann Arbor, Michigan in 1956. PAS was and is a hospital chart abstracting system which provides to participating hospitals summaries of clinical information contained in hospital records. Eisele (319) demonstrated how such data can be used to evaluate the quality of care more objectively than by use of judgment alone.

Research in the assessment of physician performance was

given impetus by Peterson (320) who conducted and reported his study of general practice in North Carolina using the technique of direct observation to determine if physicians performed in accord with standards taught in medical school. This study was important in demonstrating that the method of direct observation can be applied in the actual practice setting. It also was the first study to analyze the association of observed performances with personal, professional, and educational backgrounds of the physicians. Peterson's methods were refined and applied by Clute in Canada (321) with substantially similar findings.

Lembcke's criterion approach was adapted by Fitzpatrick, Riedel, and Payne to the study of hospital use (322). Subsequently, Payne demonstrated the utility, professional acceptability, and effectiveness of criteria in internal medical audits (323). Williamson proposed a method of relating patient care research to continuing education (324). Brown applied this approach, dubbing it the bi-cycle model, and reported on its effectiveness (325).

Price, Taylor, and associates published reports on prediction and measures of physician performance (326). These systematic criterion and predictor studies yielded unique and important information on perceptions of physicians, other professionals, and the general public.

The critical incident technique was used to define the categories of physician performance reported to have beneficial or detrimental effects on patients (327). The classification of physician performance based on reports by internists was used by Lewis, et al. (328) to compare nurse-practitioner performance with that of internists. The National Board of Medical Examiners had earlier used the critical incident technique to begin the major task of creating suitable instruments for conducting objective evaluation of clinical competence for purposes of certification (329).

Donabedian popularized the concepts of "structure," "process," and "outcome" in his definitive summary and analysis of research on the quality of care (330). His subsequent review is a valuable source of research reference material (331). Brook refined the technique for studying the process of care and replicated both his methods and his findings (332,333). Gonnella and associates (334) compared the performance of students and their teachers in an outpatient department in the diagnosis of urinary tract infection with an independent evaluation of the same patients. The number of missed diagnoses and the demonstrated lack of correlation between knowledge and performance in the study group are important observations. The same research group analyzed these performance data to test the validity of patient management problems (335).

More attention is again being given to the end results or outcomes of care as the best means of validating medical care. Shapiro has discussed the technical constraints and requirements in using end results as measures of the quality of care (336). Lipworth, Lee, and Morris (337) studied differences in case fatality rates between teaching and non-teaching hospitals. Katz has proposed and applied the index of Activities of Daily Living (338) and has reported a controlled study of outpatient care in rheumatoid arthritis (339). Sanazaro and Williamson (340) applied the critical incident technique to identify operational end results as defined by practicing internists. Thompson studied end results of obstetrical care as the basis of comparing quality of care in hospitals (341). Williamson has proposed a method of relating process and outcome which he illustrates by describing initial efforts to obtain estimates of outcomes when scientific data are not available (342).

Payne (343,344) has recently reported a study of the office and hospital care provided by a sample of physicians in Hawaii. The methods he used incorporate professionally defined criteria for diagnosis, treatment, and outcome; standard and modified statistical methods of the Professional Activity Study; and an analysis of interrelationships among age, certification, institutional setting, and source of payment.

Other contributions of note to methods for evaluating medical care are those of Solon who defined an episode of care (345) and Falk, Schonfeld, et al. (346-348), who updated the Lee and Jones study (27) by reporting current standards of care for a wide range of clinical conditions. Bunker (349) and Lewis (350) have analyzed the great variations in rates of operations between countries and within states. Coronary care units have been analyzed with respect to end results, cost, and productivity (351). Fanshel and Bush (352) have proposed a conceptual model for objectively determining outcomes. The proceedings of a conference on outcomes of care provide a perspective on the state of the art in this field (353).

The interrelationships of organization, financing, and quality have received some emphasis. Roemer and colleagues have proposed an index of hospital quality (354). Goss has summarized the literature on hospital characteristics and quality, pointing up tentative conclusions that clearly call for further study (355). Donabedian summarized the evidence regarding the quality of care in prepaid group practice (242). The Trussell and Morehead studies compare organization and type of hospital and quality of care (314,315). Huntley conducted an early study of quality of care in the outpatient department (356). Densen and Shapiro compared prematurity and perinatal mortality under the Health Insurance Plan of Greater New York and in a sample of the general population (357–359).

A special category of evaluation is work done on observer error, summarized by Garland (360).

EVALUATION BY SPECIAL TECHNIQUES

In the late 1950's and throughout the 1960's, a number of investigators applied research techniques derived from several independent disciplines to the description and measurement of patient care. Howland used the systems approach in the analysis of patient care (361) while Maloney, Trussell, and Elinson (362) and Pratt and Reader applied sociological methods (363). Reader and Goss reported on almost a decade of sociologic study of the comprehensive medical care teaching program at the New York Hospital-Cornell Medical Center (364). This is a rich source of information and references on the interrelationships between medical care and medical education in an experimental setting.

Much of the work by economists in cost-benefit studies and operations research could be classified under evaluation. Some examples are found in reports by Klarman (365) and Stig Andersen (366).

One set of studies in evaluation deserves special attention. These have in common a quasi-experimental design to determine differences in the effectiveness of organized programs in achieving specified objectives. Reader and associates compared the effects on elderly welfare recipients, of an organized program of comprehensive medical care with those of the usual, fragmented care and found no differences in mortality or morbidity (367). Haggerty and colleagues conducted a controlled trial which clearly demonstrated the effectiveness of a comprehensive health care program in reducing costs of illness and utilization (368). The controlled study by Katz and associates (339) and the randomized clinical trial by Mather, et al., (369) are examples.

The previously noted studies by Lewis of the nurse practitioner (50,51) are also controlled trials. The application of this method constitutes the most rigorous evaluation of the impact of health services delivery on individuals and groups. It is the most objective method of evaluating attributes of the care process itself, whether these be efficacy, efficiency, or effectiveness.

The cumulative contributions of health services research to improvement in methods of evaluating health care are evident in retrospect. The techniques of social science when combined with knowledge of medical care make possible evaluation of "structure," "process," and "outcome" with acceptable reliability within the constraints of current social science methods and the limitations of scientific knowledge about the outcomes of care. Individual physician performance and group performance can now be assessed reasonably well, but considerable refinement of methods is needed before they can be widely applied.

The determinants of the variations in physician performance require further research, as do the interrelationships between institutional setting (type of hospital or clinic, etc.), methods of financing, and process and outcomes of care. Performance by other health professionals, except for nurses, has not been adequately studied. A high priority for health services research remains the explication of the components of quality of care as defined by all principal parties in health care, and the determination of their implications for changes in the organization, delivery, and financing of care.

An illustration of how health services research forms the basis for R&D which aims at innovation on a national scale is

given in the description of the Experimental Medical Care
Review Program (see p. 169.).

UTILIZATION OF HEALTH SERVICES

Very few studies of the utilization of health services were
made prior to 1950. The few exceptions include the work of
two Public Health Service statisticians, Sydenstricker and Collins. As part of the Hagerstown Morbidity Studies, which were
primarily directed to the incidence of illness in the general
population of a small city, Sydenstricker in 1927 reported *The
Extent of Medical and Hospital Service in a Typical Small City* (370).
This was the first study to relate services received to illness by
diagnosis.

Three studies by Collins (371–373) reported the frequency
of specific types of health services received by 9,000 families
canvassed periodically between 1928 and 1931. Services studied were health examinations, immunizing and related procedures, and doctor's calls. A survey of 9,000 families, drawn
from eighteen states, was organized as the basic investigation
of the Committee on the Costs of Medical Care (CCMC).
CCMC publications based on the results dealt primarily with
costs, and Public Health Service publications, primarily with
incidence of illness and the extent and kind of medical care,
without regard to cost. Since costs are meaningless unless
related to the extent and nature of the services received, the
several reports do not maintain a sharp separation.

In 1939, Wiehl and Berry (374) reported an intensive study
of prenatal and postnatal care received by mothers in Catta-
raugus County, New York. Between 1940 and 1945, Sinai and
Paton studied the hospitalization experience of the people of
Hillsdale and Branch Counties, Michigan (375). During the
same period, the University of Missouri published a series of
research bulletins on rural health. Two of these (376,377)
described the use of medical services and other family health
practices in rural Missouri.

During the 1950's there was an acceleration of research on
the utilization of health services. Studies of that decade were
about evenly divided between those limited to utilization of
hospital services only and those concerned with the broader
spectrum of medical care. In the first group, Rosenfeld, Gold-

mann, and Kaprio studied reasons for prolonged hospital stay in four Boston hospitals (378), and Goldmann extended this work to four additional hospitals in other cities (379). Odoroff and Abbe reported on factors in outpatient visits to general hospitals (380). The influence of various types of insurance or prepayment plans on hospital use was studied by Densen, Balamuth, and Shapiro (381), by Roemer (382), and Roemer and Shain (383,384).

Looking at the broader picture in 1952 were Axelrod and Patton (385) and Ciocco, Altman, and Truan (386). In that same year, Larson and Hay reported on the differential use of health resources by rural people (387) in New York State and McNamara and Hassinger made a similar study in Missouri (388). The latter study was an extension of the work begun there in the 1940's. Taubenhaus made a study of one rural practice several years later (389), and Graham reported on the relationship of illness and use of medical services to socio-economic status (390). Darsky, Sinai, and Axelrod's ambitious study of the use of comprehensive health services under the voluntary health insurance plan of Windsor, Canada, was published in 1958 (391). Freidson compared the extent to which patients turned to psychiatric social workers versus nurses for help in solving their personal problems (392).

More than three times as many studies of utilization of health services have been reported since 1960 as were reported prior to that time. Interpretations continued to be highly influenced by the assumptions and background of the interpreter. As in the preceding decade, the major division of interest was between use of hospital services per se and of medical services more broadly defined. The greater number of studies was directed to hospital use. This probably reflects the growing concern during this period with the rising costs of medical care, and the fact that hospitalization is the most expensive single element of care. Solon, Sheps, and Lee (393–395) studied both problems. Williams, White, et al., studied the referral process at the University of North Carolina clinic (396,397). Several investigators looked specifically at use of health services by the aged (398–404) or by children (405–409).

The numerous studies of hospital utilization exemplify the

variety of concerns, approaches, and premises in health services research. Lerner (410) and the Massachusetts Blue Cross, Inc. (411) related hospital use to specific diagnoses of illness. Three chapters of the Michigan study of hospital and medical economics (163) dealt with hospital utilization. Fitzpatrick, Riedel, and Payne (412) studied appropriateness of admission and length of stay for 18 diagnostic categories, using predetermined criteria for evaluation of appropriateness. They also examined the character and effectiveness of hospital use from an economic standpoint (322) and studied changing patterns of care (413). Two years later these same investigators examined hospital use for six diagnoses (414). Hanchett and Torrens studied the effects on hospital use of a home nursing program (415).

Klarman investigated the effect of prepaid group practice on hospital use (416). The studies of Densen, et al. (417–419) were an extension of the work previously mentioned (381). In the later analyses, varying forms of medical organization were the subject of study. Other studies of utilization of health services under prepayment plans were made by Perrott (420,421), the Blue Cross Association (422), Hill and Veney (423), and Lewis (424).

Lewis and Keairnes (425) and McCorkle (426) compared the length of inpatient stay in various departments of the hospital. Roemer examined the effect of both bed supply (427) and physician supply (428) on hospital utilization and found positive correlations in each instance. Rosenthal (429) considered the two basic influences affecting utilization of short-term general hospitals to be characteristics of the population—age, sex, economic status, etc.—and the general organization of medical care within the community. Ro (430) postulated that hospital use is determined by interaction of patient characteristics and hospital characteristics.

Weinerman and associates (431,432), Bergman and Haggerty (433), Wingert and associates (434), Alpert, Kosa, et al. (435), Reed and Reader (436), and Torrens and Yedvab (437) concentrated on the determinants of use of hospital emergency services. Three of these were studies of pediatric emergency rooms.

Long Stay Hospital Care by van Dyke, Brown and Thom (438)

also was published during this period. Durbin and Antelman (439) used multiple regression analyses to study the effects of six variables on hospital utilization. Rafferty analyzed short-run variations to determine patterns of hospital use (440). Anderson and Sheatsley (441) considered patient and physician decisions the critical factors in hospital use.

But the interests of Odin Anderson and his colleagues have not been limited to utilization of hospital services alone. The periodic nationwide surveys of Anderson and Andersen (Ronald) have provided the most comprehensive information on the use of all forms of health services by persons of different economic categories since the report of the CCMC in 1933. The first two surveys by this group, conducted in 1953 and 1958, respectively, will be discussed under Economics, Costs and Financing of Health Care, since primary emphasis was on family expenditures and insurance, with secondary attention to utilization. In the 1963 and 1971 surveys (442–444) utilization was featured. In addition to the trend data, the most recent study compares the current utilization patterns of various subgroups in the population with respect to their use of physician, hospital, and dental care. It also relates utilization to disability. The results have clear significance for national policies in health care. The most important information revealed by this series of surveys is that the gap between persons of high income and those of lower economic strata, in terms of health services used, has steadily narrowed. Ronald Andersen's behavioral model for studying use of health services by families (445,446) is an important contribution to work in this area.

Sheps and associates (447,448) reported on utilization of health services in one large city from two points of view: families and their "regular doctors" and the patient load of internists. The Cornell University — New York Hospital (449) and Baltimore's utilization rates under two physician-payment systems (450) are other case studies of single city experiences. Lewis studied utilization of both institutional facilities and office visits to practicing physicians by patients with neurological and sensory diseases (451). Last and White examined the problem in primary practice (452).

Beginning in 1969, a number of studies concerned with utilization of medical services by the poor began appearing in the literature. Those reporting such research included: Coe and associates (453), Richardson (454,455), Andersen and Benham (446), Bice, et al. (456), Roghmann, Haggerty, and Lorenz (457), Olendzki, Grann, and Goodrich (458), and Greenlick, et al. (459). These studies reflected, on the one hand, a growing sensitivity to inequities of access to health care; on the other, an interest in determining the impact of Medicaid in correcting these inequities.

Metzner, Shannon, and Bashshur prepared a review article (460) on the concept of distance as a factor in accessibility and utilization of health care. Although this review focused on utilization, some of the studies to which it refers were beamed more directly to organization.

Aday and Eichhorn have recently completed a comprehensive critical review of the flood of research on health services utilization which has been completed during the last twenty years (461). The need for and value of such a review is apparent from the authors' own words:

> "The conclusions about the patterns of use and their determinants to be drawn from the literature are far from clear. The specific measures of utilization employed by researchers, the populations observed, sampling procedures, methods of data collection and analysis have been combined in such heterogeneous ways that few studies are truly replicative. For this reason the cleansing of the literature which normally occurs in science has not taken place. Highly suspect findings cannot be discounted finally, and confusion results as they continue to be cited."

ECONOMICS, COSTS, AND FINANCING OF HEALTH CARE

The Committee on the Costs of Medical Care was the first group to address the problems of economics, costs, and financing of health care. Between 1930 and 1933, six Committee reports dealing with various aspects of these problems were released (462–467). The several staff members responsible for these individual studies thereby established themselves as serious students of the field. Williams, of the National Bureau of Economic Research, published *The Purchase of Medical Care*

Through Fixed Periodic Payment in 1932 (468). This study was made at the invitation of CCMC. Until 1950 the most prominent investigators identified with the financing of health care were Rorem (469–473), Sinai (474–476), Michael Davis (477–482), Falk (483,484), Reed (485–487), and Klem (488–490). Of this group, Dr. Davis was a member of the Executive Committee of CCMC. Dr. Falk was Associate Director of Study and headed the research staff. Miss Klem and Drs. Reed, Rorem, and Sinai were members of the research staff. Questions explored by this dedicated band included health insurance, hospital finance, the costs of medical care, the income of physicians and dentists, family expenditures for medical and dental care, and various types of hospital service plans.

Deserving of special mention is the volume by Davis and Rorem, *The Crisis in Hospital Finance* (478), which brings together, with revisions, a number of studies previously published by one or the other author. Most of the original studies were made with the aid of a grant from the Rockefeller Foundation for investigations in the hospital and clinic field, which one of the authors had administered. Falk's *Security Against Sickness: A Study of Health Insurance* (484) is also a major work, undertaken as a sequel to the activities of the CCMC. The follow-up study was supported by the Milbank Memorial Fund.

During the mid- and late 1930's, a number of local hospital service plans were formed. Some of these were contracts of individual hospitals with designated groups of beneficiaries. By paying a predetermined annual fee to the hospital, members of the covered groups were entitled to care as needed in that hospital. In other communities, a hospital council or association organized the service plan and subscribers were eligible for care from any of the member hospitals. Central information regarding the development and characteristics of these plans was maintained by Rorem of the Commission on Hospital Service until 1938. At that time the Hospital Service Plan Commission was organized within the American Hospital Association. During the 1940's this national organization became quite active and expanded the service coverage that individual local service plans could not offer. This was the antecedent of the Blue Cross Association, which in 1957 organized as a separate entity.

During the 1940's, Franz Goldmann (491–493), Odin Anderson (475,494,495), and Mountin and Perrott (496) joined the ranks of the pioneers in this field. Simpson did an analysis and appraisal of the compulsory health insurance movement in 1943 (497) and the American Medical Association sponsored a study by Dickinson on the cost and quantity of medical care in the United States in 1948 (498).

The work of Odin Anderson (499-503) became increasingly important during the 1950's. His nationwide survey of family medical costs and voluntary health insurance, reported collaboratively with Feldman (501), updated much of the basic information obtained by the CCMC some 20 years earlier. Klarman reported his first work on the economic aspects of hospital care (504). Davis (505) and Sinai, with his colleagues Darsky and Axelrod (391), continued to build on their earlier work. The latter group examined the Windsor, Canada, experience to see whether it held implications for the United States. Klem turned to the more specialized area of industrial health programs (506-508). Langford analyzed the position of medical care in the consumer price index over a period of 20 years, 1936-56 (509).

The three-volume report of the Commission on Financing of Hospital Care was a major contribution to this period. The Commission on Financing of Hospital Care, a natural sequel to the Commission on Hospital Care (see p. 9), was also established by the American Hospital Association. Like its predecessor, it was an independent, nongovernmental group. The first volume of the Commission's report (510) analyzed factors affecting the costs of hospital care. Volumes 2 and 3 dealt with two facets of financing hospital care in the United States: *Prepayment in the Community* and *Financing Hospital Care for Nonwage and Low Income Groups.*

As in each of the previous categories of research we have discussed, the volume of research related to economics, costs, and financing of health care has increased greatly since 1960. Essentially the same problems are being studied, because the basic issues have not changed. Instead, the problems have increased in size and complexity. The roster of investigators, however, is almost entirely different. Anderson (247, 511–513), Reed (514–516), Roemer (517), and Sinai (518,519) are the only familiar names from earlier years.

The comprehensive, five-year Michigan study of hospital and medical economics by McNerney and his group at the University of Michigan (163), analyzes the specific problems of a single State. Its coverage is broad, including, as a prelude to the economics of care, attention to the consumers of health care, the character and effectiveness of hospital use, changing patterns of care, and the role of government in personal health care. To McNerney and his associates, prepayment, insurance, and government—in balance—form the economic bridge for assuring availability of health care for all who need it.

Of particular pertinence to this section is Project No. 7, *Prepayment and Insurance Organizations: Characteristics and Coverages.* This study, supported by the W. K. Kellogg Foundation, was conducted for the Governor's Study Commission on Prepaid Hospital and Medical Care Plans. Resources of the University of Michigan for carrying out research of this depth were unique. Four years after the School of Public Health was founded in 1941, there was established within it a Bureau of Public Health Economics. Under the leadership of Dr. Nathan Sinai, its first director, the Bureau soon became one of the chief research groups in the country concerned with the economics and financing of health care. It has continued to hold an important place in this field. In 1962 the Bureau, in collaboration with the University's Department of Economics, sponsored a national conference on the Economics of Health and Medical Care (520).

Other research reported in the early 1960's included Straight's examination of the effect of coinsurance on the incidence of home and office visits (521) and MacIntyre's *Voluntary Health Insurance and Rate Making* (522). A survey by Williams, Trussell, and Elinson of Columbia University School of Public Health and Administrative Medicine compared family medical care under three types of insurance (523). The National Opinion Research Center of the University of Chicago collaborated in this study.

Although the problems being studied remain the same,

modern research methods and approaches of the new generation of investigators are quite different from those used initially. A growing number of economists entered the field during the 1960's. Hence, research of this later period draws strongly on economic theory, with special attention to productivity and resource allocation. Recent studies probe much more deeply into understanding *why* particular conditions or situations exist, and what would be required to change them, than did those of the '30's, '40's, and '50's. Answers are sought by examining interrelationships of the various factors involved.

Among the recent and current health economics investigators whose work has attained recognition are Klarman (524–528), Martin Feldstein (529–532), Weisbrod (533–535), Fuchs (536,537), Reder (538,539), Ingbar (540–542), Muller (543,544), Rice and Horowitz (545–547), Paul Feldstein (548,549), Garbarino (550), Glaser (551), David Knapp (552), Newhouse (553), Piore (554), Scitovsky (555,556), Wirick and associates (557), Wolfman (558), and Lave and Lave (559,560).

Shanas (561) and Royle and Brewster (562) were concerned particularly with use and costs of medical care for aged patients. Hall (563) studied deductibles as a factor in health insurance; Williams compared hospital utilization and costs by types of insurance coverage (564); Buxbaum reported on coordinated home care benefits provided by Blue Cross (565); and Josephson described family expenditures of Federal employees for designated items of health care services (566). Yett evaluated alternative methods of estimating physicians' expenses in relation to output (567) and attempted to apply economic theory to the analysis of the market of nurses (568–571). Several years later, Conley (572) reviewed the first decade of operation (1960–1970) of the Federal Employees Health Benefits Program.

Hardwick and Wolfe, researchers with Blue Cross of Western Pennsylvania, reported the results of an incentive reimbursement/industrial engineering experiment carried out in three hospitals (573,574). Rafferty studied hospital output indices (575) and Berkowitz and Johnson examined the economics of disability (576). Stuart and Bair compared the impact of Medicaid and Medicare on distribution of health care and income in the State of Michigan with the experience for the country as a whole (577). Owens studied the effect of inflation on physicians' earnings (578). Starkweather prepared a useful review of the laws and court decisions regulating various types of health insurance plans in the State of California (579) and Mueller analyzed the status of private health insurance in 1969 (580).

Finally, the insurance industry has contributed importantly to the health services research literature. Faulkner's exhaustive history and detailed analysis of voluntary health insurance in America (581) summarized its growth to the end of the 1950's. Faulkner was President of the .Woodmen Accident and Life Insurance Company. Follman, who was Director of Information and Research of the Health Insurance Association of America, published a volume *Medical Care and Health Insurance* in 1963 (582). Angell, Associate Professor of Insurance, School of Commerce, New York University, published the second edition of *Health Insurance* (583) updating Faulkner's work. Five years later, Dickerson published the third edition (584). This work was supported by the Health Insurance Institute. The Health Insurance Council also reported periodically on the extent of voluntary health insurance coverage in the United States (585).

No assessment has been made of the influence the recent accumulation of health economics research has had upon policy or practice in the delivery of health care. Neither has the relative value of one economic theory over another as applied to the provision of health services been weighed. The sort of critical review that Aday and Eichhorn made of the empirical literature on health services utilization (461) has not been undertaken for the substantial volume of research which now exists on economics, costs, and financing of health care.

SOCIAL-BEHAVIORAL ASPECTS OF HEALTH CARE

Social–behavioral research in health care originated in rural sociology. Otis Duncan's *Social Research on Health* published in 1946 (586) was the first report directed to social research in the health field that was prepared exclusively by sociologists, social anthropologists, and psychologists. This work was initiated by the Social Science Research Council, which, as early as 1941, stimulated a number of rural sociologists to plan some social research in health.

Gordon, Anderson, et al. (587) state that "During the 1940's the health of the rural farm population became an area of social research interest. The Agricultural Extension Service of the United States Department of Agriculture stimulated a number of local studies through the Extension Departments of land grant universities. These studies were mainly staffed by sociologists with an applied interest in rural life."

The Department of Rural Sociology of the University of Missouri, in collaboration with the Missouri Agricultural Experiment Station, engaged in studies of the social conditions and situations associated with the health of rural people of that State. These rural health studies were reported in a series of research bulletins of the University over a period of 15 years (1943–1958). They have been distributed among appropriate research categories in this chapter. Lively's discussion of the objectives and methods of rural sociological research in health at the University of Missouri is pertinent here (588).

Schuler, Hoffer, Loomis, and Miller at Michigan State College were another group of active rural sociologists who responded to the need for facts about health and health care (589,590). Their decision to pursue this line of study was stimulated by the Schools of Medicine and Public Health of the University of Michigan, the public health demonstration projects of the Children's Fund, the W. K. Kellogg Foundation, and the Michigan Agricultural Extension Service.

In two rural counties of upstate New York, Olaf Larson, of the Department of Rural Sociology at Cornell University, and Donald Hay, of the Bureau of Agricultural Economics, U. S. Department of Agriculture, made similar studies (387, 591). One of these (387) has already been referred to in the section Utilization of Health Services. Saunders and Samora (592) reported the experience of a Colorado community in the establishment and maintenance of a medical care program between 1946 and 1952. The settings for all of these small-scale, local sociological health studies were rural areas and/or small towns. Among them, *The Health of Regionville* by Koos (593) is probably best known. Beyond these, very few reports on the social-behavioral aspects of health care appeared in the literature until after 1955. Coser's study of authority and decision making in a hospital (594) was reported in 1958, but there was no great concentration of effort in this area until after 1960, the year in which the Section on Medical Sociology was established in the American Sociological Association.

In 1957, Anderson and Seacat (595) noted that "The application of behavioral science research concepts and techniques in the social and economic aspects of the health field is not new in this country or in Europe. But the *momentum* with which sociologists, social psychologists, and social anthropologists are being brought into this growing research area is a new phenomenon, and has taken place mainly since 1945." This statement was based on the findings of an Anderson-Seacat survey conducted in 1956. Of the 193 persons who responded, almost 60 percent had received their degrees during the past six years. Fifty-three percent had been in the health field two years or less, and only 25 percent had been in the field seven years or more. Behavioral scientists included in the study were sociologists, anthropologists, and social psychologists. The term "social scientists" was not used because it is generic and includes economists, political scientists, and historians as well as the three groups already mentioned. A later survey by the same investigators (596) showed that about 85 per cent of the three groups of behavioral scientists were sociologists. Most were young, and had been in the field a relatively short time.

Anderson and Seacat were members of the research staff of the Health Information Foundation, chartered in 1950 to support and conduct studies to help solve social and economic problems in the delivery of medical care. The Foundation, sponsored by companies in the pharmaceutical industry, awarded a few grants, but its influence was exerted principally through the series of 27 monographs prepared by its own competent investigators. Most of these are noted in other sections of this chapter, but Freidson and Feldman's studies of the public's attitudes toward hospitals (597), health insurance (598), and dental care (599) are cited here as examples. Beginning in 1952, the Health Information Foundation for a number of years published an annual *Inventory of Social and Economic Research in Health.* This series of publications was extremely important in defining the field and putting professionals in touch with each other. The Foundation continued as an independent research agency until 1962, when it affiliated with the University of Chicago. Data for the HIF studies were drawn from a much broader base than the earlier rural health studies previously mentioned.

Also during the 1950's, the Russell Sage Foundation subsidized and gained entreé into key health settings—such as hospitals, medical schools, and schools of public health—for discipline-oriented social scientists. Freidson's study of patients' views of three medical practices in New York (600) was partially supported and the report published by this Foundation.

Freidson's interest in the sociology of hospitals led him to assemble in one volume, *The Hospital in Modern Society* (601), a collection of papers representing the scope of research on the hospital at that time. It was his hope that the collection would be provocative to social scientists, leading them to undertake both more extensive and intensive work in the human organization of hospitals. Other closely related studies by Freidson are *Processes of Control in a Company of Equals* (with Buford Rhea) (602), *Professional Dominance: The Social Structure of Medical Care* (603), and *Profession of Medicine: A Study of the Sociology of Applied Knowledge* (604).

Studies by other social scientists who entered the health care field tend to fall in one of several broad groupings:

• An effort to improve understanding of the nature and potential of medical sociology, per se
• Attitudes, motivation, behavior, and values of the consumers of health care
• Social structure, lines of authority, and communication and perceptions of the providers of health care
• Socio-cultural aspects of health care
• Physician-patient interactions and relationships

GENERAL APPLICATION OF SOCIAL RESEARCH TO THE HEALTH FIELD

Patients, Physicians, and Illness, edited by Jaco (605), a source book in behavioral science and medicine, is an example of the first group. Others are Freeman, Levine, and Reeder's *Handbook of Medical Sociology* (606); Suchman's *Sociology and the Field of Public Health* (607); *Disease, the Individual, and Society* by Gordon, Anderson, Brehm, et al. (587); Knutson's *The Individual, Society, and Health Behavior* (608); Scott and Volkart's *Medical Care: Readings in the Sociology of Medical Institutions* (609); Duff and Hollingshead's *Sickness and Society* (610); Mechanic's *Medical Sociology: A Selective View* (611); and Coe's *Sociology of Medicine* (612). The fact that these broad-gauged approaches to the entire field continue to appear seems to reflect a discipline still trying to explain its presence in a relatively new territory.

Studies of Attitudes, Motivation, and Behavior

Rosenstock laid the groundwork for attitudinal, motivational, and behavioral research in his analysis of what research in motivation suggests for public health (613), followed by *Why People Use Health Services* (614). The latter article is a comprehensive description and critique of his model. It presents research evidence that tends both to support and contradict it. The national study of health beliefs in which he participated with his associates, Kirscht, Haefner, and Kegeles (615) provided further general background against which more specific studies of this type (some of which antedated these reports) could be judged.

Particular problems to which these more focused studies were directed by more than a score of social scientists included: why people do or do not seek vaccination against poliomyelitis (616,617); public participation in screening programs and other preventive health behavior (618–620); participation in, and attitudes toward, pediatric programs (621,622); why people seek dental care (623–625); consumer satisfaction with group practice (626); prophylaxis behavior with respect to rheumatic fever (627); patients' compliance with doctors' advice (628–633); level of patients' medical information (634,635); and factors associated with choice of health care plans and insurance coverage (636–638). Other studies dealt with perceptions of and responses to illness generally and acceptance of modern medical practice (639–642). Mechanic (643,644) advanced a broad concept of illness behavior which describes how symptoms may be differently perceived and acted upon by different kinds of people. Leventhal

studied the effectiveness of fear-arousing educational material
in attaining desirable preventive health practices (645). Haefner and Kirscht conducted a controlled experiment (646) to
determine the effect of modifying health beliefs upon motivation to take pertinent health-related actions and subsequent
health behavior. Battistella reported two studies (647,648) on
the psychological readiness of older persons to initiate health
care.

STUDIES OF PROVIDERS OF HEALTH CARE

Another group of investigators concentrated on individual
and institutional providers, rather than the consumers, of
health care. Solon, et al., analyzed staff perception of patients'
use of the hospital outpatient department (649). Goss studied
influence and authority among physicians in a large outpatient
clinic and patterns of bureaucracy among hospital staff physicians (650,651); McElrath examined the perspective and participation of physicians in prepaid group practice (652). Seeman and Evans studied stratification and hospital care, looking
specifically at the performance of the medical intern (653).
The same investigators as well as Kendall were concerned with
the learning environment of hospitals (654,655); Rosengren
and DeVault dealt with the sociology of time and space in an
obstetrical hospital (656). The comprehensive study of outpatient care by Sussman and associates was reported in 1967 in
their book, *The Walking Patient* (657). Mechanic studied general practice in England and Wales (658) from the point of view
of the doctors. Freidson and Rhea studied physicians in group
practice (659,660). DuBois investigated the organizational viability of group practice (661). Glaser's cross-national study of
the hospital (662) was directed specifically to its social settings
and medical organization.

Elling and Roemer (663) made a study of 136 hospitals to
identify both internal and external factors which led to strong
community support. Suchman proposed a model for research
on community health campaigns (664). Rosner studied the
relationship of administrative control of institutional activity to
innovative practices (665). For a number of years, Colombotos
has studied the attitudes of physicians toward changes in the
delivery of health care, particularly with respect to the Medi-

care program. From his findings, he has now projected how they are likely to respond to some of the major health care issues of the next decade (666).

STUDIES OF SOCIO-CULTURAL ASPECTS OF HEALTH CARE

The effect of socio-cultural characteristics on health behavior has interested a number of social scientists who have been drawn into health services research. Lieberson was one of the first to report on differences among ethnic groups as related to the practice of medicine (667). Suchman also studied this question (668), as well as broader social patterns of illness and medical care and social factors affecting medical deprivation (669,670). Ross, likewise, examined social class and medical care (671) and Macgregor set forth a number of social determinants of health practices (672). Lewis and Lopreato concentrated on arationality, ignorance, and perceived danger in medical practices (673).

Solon analyzed sociocultural variations among a hospital's outpatients (674). Ellenbogen, Ramsey, and Danley studied health need and status in relation to subscription to health insurance (675) and Bashshur and Metzner examined patterns of social differences between persons who subscribed to particular types of prepayment health care plans (676). Coe and Wessen investigated social-psychological factors influencing the use of community health resources (677).

Kegeles reported on a field experiment which attempted to change health beliefs and behavior in an urban ghetto (678). In a later article (679) he described some of the problems encountered in carrying out this research.

STUDIES OF PATIENT-PROVIDER COMMUNICATION

Problems and gaps in doctor-patient communication were studied by Kane and Deuschle (680) and by Korsch, Gozzi, Francis, and Morris (681,682). Skipper and Leonard reported a controlled experiment which tested their hypothesis that stress of hospitalized children would be reduced by greater interaction between attending nurses and the children's mothers (683). With more information, obtained from the nurse, the mother was in a better position to reassure the child.

Caplan and Sussman studied the relative importance of

selected variables in contributing to patient and staff satisfaction with outpatient service (684).

The second editions of two basic source books in the social-behavioral area of health services research have recently been published (685,686). The major additions to Jaco's new edition (686) are the articles on societal and community efforts to organize and manage health care services and on problems related to maintaining the total health care "system" in society. A number of the studies cited have implications for the development of public policy toward health care.

In Freeman, Levine, and Reeder's new book (685), the chapter by the editors, *Present Status of Medical Sociology,* summarizes some of the changes that have taken place since publication of their first edition. They point to the "prolific outpouring" of monographs and articles "during the past decade and the increase in the number of journals that publish reports for sociological research." They note, however, that there "continues to be considerable need for systematic study of the development of the field of medical sociology and the day-to-day work as sociologists in health." This is because the growth of the field has not been "uniform and orderly."

NURSING HEALTH SERVICES RESEARCH

Nursing health services research is an attempt to find ways by which nurses and nursing care can contribute more effectively to the entire spectrum of health services delivery. The first significant nursing contribution in health services research was made by Florence Nightingale in 1858 (687). Her report provided the first effort to document the method and rationales for the collection of hospital statistics.

Health services research has been conducted under the auspices of nursing organizations, public, and private institutions and agencies. Complete references to research conducted in nursing can be found in Abdellah-Levine, *Better Patient Care Through Nursing Research* (Macmillan 1965) (688); Abdellah, "Overview of Nursing Research, 1955–1968," *Nursing Research,* January–June 1970 (689); and *Research in Nursing 1955–1968* (690).

UTILIZATION OF SERVICES

The first comprehensive survey of American nursing was made by Nutting in 1912 (691). A comprehensive hospital and health survey was carried out by Josephine Goldmark in 1920 under the direction of Dr. Haven Emerson (692). This study identified inadequacies of nursing services. The first recorded time study of institutional nursing was released by the New York Academy of Medicine in 1922 (693).

The Committee for the Study of Nursing Education in 1923 reported the first representative study of schools of nursing and public health agencies with firsthand observation of nurses at work as public health nurses, as teachers, and as administrators. This study was subsequently used in carrying out national nursing surveys. The final report was published in 1923 (694).

The Committee on the Grading of Nursing Schools appointed May Ayres Burgess to direct a monumental study of the ways and means for assuring an ample supply of nursing service at a level essential for the adequate care of the patient (695,696). The study encompassed the supply and demand for nursing service; job analysis; and the grading of nursing schools. The first project was reported in the now classic publication *Nurses, Patients, and Pocketbooks* (697). The second project was reported in the publication *An Activity Analysis of Nursing* (698). The third project utilized a survey approach comparable to the Flexner Report in medicine and was the first to give attention to the quality of practice settings (699).

The first systematic study of the practice of hospital nursing was by Pfefferkorn and Rottman at Bellevue Hospital (700, 701). They sought to use a nurse-patient ratio as a quantitative index of nursing care. Feyerherm (702) proposed the use of a mathematical model to study changes in activity patterns for nurses and aides.

The Brown report (1948), scholarly and objective, brought to a focal point many of the issues facing nursing education and nursing services for the past half century (703). Many subsequent studies of inservice education, nursing functions, nursing teams, practical nurses, role and attitude, the nurse technician, nurse-patient relationships, hospital environment, and economic security had their roots in the recommendations of the Brown report.

Studies such as *Change and Dilemma in the Nursing Profession* (704), *The Give and Take in Hospitals* (86), and *Human Problems of a State Mental Hospital* (705) provide information on the problems faced by nursing in the complex and changing character of the modern hospital. A social anthropologist, Dr. Leo Simmons, and a renowned expert nurse teacher and practitioner, Virginia Henderson, directed a survey to find, classify, and evaluate the research in nursing during the preceding decade (706).

HEALTH MANPOWER

In 1936 in response to the growing demand for nursing services, the U. S. Public Health Service undertook the task of maintaining a census of public health nurses (707). In 1940, this agency, in cooperation with the state nursing associations, conducted a national inventory of all registered nurses (708). The National Organization of Public Health Nursing made a survey in 1943 of needs and resources for home care in 16 communities.

The increased employment of the graduate staff nurse in giving care to patients in hospitals led to a major study in 1944 of general staff nursing by the American Nurses' Association and the National League for Nursing Education, in cooperation with the American Hospital Association (709).

Following World War II (1945–1955), to alleviate the nursing shortage, efforts were directed toward the development of programs at each level of practice, e.g., practical nursing and technical nursing (710). White and Goldsen (711), concerned with nurse manpower and holding factors in the profession, studied differences in identity as they influence occupational choice, career planning, and work-role orientation to women. Flitter (712) developed a basic cost methodology initially for nursing and later adopted by other health professions. Nahm, Olesen, and Davis (713) sought to discover and interpret the significant experiences underlying the educational process whereby lay persons are transformed into professional nurses.

EVALUATION AND QUALITY OF SERVICES

The first significant early attempt to measure quality of

nursing care was made by Reiter and Kakosh in 1950 (714). They identified 12 components of nursing care to define some standards for appraising observed nursing care. Industrial engineers and nurse researchers have joined forces to develop measures to evaluate patient care. Howland and McDowell, as previously indicated (361), conceptualized the nurse-patient-physician triad as a servo-system in which the patient generates signals to the monitor.

Dorothy Smith (715) developed a nursing analysis tool (Nursing History Form) which contributes to the evaluation of nursing care by organizing information from patients to permit the development of an effective nursing care plan. White (716) extended the earlier work of the development of a progressive patient care system by constructing a simplified check-list of five nursing criteria to classify patients into intensive, intermediate, or self care.

Wandelt (717) explored the problem of uninterrupted patient care and nursing requirements. Klaus (718) applied a variety of techniques (task analysis; critical incident) to the definition of instructional objectives concerned with adequate patient care. A long-range study to measure quality nursing practice was initiated by Aydelotte and Simon (719) at Iowa. Using an experimental approach, they found that there is a limit to the contribution that nursing care can make to patient welfare and that this limit is much closer to the existing level of care than was formerly thought. Simon (720) continued the work by studying activity patterns of hospitalized medical and urological patients with the aim of deriving patient activity indices that might be used as measures of patient welfare.

Bryant and New (721) replicated some aspects of the Iowa study by testing the effects of minimal nursing care. Attempts to evaluate nursing by the effect of nursing care upon patient recovery were reported by Dumas (722) and Elms (723). Flitter and Tate (724) developed an instrument for use by hospitals for evaluation and guidance related to the general staff nurse.

Kinsinger, Griffin, and Perlmutter (725) conducted an exploratory study using closed-circuit television for data collection and identification of criteria for nursing practice. This study extended the earlier work (*Clinical Nursing Instruction by Closed Circuit TV* by Matheney, Griffin, and Kinsinger) that successfully tested the feasibility of using closed-circuit television to enable an existing number of nursing instructors to teach an increased number of students. The study does provide an objective tool to document what actually happens in a nursing situation. The pioneering research of Chow (726) (1967-1968) on patients undergoing open-heart surgery at Ohio State University supports the findings of this study, namely that video-tapes and closed-circuit television offer promising tools to provide objective documentation and may be a major breakthrough in the measurement of the quality of nursing care. Meltzer, Pinneo, and Kitchell (727) defined the role of a nurse in a system of intensive coronary care which reduced the death rate from the complications of acute myocardial infarction.

Hospital Based Studies

A variety of organizational patterns that were hospital based have been explored. Wooden (728) studied the nursing function in relation to the hospital and to the patient, focusing on the impact of care management patterns on the hospitalized patients.

An early demonstration study of the reorganization of a nursing unit by Throne (729) introduced the floor manager pattern to determine if patient care could be improved. A modification of the floor manager pattern was studied by McKenna and Brodt (730), comparing the efficacy and costs of centralized management under the head nurse and a dichotomized management under a service manager. The two systems were evaluated by a patient welfare measure developed by Brodt that utilized the Aydelotte measures of patient welfare.

Outpatient and Extra-Hospital Based Studies

Two important studies in public health nursing include *Survey of Public Health Nursing Administration and Practice* by Tucker and Hilbert (731), and *An Analysis of First Level Public Health Nursing in 10 Selected Organizations* by McIver (732). Freeman and Mickey (733) used a single nursing interview of a random sample of the population of one county, chosen because it was representative of the country as a whole on a number of characteristics, to estimate the extra-hospital nursing needs of the general population.

Working out efficient plans for referral of patients from hospitals to home nursing service came under scrutiny in 1957–1960 by Bunge and Smith (734) who used interviews of hospital personnel and public health nurses and patients to obtain data about instructions and communications relating to home-going orders. A monumental study conducted by Johnson (735) used taped records of the entire verbal interaction of 287 public health nursing visits.

Katz, Ford, Downs, et al. (736) conducted a controlled, longitudinal study of the effects of regular visits by a public health nurse on the status and function of chronically ill patients. Important benefits were observed. Holliday (737), seeking to improve home care, used questionnaires and interview schedules to find that there were significant attitudes underlying nurses' preferences in caring for different types of patients. Wilson (738) used the case study method to analyze the Community Nursing Services program in a large metropolitan area.

Abrahamsen and Simon (739) studied the feasibility of analyzing the effects of nursing service on the outcome of student health problems and confirmed some of the methodological problems encountered in field studies.

Most of the studies in this category were conducted between 1955 and 1965. Hagen and Wolff (740) looked at behaviors of nursing service administrators, supervisors of nursing service, and head nurses. The critical incident technique was also used to identify specific behaviors (effective or ineffective) of nurses in leadership positions in nursing service.

The patient satisfaction scale developed by Abdellah and Levine formed the basis of a Guttman type scale (Interpersonal Influence and the Nursing Function, 1959) used by Tannenbaum, and reported by Meyer (741), to examine the connection between aspects of interpersonal relations in nursing, the social climate of the hospital, and the effectiveness with which the nursing function is carried out.

Spaney and Matheney (742) provided well-designed instruments to compare the employer's expectations with actual performance of staff nurses according to their training: graduates of basic baccalaureate, diploma, and associate degree programs. Dodge (743), building on the work of Spaney and Matheney, investigated the relationship between attitudes on the one hand and performance or behavior on the other.

In an impressive study extending over a seven-year period, Strauss, Quint, and Glaser (744) used anthropological methods to study the attitudes of hospital personnel toward terminally ill and dying patients. This work has stimulated much discussion in the literature, particularly about the methods used to conduct "qualitative" research. Sindberg and Enos (745) sought an extended and broadened role for the professional nurse caring for mongoloid and cerebral palsied children. The Barker and Englund Speech Therapy Instrument and Rembolt Motor Skills Achievement Test (RMSAT) were successfully used to make this assessment. Significant differences were found in the motor development and skills of the experimental subjects.

Bennis and Berkowitz (746) analyzed the effects of interpersonal and organizational concepts upon patient care and patient teaching in an outpatient department. Hardin (747) directed a monumental field study of behavior of public health nurses and patients in a face-to-face situation to discover what public health nurses and patients do and say to each other. A useful instrument was also provided to measure turnover among public health nurses. Hassinger (748) studied the role of the local public health nurse—how this role developed within the three-fold reference system that included the formal organization of the State divisions of health, the nursing profession, and the local community.

Little (749) demonstrated ways of creating and providing a more effective therapeutic nursing environment based on the identifiable needs of the patient population.

Social Behavioral Research

Richardson (750), using experimental control and study groups, determined if Alabama Negro mothers of premature infants actually carried out nursing procedures as taught at ten weekly home teaching sessions. Schwartz and Henley (751) produced what has come to be recognized as a classic descriptive study of the psychosocial needs of elderly, ambulatory, chronically ill patients.

Influenced by Orlando's theory of nursing practice, Dumas (752) tested the effectiveness of three different nursing approaches to the patient and found that to measure the effectiveness of care, a distinction must be made between patient welfare and the effect of the nurse on the patient. Bales' Interaction Process Analysis (IPA) was used by Conant (753) to study the development and nature of the role relationships of public health nurses and patients in home visits. Kelly and Hammond (754) applied the Brunswick Lens Model to the study of the inferential process of the nurse to determine the specific kinds of inferences made by nurses, and how they select and utilize information available to them in making the inferences. Nurses' notes were selected for analysis by Walker and Selmanoff (755) as a way of studying ritualistic behavior.

ECONOMICS AND FINANCING

Economic security was under scrutiny in 1938 by the American Nurses' Association, which conducted a study of incomes, salaries, and employment conditions of nurses (exclusive of public health nurses). These data served as a basis for arriving at costs of delivering nursing health services.

An important advance in providing basic information about the cost of delivering nursing health services was made in 1940 by Pfefferkorn and Rovetta (756). The earlier study by the Committee on the Costs of Medical Care (757) included nursing service in its report of the overall costs of medical care. Several of Yett's economics studies (previously cited) (568–571) dealt specifically with availability of and payment for nursing care.

DENTAL HEALTH SERVICES RESEARCH

Research in dental health services is closely related to medical and social research. As advances were made on the broad social front to bring medical and social services closer to those who need them, dental services, to a lesser extent, were included as an important and necessary partner.

Research on the problems of providing dental health services follows the same general pattern as for health services at large. But the chronological development of, and emphasis on, the several major categories are somewhat different, and this is taken into account in this summary. This section omits mention of research carried out in relation to fluoridation because such studies are directed more to environmental and clinical problems.

Research in the more productive utilization of dental manpower has already been discussed in the section Health Manpower Research (p. 4).

ORGANIZATION AND ADMINISTRATION OF DENTAL HEALTH SERVICES

Dental services for children have received the most intensive study over the years, beginning with the Child Hygiene Studies of the Public Health Service in 1919 (758). About 15 per cent of the children examined were found to be in need of urgent medical, surgical, or dental attention. In those days minor dental corrections were not reported. Not until 1937 was a formal public health dental program initiated in the Public Health Service.

One of the two greatest achievements in the dental field in the first half of the 20th century was the development of the DMF index by Drs. Klein, Palmer, and Knutson (759). The DMF index, a tool for measuring caries experience in population groups, makes it possible to analyze incremental problems, rates of accumulation of dental caries experience, and to evaluate the effectiveness of caries preventive programs. Wisan (760) in 1938 recommended the use of the National Dental Inspection Chart for school children as a reliable, valid, and practical means of evaluating dental programs among school children. Of more recent date, Pickles (761), in his study of caries prevalence data and diagnosed treatment needs in a child population, concluded that primary teeth scores present a more reliable relationship to clinical diagnosis as a prediction of treatment needs than do permanent teeth.

Beginning in December of 1946 and extending over a five-year period, dental care study projects were undertaken to throw light on the problems of accumulated and maintenance dental needs of school children (30–33, 762). Numerous dental surveys in the 40's demonstrated that the prevalence of dental caries varied greatly from community to community as well as racially (763–765).

Smith, Fuchsberg, and Ake (766) and Schoen (767) evaluated a pilot program of dental care for children under 15 years of age offered under alternate financing plans. Rogers and Daniels (768) found that participating dentists approve of dental care plans even on short experience and are more likely to approve of closed panels. This study also includes findings of patient satisfaction with open panels vs. closed panels. Brusseau, Hoggard, and Gribble reported a nationwide survey of group dental practice in the United States in 1971 (768a).

The success of the Head Start program for pre-school children in meeting the children's total dental needs was studied by the Division of Dental Health of the Public Health Service (769). Experience in the following cities was the subject of separate studies: New York (770), Boston (771), Tucson (772), and Los Angeles (773).

SOCIAL AND BEHAVIORAL STUDIES OF DENTAL CARE

Research has been carried out on school dental health education. Rayner and Cohen (774) have charted this neatly from 1953 to the present, and have identified crucial gaps in this field. In a controlled study of fourth, fifth, and sixth grade children on Indian Reservations, Stolpe, Mecklenburg, and Lathrop (775) combined mouth examination with a test for knowledge about oral structures.

How to motivate parents to procure dental care for their pre-school children was studied by Stadt, et al. (776). Direct mail was used in reaching dental practitioners in a study by Cohen (777), who found it *not* effective in increasing the use of oral cytology. A study by Cassidy (778) on the psychological factors in preventive dentistry indicated that as a solution to oral disease preventive dentistry will need to concentrate on patient education and professional education relative to communicating the real meaning of dental problems. Of more recent date, Ramirez, Wershow, and Pelton (779) showed the relationships between social and psychological variables and the concept of prevention. O'Shea (780) studied dental patients' attitudes and behavior concerning prevention.

Many studies have examined beliefs about dental health and reasons why people do, or do not, seek dental care. The 1966 study of John Kirscht, et al. (615), used the Rosenstock-

Hochbaum formulations[6] concerning individual perceptions about dental care. Using the same Rosenstock-Hochbaum formula, Kegeles collected belief and attitude data from a random sample of factory employees to predict whether these employees would make preventive or symptomatic visits to dentists over a 3-year period. Three years later, the original sample was studied along with a control group from the same company (624, 781). Haefner, Kegeles, Kirscht, et al., in their study (782) found the influence of the social group weighs heavily on behavior in seeking dental care. In a statewide household survey, Tyroler (620) in 1965 studied levels of tooth salvage among different ethnic and social groups. A series of interlocking community dental studies of public dental clinics and attitudes of private dentistry toward them was conducted at Brandeis University (784–787).

Lambert and Freeman (788) studied 624 families in Brookline, Massachusetts to determine whether patterns of dental care established for young children carried over into the teen years. Cohen and Fusillo (789) found that between 1959 and 1968 the public attitude toward tax support for dental care for children became more negative.

Images of dentist-patient relationship as perceived by dental students from formal and informal school experiences were studied by Quarantelli (790). Simonds (791) presents a plan for delineating the patients' perception of his problem. Another study concerning motivation to seek dental care was reported by Goulding (792). Brunswick, in studying the adolescent's perception of his health needs (793), included self-appraisal of the general condition of teeth.

Two recent volumes, one edited by Richards and Cohen (794), the other by O'Shea and Cohen (795), contain an inclusive review of the current literature on the social–behavioral aspects of dental health services. For additional references pertinent to this section, see Social–Behavioral Aspects of Health Care (p. 35).

UTILIZATION OF DENTAL SERVICES

Utilization of dental services is closely allied with motivation-

---

[6] The psychological state of readiness to take action, situational factors, such as symptoms, and environmental conditions, such as availability of service.

al factors. Newman and Anderson, in their survey (796), built on the pioneer work of the Committee on the Costs of Medical Care (757) and Andersen and Anderson's *A Decade of Health Services* (443). Suchman and Rothman (797) in a survey on utilization of dental services in New York City found dental care lagging behind medical care in its preventive aspects. Kreisberg and Treiman (798) studied the influence of socioeconomic status on the utilization of dental services. Hochstim, Athanasopoulos and Larkins (799) also studied income and race as determinants in utilization of services.

In a study of utilization of dental services by welfare recipients in a private dental office, Bodnarchuk's (800) experience showed much unproductive chairside time. Failure to complete treatment, "no shows," and the like, resulted in loss of fees to private dentists. Schonfeld and Milone (801) studied records of patients under age 22 to understand interactions between family and program and the impact of oral hygiene counseling. Leverett and Jong (802) reported on a study of variations in the use of dental care facilities by low-income white and black urban populations. Nikias (803) referred back to 1960 and 1965 studies to relate dental practices to ethnic and income influences. Morrison, Gurley, Ragsdale, et al. (804), studied patients' records to determine the most prominent characteristics of a metropolitan dental clinic population.

Based on a four-year dental project for the institutionalized and homebound chronically ill and aged, Lotzkar (805) points out that when dental care is offered, such patients not only accept it but want it. Kegeles, Lotzkar, and Andrews (806) tried to pinpoint certain characteristics which could be termed "predictors" of which groups would and/or would not accept dental care or health care. Waldman (807) reported on a demonstration of dental care for the homebound chronically ill and aged patients. The American Dental Association Council on Dental Health in 1965 reported on a survey regarding the availability of dental care for residents of nursing homes (808).

ECONOMICS, COSTS, AND FINANCING OF DENTAL CARE

Studies of payment mechanisms for dental services are

closely allied to a variety of prepayment plans, group practice, and the question of open and closed panels. Reference has been made earlier to the pilot program of dental care for children under 15 years of age (766). Studies of three types of plans—dental services corporations, group practices, and insurance company indemnity arrangements—present a distinct series of differing advantages and disadvantages (809) and differing utilization (810,811). Zalk (812) reported on the benefits of a 1958 Teamsters Union agreement with trucking companies concerning dental care coverage in north New Jersey.

The Group Health Association of America has summarized its experience with a wide age range in its sample (813). Schoen has analyzed group practice and prepayment (814), utilization and quality of dental care in groups (815), and factors responsible for a decrease in extraction rates in children (767). Genet (817) analyzed capitation prepayment and private group practice. Simons studied consumer attitudes toward prepaid dentistry (818).

Other studies of interest in the area of prepaid dental care are: *Insured Dental Care* by Avnet and Nikias (819) and *Social Class and the Use of Dental Care Under Prepayment* by Nikias (820). Nikias (821) confirmed earlier findings of Smith, et al. (810). Draker (822–824) studied family expenditures for dental care in New York State. Another type of group purchase of dental care is the Dental Service Corporation (825). Vidmar (826) reported on the Corporation and its role in the delivery of oral health services. Baum studied dental care under Medicaid in Boston and its suburbs (827).

EVALUATION AND QUALITY OF DENTAL SERVICES

Schonfeld (828) referred to the Yale studies (829) indicating the need for standards of quality to measure dental care. Jong and Leverett (830) attempted to determine whether dental treatment could be organized more cheaply in one of Boston's neighborhood health centers than in private practice. Williams, Wechsler, and Avery (831), reporting on a survey in Boston Standard Metropolitan Statistical Area (SMSA), found that expanding dental practice would encourage the hiring of auxiliary personnel rather than lengthening the hours of the dentist.

TECHNOLOGY

Christopher (832) reviewed efforts in using computers in treatment, oral pathology, dental education, dental research, and in designing dentures. Pelton and associates (833) developed and tested a simulation model as a tool for analyzing the economic consequences of using various dental care team mixes in dental practice.

PHARMACY-RELATED HEALTH SERVICES RESEARCH

The first identified pharmacy-related health services research was the 1953 study by Furstenberg, et al. (834), of the prescribing patterns of physicians as an index to the quality of care provided. Several years later, Teplitsky (835) used a mailed questionnaire to determine the merits or shortcomings of drug detailing in hospitals, and Coleman, Menzel, and Katz (836) conducted a pioneer study of the "diffusion" process by which a new drug is introduced into the prescribing patterns of midwest doctors. Subsequently, Winick (837) studied the "diffusion" process among physicians in a large city, using different methods and obtaining different results from those of Menzel and Katz (838). Others who studied sources of physicians' information about drugs were Bauer and Wartzel (839), Ferber and Wales (840), and Burkholder (841).

Wilson and colleagues (842,843) in Great Britain used operational research methods to study the influence of pharmaceutical mailings, journal advertising, detailmen, and other factors, upon the prescribing patterns of general practitioners. Martin (844) in Great Britain analyzed a large number of prescriptions issued under the National Health Service and found large prescribing variations in different regions. His findings were confirmed by Wilson, et al. (845), Lee (846), and Lee, et al. (847).

A study conducted by the Committee on Enquiry into the Relationship of the Pharmaceutical Industry with the National Health Service attempted to estimate the influence of detailmen, promotional material, journal articles, and expert recommendations on the prescribing patterns of general practitioners (848).

The prescribing patterns of physicians were studied by

Muller (849), Cluff (850), Stolley, Lasagna, et al. (851,852), and Maronde and associates (853,854). Kunin and Dierks (855) reported on an experimental physician-pharmacist voluntary program to improve prescription practices. Safren, et al. (856) used the critical incident technique to study hospital medication errors.

Drug formularies are used mainly by hospital staffs to promote rational prescribing and are considered an effective tool in controlling drug costs. Muller and Westheimer (857) analyzed responses from 104 short-term general hospitals to determine effectiveness of the use of formularies on decision-making of physicians, and the cost effectiveness of such use. Muller (858) also studied the factors which influence the choice of drugs purchased by the institutional pharmacy. In 1965 Lamy and Flack (859) conducted a mail survey of the hospital formulary system to find how many hospitals had a Pharmacy and Therapeutics Committee and a formulary or drug list. Furstenberg (834) showed researchers how prescription records, as part of the formulary system, could be used as an index of rationality of drug therapy when compared with official listings of acceptable drugs.

The unit dose concept was an outgrowth of concerns over medication errors and an effort to provide an element of safety. Simon, et al. (860), looked at the attitudes of nurses, physicians and pharmacists toward a unit dose drug distribution system. Durant and Zilz (861) studied the unit dose concept utilizing the pharmacist on the wards. Slater and Hripko (862,863) determined whether basic changes in the pharmacy and on the nursing unit are necessary to the successful operation of such a system. Barker and Heller (864) attempted to raise the quality of drug therapy in hospitals through the study and improvement of methods by which physician medication orders are carried out.

With adoption of the unit dose packaging program, the pharmacist moved into the mainstream of patient care and became an important member of the hospital team. Black and Tester (865) found he became a valuable source for good drug information for hospital staff. Greth, Tester, and Black (866) studied decentralized pharmacy operations and drug information services and utilization in a decentralized pharmacy substation. In 1962 Burkholder (867) studied the establishing and functioning of a Drug Information Center at the University of Kentucky Medical Center using the hospital pharmacist as the knowledgeable resource in drugs.

Drug information services in hospitals have been developed in a variety of ways. Benson and Kabat (868) showed all staff used such an information service two or three times a week. Bell, et al. (869), developed a mechanism for dissemination of drug information to the practicing physician. The pharmacist as an active member of the medical team involved in bedside patient care presents the physician with drug issues which he might not otherwise consider.

Another study of the pharmacists' new role in patient care was reported by Owyang, Miller, and Brodie (870). The nurse was returned to bedside nursing by involving the pharmacist in the administration of medications. The Task Force on the Pharmacist's Clinical Role (871) reported that pharmacists' participation in patient care is associated more with hospital practice than non-hospital. White (872) reported on the pharmacy station as a complete educational station, with pharmacists actively engaging in decisions, research, and work of the clinical care teams of the health center.

Drew and Shapiro (873) studied sociological determinants of drug utilization in a university hospital. Using records as their data source, they found administration of drugs for all patients, public and private, was constant, although public clinic patients were more accepting of pain and needed fewer supportives. Greenlick and Darsky (874) in the study of Prescription Services, Inc. of Windsor, Ontario, found drug utilization among the aged to be predictably higher. In a working class housing estate in Great Britain, Jeffreys, Brotherston, and Cartwright (875) inquired about the kind of medicines taken in a certain period. Brewster, Allen, and Holen (876), studying records of the Group Health Association of the District of Columbia, found the number of prescriptions increased steeply with advancing age and that the average prescription price was considerably above the national average. This probably reflects the prescribing of more expensive drugs in larger quantities for enrollees, exceeding the deductible amount. Greenlick and Saward (877), analyzing the Oregon region of the Kaiser Foundation Health Plan, found where Plan members utilized pharmacy services, a reduction in cost per prescription effected a savings to members and still showed a profit in operation.

Slavin (878) reports various ways in which automation was applied in pharmacy related services: cutting down on clinical paperwork; availability of pharmacological reference data; accessible formulary data via TV screens; printouts of formularies for use on wards; and pre-packaging of drugs and containers. McEvilla (879) attempted to determine whether information contained on filled prescription orders could be collected, recorded, and retrieved easily and what multiple investigational techniques were applicable to this research. Allen, Hurd, and Dodds (880) described a demonstration of a feasible method of obtaining prescription information from pharmacies in a form readily adaptable to the production of periodic reports of pharmacy activity or special research studies. Flack (881) evaluated the several methods by which hospital formularies may be printed, finding other benefits accruing from EDP application to the hospital formulary—such as inventory control, purchasing, patient billing, drug surveillance, and adverse drug reaction reporting.

Seibert, Brunjes, Soutter, et al. (882), developed a program for processing prescriptions. Using a computer, it was possible to store data related to the prescribing physician, patient, clinic visited, and drug and quantity prescribed. In five Boston hospitals (883), a comprehensive surveillance program was undertaken in 1966. Information was obtained on efficacy and toxicity of pharmacologically active agents and on sub-populations which react positively or negatively to different drugs. California Medicaid (Medi-Cal) was studied by Preston and Boisseree (884) in the San Joaquin area. The potential for significant savings in the administration of public medical assistance was illustrated. Bartel and Fahey (885) reported on a study to reduce paperwork at nursing stations by computerizing admissions, nursing stations, laboratories, and pharmacy areas.

Knapp, Wolf, and Rudy (886) surveyed 36 pharmacies in a large metropolitan area. They found a lack of patient orientation among pharmacists, who kept to traditional functions, such as dispensing drugs, rather than maintaining drug records on patients, alerting physicians, and cautioning patients concerning contradictory reactions. Galloway and Eby (887) surveyed households of residents in urban and rural poverty areas to determine the need for nontraditional roles for pharmacists in such areas, and the acceptability of such roles. Nelson and Watkins (888) undertook to determine why people select pharmacy as a career. In the report of the Task Force on the Pharmacist's Clinical Role (871), several projections were made concerning the future role of pharmacists.

One of the most significant series of studies relating to prescription drugs came from the Task Force on Prescription Drugs established in May of 1967. Acting upon a Presidential directive, the Secretary of Health, Education, and Welfare charged the Task Force to "Undertake a comprehensive study of the problems of including the cost of prescription drugs under Medicare." The information derived from these studies serves as the basis for the findings and recommendations of a series of separate publications (889). *The Drug Prescribers* (890) covers the prescribing patterns of physicians and the types of training and sources of information available to them, a consideration of drug quality, and the drug formularies available to them. *The Drug Users* (891) delineates the drugs actually used by elderly men and women. *The Drug Makers and The Drug Distributors* (892) combines studies on the manufacture and the distribution of prescription drugs. *Approaches to Drug Insurance Design* (893) studies some of the chief elements in designing a drug insurance program and presents various alternatives for consideration in developing a program blueprint.

HEALTH CARE TECHNOLOGY

Health care technology is the newest component of health services research. Following World War II, there was much interest in converting the new technologies developed for military purposes, particularly mathematical computers, to peacetime use (894,895). The health care field seemed to offer wide opportunity. Dating from 1948, research was first centered on use of computers for mathematical biology. Since analysis of biological systems and the study of physiology as a mathematical science are technically not in the realm of health services research, no effort is made here to identify the basic research addressed to these problems. Neither have we traced the development of biomedical engineering in such areas as bioinstrumentation, technology for individual tests and procedures, such as EKG, EEG, or spirometry, the development of prostheses or mechanical aids for the disabled, nor engineering research in radiology, surgery, or other disciplines concerned with the direct care of patients.

Instead, this overview is limited to health care technology which has the potential for (1) increasing productivity and efficiency in the delivery of health services, (2) improving access to health care, and (3) improving the quality of care. There remains a large element of R&D even within these limited categories, but the overall contributions of this field are more readily seen when examined from the perspective of research. Within these boundaries, the major area of research and exploration has been the application of computer technology for the automation of: medical diagnosis, screening for disease detection, clinical laboratories, patient monitoring, medical records, medical history taking, and hospital information systems. Development of these several areas has been guided by a common need for more efficient means of obtaining, storing, retrieving, and communicating large quantities of information.

Several characteristics distinguish research in health care technology from the other categories of health services research:

• The work has been concentrated in a relatively small number of sites

• Investigative teams, of necessity, have drawn from the medical and engineering professions and a wide variety of disciplines

• Research units of private industry frequently collaborate with the investigators from health care institutions

• Because of the great expense involved, federal support has figured more prominently in the development of health care technology than in any other area of health services research.

By 1955, the need to develop more efficient ways of classifying, correlating, storing, and retrieving available medical information for adequate provision of health care was recognized. Modern medical care had become increasingly complex. The many new discoveries emanating from biomedical research had greatly expanded the base and multiplied the sources of medical knowledge. Automation of information handling, to the extent feasible, and development of data management systems began to hold considerable appeal both for the diagnosis and treatment of individual patients and for the management and evaluation of groups of patients as they moved through the health care delivery system. The important feature of this form of health care technology is that the quality and quantity of data handling far exceeds the capability of human operators. It is economical feasibility that still remains to be tested (cost/effectiveness).

Several pioneering groups began to explore the potentials of computer technology for the acquisition, integration, and processing of medical data for: medical diagnosis, screening for disease detection, and patient monitoring. Only Lipkin and Hardy (896) and Ledley and Lusted (897) reported on their initial work prior to 1960. Both of these teams concentrated on the correlation of data for medical diagnosis. Since 1960, and particularly since 1966, there has been a steadily growing literature reporting experience in the development of health care technology. Most of these reports were descriptive in nature, and few could be classified as scientifically evaluated demonstrations.

Application of computer technology to medical diagnosis was reported by Lipkin, Engle, et al. (898); Caceres and associates (899–903); Horvath (904); Cooper, McGough, et al. (905); Dickson and Stark (906); Lincoln and Parker (907); Gorry and Barnett (908,909); Lusted (910); Gleser and Collen (911); Bishop and Warner (912); and Warner, Rutherford, and colleagues (913,914). Not all of the early expectations of automated diagnosis were realized. Barnett's review article *Computers in Patient Care* (915) presents a critical analysis, as of 1968, of the potential and the problems of medical diagnosis by computer. Bleich's computer-based consultation in diagnosis and management of medical problems is a working, sophisticated, and useful program (916).

Some of the first and most sustained work on automated multiphasic screening has been done by Collen, Ruben, Davis, et al., of the Kaiser-Permanente Health Foundation (917–919). Other researchers who addressed themselves to this problem are Brodman and van Woerkom, who reported their experience with computer-aided diagnostic screening for 100 common diseases (920), and several members of the Caceres group. Hochberg, Calatayud, et al., explored the use of computer-based electrocardiogram analysis in rapid mass screening (921) and Silver, Schonfeld, et al., reported on a survey for chronic obstructive lung disease in a clinic population (922).

Because automated health testing offered a promising method of disease detection in its early stages for large population groups, there was strong pressure to introduce such programs on an operational basis before they had been thoroughly researched and evaluated. A group of scientists of the United Kingdom published, in 1968, a critical review of the tests most commonly used in screening programs (923). Two years later, the National Center for Health Services Research and Development sponsored an invitational conference of distinguished consultants to distill the best of current knowledge and experience in the form of provisional guidelines for automated multiphasic health testing and services. These guidelines, published in three volumes (924), have been widely distributed to health care provider and consumer groups, third party payers, and commercial firms. The provisional nature of these guidelines is emphasized because it is expected that additional experience will require their revision.

Spencer, Vallbona, and colleagues of the Baylor University College of Medicine and the Texas Institute for Rehabilitation and Research were among the first investigators to automate measurement and collection of biological data in a clinical setting and to integrate it with other information for purposes of analyzing and improving clinical and institutional management (925–928). This remains the only operational example of a total hospital information system.

The goal of the computer project of Massachusetts General Hospital also was improvement of patient care. As described by Barnett and Hofmann (929), it was so all-encompassing that the entire effort might be classified most appropriately as a computer-based hospital information system. However, segments of the project contribute to knowledge regarding particular elements of the total system. For example, Greenes, Pappalardo, et al., dealt specifically with the management of clinical data (930); Greenes, Barnett, et al., with physician-computer interaction in the provision of medical care (931); and Betaque and Gorry (932), with analysis of decision problems in both medical diagnosis and treatment.

Weil, Shubin, and Rand (933) found a digital computer system used at the bedside efficient for monitoring the physiological conditions of critically ill patients in shock. Warner, et al., have developed a system for computer-based monitoring of patients in a six-bed intensive care ward to which patients return after open-heart surgery (934).

Lipmann and Preece (935) have tested on a pilot basis a computerized medical data system which permits general practitioners within a 200-mile area to maintain centrally-stored clinical data and to retrieve, by telephone, information as needed for day-to-day patient management. This prototype remote control system will be used in larger-scale experiments in which family doctors and hospitals will be linked into a computer network with a central bank of clinical documents and patient records.

Another facet of patient care to which computers have been applied is the electronic processing of clinical laboratory data. Automation of laboratory data has been stimulated by a rapidly increasing volume of work and concomitant manpower problems. Advantages of automated processing, in addition to reducing the need for ever-expanding staff, are more rapid service and minimal error. Lamson (936) discusses the collecting, organizing, and recording of laboratory medical data in his chapter of Stacy and Waxman's *Computers in Biomedical Research* and describes the experience of the University of California Hospital, Los Angeles, in developing and implementing an automated laboratory data system.

Hicks and associates of the Department of Medicine, University of Wisconsin, reported their experience with on-line data acquisition in the clinical laboratory (937). An earlier report (938) had discussed the routine use of a small digital computer in the clinical laboratory. Seligson and colleagues of the Yale University School of Medicine have done extensive work, using alternative approaches, on automation of data processing in the clinical laboratory (939-944). The purpose of their work has been to increase precision and accuracy of tests, enhance communication of information from laboratory to physician, and improve efficiency of laboratory operations. Rappoport, Gennaro, and Constandse have reported a number of times to the hospital community on the methods used by the Youngstown, Ohio Hospital Association in automating the hospital laboratory (945-949). In his book, *The Computer and Medical Care* (950) Lindberg has described technical aspects of the computer laboratory data transmission system used by the University of Missouri Medical Center.

An excellent overview of the British experience has recently been published (951).

Preparation, transmission, and review of traditional basic medical records or charts have long been problems in the provision of medical care. Too often records are illegible, and either incomplete or overwhelmingly detailed. Synchronizing their transfer with the movement of the patient from one source of care to another has been difficult. In order to improve the accuracy and utility of medical records and to make manageable a larger volume of data, computers have been used to store and analyze defined abstracts of individual medical records and to link significant information from separate records. Acheson's study of medical record linkage (952) is a landmark. Others who have contributed importantly in dealing with this problem are: Levy, Cammarn, and Smith (953); Slee (954); Korein, et al. (955); Slack and colleagues (956); Collen, Davis, and associates (957,958); Weed (959,960); Kiely, Juergens, et al. (961); Robinson (962); and Warner and Morgan (963).

Chief difficulties encountered in the automation of medical records have not been with mechanical processing or retrieval of information, but with the selection, classification, and coding of original data to be captured.

Development of automated systems for obtaining the medical histories of patients has been stimulated primarily by the need to conserve medical manpower, since history-taking consumes a substantial portion of a physician's time. Secondarily, it was believed that automated history-taking could serve as a screening device in the early detection of disease.

To a large extent, automated medical history-taking has been developed by several of the same teams that have pioneered in other aspects of health care technology, notably Slack, Hicks, and Van Cura; Collen, Cutler, and Siegelaub; and Grossman, Barnett, and Swedlow. The Slack team was particularly interested in patient reaction to computer-based medical interviewing—nonverbal behavior—as well as keyboard responses (964–967). Of primary concerns to the Collen group was the reliability of a self-administered medical questionnaire (968). Grossman, Barnett, et al., concentrated on evaluation of computer-acquired patient histories (969) and on simplification of programming for automated medical histories (970). Others who have reported work on automated medical histories are: Mayne, Weksel, and Sholtz (971); Kanner (972); Coombs, Murray, and Krahn (973), and Gottlieb, Beers, Bernecker, et al. (974). The recency of all this work is worthy of note. None of these reports appeared prior to 1966.

The development of automated hospital information systems (HIS), perhaps more than any other segment of health care technology, has been spearheaded by private industry. It appeared that systems already developed for the management of large, complex industries could easily be adapted to the operational needs of hospitals, themselves complex institutions. This expectation has not yet been realized. The review of hospital information systems made by DeLand and Waxman in 1970 (975), describes some of the difficulties encountered and identifies a few sites where progress is being made toward development of a total HIS. The system being developed by Barnett, Hofmann, et al., at the Massachusetts General Hospital (929) is an example.

A total HIS is very broad. It encompasses any phase of communication or information gathering and data management within the hospital, and comprises a number of components or subcategories. The development of technology for several of these (medical diagnosis, patient monitoring, processing of clinical laboratory data, storage and retrieval of medical record data, and automated history-taking) has already been discussed. In most instances these have been developed as discrete entities and have not been coordinated to form the nucleus of a total HIS. Instead, hospitals have tended to give priority to automation of business office transactions such as payroll, billing procedures, accounting, and personnel operations. These procedures are most like computerized systems elsewhere in industry, hence have been the easiest to adapt. For this reason, their installation has frequently not included a research stage. Inventory control and distribution of supplies and equipment have also been automated in a number of hospitals. Still other uses of modern technology include the development of efficient schedules for outpatients, ambulatory clinic patients, patient admission and interview, and bed utilization. Cronkhite (976,977) has reported on the automation of clinic appointment systems and Leighton and Headly (978) on computer analysis of length of stay.

In spite of the difficulties inherent in the establishment and coordination of total information systems within individual hospitals, a few investigators have recognized the importance of developing information systems for ambulatory care by establishing information linkage among multiple provider sites (979–983). Such multifacility systems are in their infancy. They have yet to be demonstrated at a level of operational sophistication that will satisfy the needs of physicians and nurses dedicated to traditional concepts of good quality medical care. The basic problem is not one of technical refinements. Rather, it is the inability of the providers of care to specify their data needs and to agree upon uniform methods of data management.

As can be seen from this overview, the development of health care technology to date has been directed primarily to the acquisition and management of information for a variety of purposes in the delivery of health care. The brief history of this development has been characterized by both promise and disappointment. Numerous conferences, symposia, review articles, and books by the recognized leaders in the field (915, 929, 951, 975, and 984–997) have been devoted to exchange of experience. Characteristics, advantages, and disadvantages of alternative methods and systems — including their acceptability to the medical profession — have been freely discussed. Even so, until very recently, effort has been relatively unfocused. Almost no complete system exists in any part of the medical care complex. The dearth of data on the cost/effectiveness of these new systems, which represent a tremendous monetary investment, has been of particular concern.

Looking ahead, it is clear that the potential and the direction of health care technology require reassessment. Cost/productivity must be directly addressed, beginning with a cost/benefit analysis of technology already in use. Most basically, health care technology R&D must be channeled to specific aspects of health services where economic and patient benefits are predictable. Health services data systems, automation of laboratory services, and management information systems for out-of-hospital care of defined populations are among the priority needs.

RESEARCH METHODS

The substantive results of health services research, as in all investigative fields, are qualitative and/or quantitative, expressed in terms and forms that depend upon the particular design and methods of research and analysis. Health services research methods have two main origins: (a) epidemiology and biostatistics and (b) social science research and surveys.

Epidemiology is a derivative science and draws upon biology and clinical medicine in its description of the distribution of disease in defined populations and in formulating and testing etiologic hypotheses. Respectively, the method helps define the needs for health care and it suggests approaches to prevention based on the knowledge of causal factors. It relies upon the statistical approach and use of standard mathematical methods of analysis. The techniques of epidemiology can be adapted to studies of the distribution and characteristics of health personnel, facilities, and services (998). Epidemiologists are not all agreed that one of epidemiology's main uses can be to help social institutions, by applying scientific methods to the description and analysis of their own workings.

In contrast to this situation, the collective techniques of the social and behavioral sciences are generally acknowledged to be the foundation stone of contemporary health services research. The earliest studies addressed to a particular segment of the delivery of health services were simple descriptive surveys. Analytical case studies followed. For the most part, descriptive studies and analyses of individual components of health services provided insufficient explanation of observed findings to warrant direct action. But these earlier studies were enormously valuable in identifying critical problems, opening up new fronts of inquiry and discussion, and in forming the basis for a second level of research: the formulation and testing of hypotheses, particularly those relevant to causal relationships.

This second level of health services research draws on the methods and skills of social sciences. With the entry of many more social scientists to the health care field during the late 1940's and 1950's, theoretically oriented research and hypothesis testing became much more popular. Most of the studies cited in Social-Behavioral Aspects of Health Care, an earlier section of this chapter, involve the application of social research methods to a particular problem in the delivery of health care or to the field as a whole. Elinson's chapter, *Methods of Sociomedical Research,* in Freeman, Levine, and Reeder's book (606) should be reexamined from the standpoint of method, per se. Campbell's article on the validity of experiments in social settings (999) discusses the interactive effects of extraneous variables and the susceptibility of various experimental designs to these effects.

Part III of *Readings in Evaluation Research* edited by Caro (1000) is of particular value in dealing with methodological issues, especially those of measurement and design. Likewise the review volume *Program Evaluation in the Health Fields* by Schulberg, et al. (1001), contains a number of important articles on evaluation research methods and techniques. Other social scientists whose work has contributed to greater understanding and to the interplay, cross-fertilization, and unification of medical and social research techniques are Hyman and associates (1002–1004) and Freeman and Sherwood (1005).

The family or household survey has been used since the 1930's as a method of determining need for health services or extent to which a population used or benefited from a designated set of services. It was used, for example, by the Committee on the Costs of Medical Care and the National Health Survey and in the Hagerstown, the Brunswick-Greenville, and the Forsyth, Fairfax, and Montgomery County Health Studies of the Public Health Service. All of these have been discussed earlier in this chapter. From the beginning, investigators recognized certain limitations in data obtained through household interviews. Pennell (1006,1007) and Hoffer (1008) were among the first to point out some of the flaws as well as the usefulness of the family survey. Sanders (1009) also raised some provocative questions. But actual testing of the degree to which diagnostic information obtained by household interviews could be confirmed by clinical examinations did not take place until the late 1950's. This was an important contribution of Elinson and Trussell (1010,1011). Others who critically examined survey and interview techniques as used for various research purposes are Feldman (1012), Hutchinson, Shapiro, and Densen (1013), and Solon, Sheps, Lee, et al. (1014). Haggerty has critically reviewed research methods for determining family morbidity and function by survey, and has identified important contributions (1015).

Bergman and Werner (1016) studied the reliability of information obtained by family interview with respect to children's compliance in taking prescribed penicillin medication. The interview technique was found to be unsatisfactory for assessment of drug utilization. The method chosen by Charney and collaborators (633) as a test of compliance was examination of the child's urine for the presence of penicillin. Charney addressed the same question as had Bergman and Werner, but used an objective criterion.

The validity of the information obtained as well as the cost per personal interview has been questioned. By experimental comparison, Colombotos (666,1017) found that interviews of physicians by telephone had essentially no difference in the responses obtained, as well as being less expensive. His experience has since been verified by others.

Although Perrow (1018) expressed grave reservations concerning them, controlled studies reached a new level of sophistication during the 1960's. The controlled experiment requires comparison of randomly selected populations. One group receives the service being tested, the other does not. Illustrative of this highly developed type of research are the reports by Shapiro, Strax, and Venet, of the Health Insurance Plan of Greater New York, on the evaluation of their program of periodic breast cancer screening with mammography (1019, 1020). Large scale controlled studies of the effect of organization of health services are found in the Family Health Care Program, Harvard Medical School, and Children's Hospital Medical Center, Boston (406,407,1015,1021,1022) and the study of welfare medical care by Reader and associates (367). Other examples of controlled trials are the manpower utilization studies by Charney, Kitzman, et al. (52) and Lewis and Resnick (50).

In contrast to controlled trials are the methods available to economists, as illustrated by Klarman (1023) and Yett (1024) in looking at health manpower problems. Here, controlled studies are not possible, and economists are largely dependent upon available data and methods used in other not entirely comparable fields.

A number of studies of health services utilization, particularly utilization of inpatient hospital services, are best classified as contributing to standardization of data (1025) and improvements in methods. Among the latter may be cited Hess, Riedel, and Fitzpatrick's *Probability Sampling of Hospitals and Patients* (1026), Fitzpatrick and Riedel's *General Comments on Methods of Studying Hospital Use* (1027), and Odin Anderson's *Research in Hospital Use and Expenditures* (1028). Fitzpatrick, Riedel, and Payne were the first to apply professionally defined criteria systematically to an analysis of the appropriateness of hospital admissions (413). This work was a partial outgrowth of the earlier work of Lembcke, proposing and applying statistics and explicit criteria for evaluating care provided in hospitals (309,310).

The difficulties of evaluating social action programs have challenged the research methods of social scientists and the health professions alike. Mann examined both technical and social difficulties in the conduct of evaluative research (1029). Horvitz (1030), Packer (1031,1032), and Rossi (1033) also wrote on this subject.

The Seminar on Research in Patient Care sponsored by the

Association of American Medical Colleges in 1965 (1034) devoted much attention to methods of integrating concepts and techniques of sociology in the evaluation of patient care. Problems of the reliability and validity of clinical judgments, sampling, generalizability, experimental design, and control of variables were addressed.

Another conference which contributed to the growing body of knowledge regarding health services research methodology was the 56th Ross Conference on Pediatric Research— *Assessing the Effectiveness of Child Health Services* (1035).

The work of Shapiro (336) and Sanazaro and Williamson (340), recognized in the earlier section, Evaluation of Health Services, was specifically concerned with methodology in measuring the end results of patient care. Berkowitz, Malone, and Klein proposed that evaluation of patient care be approached by relating selected aspects of care to specific dimensions of the medical facility involved (1036).

Methods used to study hospital costs were reviewed by Judith Lave in 1966 (1037). Several years later, with L. B. Lave, she extended her work on hospital cost functions (1038). Rice also reported on methods for measurement and application of illness costs (1039).

As the need for a systems approach to current problems of health care delivery has become apparent, a number of investigators have adopted the methods of systems analysis and model formulation. Application of operations research methods to health services systems, particularly the functioning of hospitals, has been discussed by Flagle (1040,1041), Bailey (1042), and Horvath (1043).

van Woerkom and Brodman (1044) and Gorry (1045) developed methods for modeling the diagnostic process, and Chiang (1046,1047) developed mathematical models of an index to health. The model building techniques of Martin Feldstein (1048,1049), Anderson and Kravits (1050), and others are important advances. At the International Symposium on Record Linkage in Medicine (1051), held in Oxford, England, in 1967, a number of questions of research methodology were addressed.

A major source of continuing refinement of research methods in vital and health statistics is Series 2 of the Vital and

Health Statistics Series, published periodically by the National Center for Health Statistics. Titled *Data Evaluation and Methods Research,* Series 2 now contains 51 separate reports.

Although many people have contributed to the improvement of health services research methods, and to their problem-oriented application, the number of different basic methods on which HSR can draw is really very small. One does not find the same proliferation of methods in health services research that has characterized the whole biomedical research field. But as a result of continuing refinement, the research methods and designs being used today are more elegant and sophisticated than those of earlier years. Involvement of multiple disciplines is necessary because health services research itself has no unique methods or theories. Whether separate disciplines can ever be or even should be welded together for smoothly functioning *inter*-disciplinary research is an open question facing those responsible for advancing health services research as an effective academic function. So far, the evidence is mixed, but instances of such collaboration are relatively few. What is called "medical care research" does represent a tested and productive amalgam of clinical methods and social science methods (606).

This difficulty should be greater in health services R&D, the most recent technical development for bringing about improvement by actual change in the operations of health services. Here, not only must several research disciplines and approaches be integrated, but these—in turn—must be synchronized with practical day-to-day service operations. Yet initial experience indicates that practical constraints and fixed deadlines in R&D facilitate decisions as to how health services research methods can best contribute. Methods employed in the conduct of health services R&D will be discussed in detail in Chapter VI.

EMERGING CONCEPT OF
HEALTH SERVICES RESEARCH

The classification of research categories which the authors selected for this chapter is somewhat arbitrary because the categories are not mutually exclusive. The several areas of health services research have not evolved completely isolated one from another. The headings represent a mixture of disciplinary approaches (e.g., economics, social-behavioral) and component areas of health care (e.g., manpower, facilities). A single research report could well be classified either under the disciplinary heading or the subject being studied. Moreover, any one research paper may have referred to more than one component area in the delivery of health care. When such overlapping occurred, the primary objective or emphasis of the study was the determining factor in its assignment to a designated category.

In reviewing the origins and evolution of health services research, one is struck by the broad spectrum it now covers. It ranges from theoretically oriented research, through descriptive, analytical studies, to controlled trials and evaluations of health services within the community. All of these stages are interconnected by two-way feed-back loops: results of analytic research may lead to important improvements in health services, but—equally important—results of evaluations may uncover new questions which can best be answered by a more basic form of theoretically oriented research.

In examining how its content and methods have changed over the years, one can identify clearly two parallel developments which together form the basis for what appears to be an emerging concept of health services research. The first is the phenomenon common to all areas of scientific research, namely, the progression from observational or descriptive studies to the explanatory or analytic level of research. That portion of health services research that involves studies of individuals or groups has begun to make use of comparison methods and controlled studies based on random allocation of subjects. The use of increasingly sophisticated methods of collecting and analyzing data and more quasi-experimental designs constitutes one aspect of the current concept of health services research.

This combination in itself is adequate basis for advancing knowledge and theoretical frameworks of the parent disciplines, whether these be sociology, epidemiology, economics, social psychology, etc. The aim of health services research, however, is to improve health services through greater knowledge and understanding of health services as they exist.

"Health services" is a seamless interconnection of people to providers and institutions through services which are financed in some manner in a particular geographical, social, economic, and political setting. Health services research must address real problems or questions by obtaining and analyzing data which reliably depicts existing situations. If the research addresses only one area of health services, such as the attitudes of patients, or organization of hospitals, or efficient scheduling in clinics, the results may be important to the parent research discipline in advancing substantive knowledge, theories, or methods. Such research may also be of immediate use to the particular setting in which it was carried out. However important this reductionistic approach may be in advancing research, it has created a dilemma: despite the growing body of facts, concepts, constructs, and hypotheses, the fact of their being derived from differing disciplines and differing theoretical frames makes it literally impossible to aggregate the research results into a coherent empirical characterization of the existing health services delivery system. Further, results of research limited to a single aspect of health services are clearly less useful in formulating alternative policy decisions.

What can be observed, in historical perspective, is the increasing tendency by investigators, whether they represent individual disciplines or a mixture (e.g., medical care research, operations research) to interrelate two or more components or functions in health services in their studies. This deliberate interrelating of several areas of health services delivery is the second defining characteristic of the current concept of health services research. This concept may best be described as *analytic-integrative,* referring, respectively, (1) to the use of sophisticated research methods in describing or analyzing; (2) the establishment of interrelationships among health services components (patients, providers, institutions), functions (services, utilization, financing), and attributes (individual and institutional characteristics, incidence or prevalence of diseases, quality of care, costs).

The origins of this analytic-integrative concept extend back four decades to the Committee on the Costs of Medical Care, several of whose reports are the first identified precursors to health services research as we know it today. From its very beginning, the Committee recognized that it would be essential to have accurate information on the incidence of sickness, the receipt of medical care, and the costs of such care in the experience of representative family groups. The Committee's comprehensive community surveys and Reports Number 26 and Number 28 (757,1052–1057) address interrelated program areas. The community surveys covered areas that were widely separated geographically, with dissimilar economic and demographic conditions. Each survey examined both public and private resources for care. The Committee noted that "Although many valuable hospital and health surveys have been made in the last two decades, no previous study has included all medical facilities, for most have omitted data on private practitioners of medicine, dentistry, nursing, and pharmacy."

Ten years after publication of the last CCMC report in 1933, a special Committee on Medicine and the Changing Order was established by the New York Academy of Medicine to make an intensive study of medical care in the United States. Objectives of this Committee were:

• To explore the possibilities and to formulate methods of maintaining and improving standards of quality in medical service, including: medical research, medical education, the maintenance of health, both physical and mental, the prevention of disease, and the treatment of disease.

• To study the means of making available to larger groups of people and to the country as a whole the best known practice in preventive and curative medicine.

• To explore the possibilities and to formulate proposals of distributing these services not only to a larger number but also at a lower per capita cost than the present system permits.

Convinced of the need for systematic and objective data pertaining to the various aspects of medical education, medical research, and medical service, the Committee commissioned a number of recognized experts in their respective fields to prepare a series of monographs devoted to the major medical problems of the day. Several of these monographs, all published by the Commonwealth Fund, have been mentioned in earlier sections of this chapter (85) (197). Three, prepared by Dr. Bernhard J. Stern, a sociologist, reflected the evolving concept of HSR. The first of these (1058) examined American medical practice in relationship to the technical, social, economic, and political forces of the day. The next two (1059,1060) were addressed, respectively, to industrial medicine and to medical services by government. In each of these, the reciprocal interplay of the same forces was analyzed.

Several years later Mott and Roemer (1061) conducted a nationwide study of rural health and medical care, using a descriptive, integrative approach. Concurrently, Sinai and Anderson were studying the experience of the wartime Federal Emergency Maternity and Infant Care (EMIC) program (1062) to determine what lessons might be learned for guidance of a possible national health plan of the future. Aspects of the program examined included administrative techniques; the development of national, State, and local policies; the basis, method, and amount of payment for care; procedures for professional and public relations; and standards governing the quality of service.

In the early 1950's, Weinerman's study of *Social Medicine in Western Europe* (1063) and Klem, McKiever, and Lear's detailed examination of industrial health and medical programs (1064) embodied the integrative HSR approach. The Health Information Foundation explicitly addressed itself to studies interrelating the general public, their use of services, providers of service, the cost of care, and insurance coverage (Anderson and Feldman (501) and Anderson (442)).

The Commission on Chronic Illness in Hunterdon, New Jersey (1011) and Baltimore City (1065) determined the prevalence of chronic disease in representative populations and the needed categories of services as well. These two studies also advanced the survey and statistical methods of health services research. Careful comparisons were made of the data obtained by family interview and by multiple screening with that obtained by subsequent clinical evaluation.

Winter and Metzner's survey of institutional care for the long-term patient in Michigan (1066) covered both hospitals and nursing facilities. It considered such interrelated elements as levels of need; population characteristics; availability of facilities, medical and nursing personnel; characteristics of hospital service areas; utilization of facilities; and interaction between hospitals and nursing facilities.

A seminar on needed research in health and medical care held in Chapel Hill in September 1952 appears to have had a long-range influence on the evolving concept of HSR (1067). Financed by a grant from the Rockefeller Foundation, this conference presaged the development of systematic research on the problems of medical care. As this research effort evolved and broadened, it would be known variously as research in medical care, patient care research, research in community health services, and, since 1959, health services research.

Impetus was given to this development when federal funds from the Hill-Burton Hospital Construction program became available in 1955 for grant support of research in hospital operation and administration. Also in 1955, funds were set aside in the Division of Research Grants, National Institutes of Health, for a nursing research grant and fellowship program. Study sections were established to review research grant applications received in each of these programs. The National Institutes of Health also supported a few research projects dealing with other aspects of the delivery of health care.

About the same time, there was established in the Division of Community Health Services, Bureau of State Services, a multidisciplinary intramural research unit to conduct studies of community health services where the conventional local public health organization had never flourished. The major effort of this group was a study of the health needs and methods of meeting them in Kit Carson County, Colorado (1068).

In 1959, the scope of the Hospital Facilities Study Section was widened and its name changed to the Health Services Research Study Section. Dr. Cecil G. Sheps, then chairman of this body, and Dr. Ruth Freeman, chairman of the Nursing Research Study Section, collaborated closely in interrelating the research programs being developed by these two groups. They were particularly impressed by the need for more research on problems directly related to patient care. Of equal concern was the fact that the term "patient care" was not uniformly understood, nor were the complexities of its problems fully appreciated. In 1961, a small interdisciplinary group was convened to try to delineate the field. The report of this symposium did not appear until two years later (1069), but then received wide distribution.

Throughout the 1960's, the HSR concept was further clarified and refined, largely as a result of increasing federal support. A bureauwide research grants program in community health services was initiated in 1963 by the Bureau of State Services. Each of its divisions was authorized to support research relevant to its mission, as the divisions of nursing and of hospital and medical facilities had been doing since 1955. The scattered health services research projects formerly supported by the National Institutes of Health were transferred to the appropriate program within the Bureau.

During his tenure as chairman of the Health Services Research Study Section (1963–1966), Dr. Kerr L. White stimulated several special projects designed to give greater visibility to health services research and to attract competent investigators to the field. Examples of these were the 1964 Symposium on Medical Care Research (1070) and the series of health services research papers commissioned by the study section, edited by Mainland, and published by the Milbank Memorial Fund in 1967 (1). Collectively, and in juxtaposition, these papers cover the major elements of HSR. In this chapter, the individual articles have been distributed among the respective research categories to which each belongs.

A number of articles published by Dr. White during the 1960's explained further the types of research required to improve health services systems, to identify problems in carrying out such research, and to assess the methods in use (4,1071–1074).

The next major federal impetus in giving shape, meaning, and substance to health services research was the establishment of the National Center for Health Services Research and Development. Here, the next step was taken in directing the spectrum of research to the full range of health services in a more rational, more cohesive program. Events that led to the Center's establishment and the rationale and strategy of its R&D program are described in Chapter VI of this volume. Dr.

Sanazaro, author of that chapter, was the first Director of the Center and the chief architect of the first four years of its development.

The increased leadership given by the Public Health Service since 1960 to the nurturing and clarification of health services research has been paralleled by its growth throughout the professional and scientific communities. A greater number of investigators have undertaken complex studies of the interrelated elements of health services systems during the past 12 years than at any prior time. Among them were Lerner, who studied the experience of the Indiana Blue Cross (1075,1076) and health progress in the United States between 1900 and 1960 (1077). Lerner also examined three forms of health care coverage in four dimensions of performance: use of services, cost of these services, their quality, and subscriber satisfaction (1078).

Others who reported multidimensional studies in the early 1960's were: Lindsey—*Socialized Medicine in England and Wales: The National Health Service, 1948-1961* (1079); George Silver—*Family Medical Care: A Report on the Family Health Maintenance Demonstration* (1080); Querido—*The Efficiency of Medical Care* (8); Horvath—*British Experience with Operations Research in the Health Services* (1081); Klem—*Physician Services Received in an Urban Community (the Washington Heights District of New York City) in Relation to Health Insurance Coverage* (1082); Gottlieb and Spaulding—*Controls Within and Upon the Voluntary Health System* (1083); Charron—*Health Services, Health Insurance, and Their Interrelationship: A Study of Selected Countries* (1084); Wirick and Barlow—*The Economic and Social Determinants of the Demand for Health Services* (1085); and Robert Morris—*Basic Factors in Planning for the Coordination of Health Services* (1086). Odin Anderson explicitly urged that utilization research take into account organization, financing, and social-psychological variables (442). A decade later, in an updated report, Anderson and Andersen (1087) documented the additional knowledge and understanding of utilization made possible by this approach and advocated further application of the "systems approach."

During the latter half of the 1960's and the early 1970's, more and more studies were devoted to the factors and process of health services planning, including the application of systems analysis and model building techniques. Here was a new generation of health services research. Opening the frontier were Martin Feldstein (1048,1049), Odin Anderson and Kravits (1050), Navarro (1088–1093), Gue (1094), Wirick (1095), Jelinek (1096), Paul Feldstein and Kelman (1097), Zemach (1098), and James G. Anderson (1099). Jaeger used the systems approach for evaluating national hospital policy (1100).

Additional investigators who applied the combined analytic-integrative HSR concept to current problems of health care delivery during this period were Sasuly and Hopkins (1101), Gibson and associates (1102), Haggerty (3,1103), Hurtado, Greenlick, and Saward (1104,1105), Curran, Stearns, and Kaplan (1106), Weinerman (1107,1108), Roemer and DuBois (1109), Pauly and Drake (1110), Goodrich, Olendzki, and Reader (367), Goss (355), Rosemary Stevens (1111), Gartside (1112), Hardwick, Shuman, and Barnoon (1113), McDermott, Deuschle, and Barnett (1114), and Kane and Kane (1115). The best single overview of the analytic-integrative concept of HSR can be obtained by examining changes over time in research on indices and correlates of utilization of health services (461).

It is likely, given the evidence of a continuing trend, that this emerging concept of HSR will soon have to meet a critical test. That will be whether HSR is generating knowledge which can accurately predict future states in health services, depending upon specified changes in any particular component or function, such as may occur with some form of national health insurance. Such capability must be demonstrated before the results of HSR can be used to support major policy decisions. Greater use of quasi–experimental designs and sound analyses of interactions among major components and functions of health services should increase the likelihood that policy-oriented HSR passes this test.

Less rigorous HSR is needed to contribute to improvements in the operations of health services, but the "systems approach" remains the central guiding principle. Deep understanding of one narrow aspect of health services is demonstrably less useful in the field of health services than more superficial but documented valid relationships between two or more broader variables.

The goal of HSR is progressively greater understanding of all interrelationships in health services to be derived from social, political, medical, financial, economic, legal, organizational, operational, and theoretical perspectives. Individual disciplines must continue to provide both the theoretical guidance and the constantly growing power of good design, rigorous execution, and proper analysis. The integration of the results of such discipline-oriented research into a coherent theoretical framework is a challenge. Results of research from differing theoretical frames lead to widely differing implications for intervention (1116). The growing body of results from the analytic-integrative form of HSR should expedite resolution of both of these difficulties by facilitating validation of conclusions both within and between disciplines.

Chapter II
Influence of Philanthropic Foundations and Professional Organizations, the Federal Government, and Various Commission Reports

E. Evelyn Flook

Many forces have influenced the evolution of the separate strands of health services research and the interweaving of these strands to address more effectively today's complex problems in the delivery of health care. Philanthropic foundations and professional organizations have had important early and continuing effects on the directions of health services research. The Federal Government has recently provided substantial support. Numerous commissions have, in the past decade especially, represented private and public interests in sponsoring studies and in identifying policy issues in need of research. This chapter will examine the impact of these several forces and note the shift of influence at various points in time.

PHILANTHROPIC FOUNDATIONS

More than a dozen private foundations have played an historic role in pioneering support of activities contributing to the advancement of health services research. The extent of

82

participation has been quite variable. It ranges from episodic, collaborative financing of major, nationwide studies to sustained programs of support, over longer periods of time, for localized innovative efforts. A few foundations have contributed in both ways.

The landmark studies of the Committee on the Costs of Medical Care, the Commission on Hospital Care, the Commission on Chronic Illness, the Commission on the Survey of Dentistry in the United States, and the National Commission on Community Health Services—to name a few—would have been impossible without foundation support. Eight such organizations—The Carnegie Corporation, Josiah Macy, Jr., Foundation, Milbank Memorial Fund, New York Foundation, Rockefeller Foundation, Julius Rosenwald Fund, Russell Sage Foundation, and Twentieth Century Fund—contributed to the financing of the Committee on the Costs of Medical Care.

Three foundations—the Commonwealth Fund, the W. K. Kellogg Foundation, and the National Foundation for Infantile Paralysis—financed the work of the Commission on Hospital Care. The Commonwealth Fund and the Rockefeller Foundation contributed to the Commission on Chronic Illness.

The Survey of Dentistry was supported by the Kellogg Foundation, the Rockefeller Brothers Fund, the Louis W. and Maud Hill Family Foundation and the American Dental Association. (The last of these is a professional organization, not a foundation, and will be treated more fully in a later section of this chapter.) Major foundation contributors to the work of the National Commission on Community Health Services were the Commonwealth Fund, the Kellogg Foundation, the McGregor Fund, and the New York Foundation. Two agencies of the Federal Government, the Public Health Service and the Vocational Rehabilitation Administration, also contributed substantially to this work. Participation by the Public Health Service in studies initiated by voluntary agencies or organizations conforms to a pattern established more than 40 years earlier (see p. 12). Such assistance was sometimes in the form of financial support; sometimes, by assignment of staff.

The practice of most foundations has been to open up an area of activity and to support it for a limited period—either until it has served its need, or until other financial resources become available. Initial foundation sponsorship has frequently led to the growing recognition of the importance of a field by other sources of support. Many health programs of the Federal Government have been sparked by foundation initiative during the exploratory stages. Once the Federal Government became the sponsor of a nationwide program, foundation support was greatly reduced or discontinued.

The Commonwealth Fund, Kellogg Foundation, Milbank Memorial Fund, and Rockefeller Foundation have had especially active programs in the health field since they were first established. Health services research, per se, was not always the primary focus. But there have been subsidiary research benefits derived from a broader and deeper interest in one or more of the following:

• study and control of specific diseases
• training and education of professional health personnel
• improvement of health facilities and services (not necessarily through research)

THE MILBANK MEMORIAL FUND

The Milbank Memorial Fund, founded in 1905, has the longest history of supporting programs and activities in the field of health. Through these, it has advanced health services research. It has had a relatively small budget, but its impact has been substantial. From the time of its founding, the Fund "has chosen successive areas of concentration in response to the continually shifting patterns of the growth of knowledge, the emergence of new problems and public needs, the changing potentials for significant advance and the availability of resources" (1117). Only those which have influenced health services research will be cited here.

During the early 1920's, the Fund concentrated most of its resources on the support and evaluation of demonstration projects in the organization of local public health services in New York State. This represented some of the earliest efforts to address systematically the problems of medical care and health service delivery. Beginning in 1928, and continuing for four decades, the Fund investigated population problems. It conducted demographic studies through its own technical staff; made grants to others engaged in demographic research; and financed conferences and publications on the subject. Recently, as other sources of support became available for demographic projects, the Fund shifted its support to other activities.

During the 1960's, Milbank Faculty Fellowships supported the development of young medical educators skilled in the social and preventive aspects of medicine, and committed to full-time academic careers in this field. Although this program was not large, it was unique and had direct influence on both the volume and type of research activities of medical schools during the latter part of that decade and the early 1970's.

Other types of projects supported during recent years included those directed to the study of organizational development, assessment of health manpower utilization, and the study of medical education. For example, the Fund contributed substantially to the Montefiore Family Health Maintenance Project (1080).

Throughout the years, the publication program of the Milbank Memorial Fund has served as a vehicle for bringing the results of health and medical research, especially health services research, to the attention of workers in the field. Its technical journal has provided an opportunity for publication of long monographs and proceedings of important conferences and consistently carries excellent reviews of reported research.

Currently, the Fund is concentrating its efforts upon the exploration of more effective utilization of health services by consumers, with particular emphasis upon acquisition and application of knowledge about the accessibility and acceptability of such services to consumers. In the development of new ideas and concepts, the Fund provides support to individuals for study and writing and to groups for the exploration of issues through round tables and symposia. It provides research support for the development of meaningful hypotheses and the conduct of orderly and rigorous studies. Thus the Fund's resources are now being channeled directly into the mainstream of health services research.

The Commonwealth Fund

Since the Commonwealth Fund was founded in 1918, most of its grants have been in the broad field of health (1118). In the 1920's, Commonwealth began four 5-year demonstrations of child health service. In each, temporary staff were recruited to give preventive and educational pediatric service, nursing service for children and mothers, and health education leadership in the schools. The records set up as tools for evaluating the demonstrations (196) came to the attention of state and federal health authorities and were used in the development of State record systems. Full accounts of these demonstrations were published by the Fund (1119–1124).

As a result of this experience, the Commonwealth Fund concluded: (1) that such demonstration programs could be more productive if conducted in collaboration with State health departments than as isolated ventures, and (2) that its efforts at strengthening public health work should not be limited to services for children. Therefore, during the 1930's, public health programs were supported in three rural counties in Tennessee, three in Mississippi, and two in Oklahoma through cooperation with the State health departments. The State health agencies, reinforced for the purpose by new traveling field units and by statistical and epidemiological services, supervised developments in these counties and carried the lessons they taught to other areas of their respective States.

These "Commonwealth Counties" became the models for organizing new and strengthening existing rural local health departments, which developed rapidly between 1935 and the late 1940's. By that time, public health as a professional field had become well established and was receiving strong support from local, state and federal sources. There was no longer the need for the pioneering kind of assistance that the Fund had given in its earlier years. Its interest in local health services continued, however, and it supported much of the early evaluation work of the Committee on Administrative Practice of the American Public Health Association.

The most serious problems encountered by the Commonwealth Fund in the early years of its public health service demonstrations were a lack of facilities for medical and surgical care and a shortage of doctors in these rural areas. Consequently, in the mid-1920's, the Fund embarked upon a limited program of assistance to rural areas in the construction or remodeling of small hospitals. This program did not experiment with new forms of health service. It took the best that hospital experience had to offer and adapted it to the rural community or small town (1125). Over a period of 20 years, interrupted in the early 1930's by the great financial depression, 15 hospitals were built with financial aid from Commonwealth.

The importance of the hospital being a local institution, locally maintained, was emphasized. Each was expected to function as a health center, with public health and hospital services developed collaboratively. Care was provided without restriction as to race, color, creed, or economic status of the patient. Local physicians were given fellowships by the Fund for postgraduate study. Consultation was provided to facilitate good operation and administration of the hospitals. A fixed or inclusive rate schedule was introduced at most of the hospitals (1118).

From its work with small community hospitals, the Commonwealth Fund was convinced that the concept of "community" needed to be broadened to encompass a region for effective planning of hospital building and expansion. This led the Fund to support the development of regional hospital councils. The Rochester, New York, Regional Hospital Council was one of the first of these. The regional council concept included the joint operation of institutional services and the pooling of clinical, administrative, and technical skills among the hospitals of small cities and towns and those of the metropolitan center of the area. The results of the Rochester experience were reported by Rosenfeld and Makover in 1956 (87).

Commonwealth next moved to the support of experimentation in the provision of comprehensive health services, provided by both the public and private sectors. Among the innovative efforts supported during the 1950's were:

• The Hunterdon Medical Center in Hunterdon County, New Jersey (1011)

• The home care plan of Montefiore Hospital in New York City (1080)

• The program of the Richmond, Virginia, Department of Public Health for medical care of indigents

• A study by the Health Insurance Plan of Greater New York of family experience with medical care

• A survey of chronic illness in Baltimore by the Commission on Chronic Illness (1065)

• The experimental use of hospital statistics for evaluating medical care within hospital service areas in the Rochester region (309)

• A program by the Tennessee Medical Foundation for improvement of medical care in medically underprivileged areas

All of these were important contributions to the field of health services research.

Other activities of the Commonwealth Fund included grants for biomedical research, medical and nursing education—including fellowships—and mental health projects. Most of these activities are beyond the scope of this review, but a number of Commonwealth fellows have contributed actively to health services research. Since 1955, medical education, particularly the demonstration of comprehensive medicine, has been given high priority, largely through the influence of Dr. Lester J. Evans. Dr. Evans was the first physician on the staff of the Fund, and had been director of the Fargo, North Dakota, demonstration of child health services in the mid-1920's. Like the Milbank Memorial Fund, the Commonwealth Fund has encouraged research and researchers in the health services field by supporting the publication of their findings as research monographs.

THE W. K. KELLOGG FOUNDATION

The W. K. Kellogg Foundation, established in 1930, followed much the same pattern as the Commonwealth Fund in its support of health activities, but with different points of emphasis. Also, the Kellogg Foundation supported other fields of endeavor such as education, welfare, recreation, and agriculture as well as health. Influenced by Commonwealth's leadership in the development of local health units, Kellogg supported the establishment of similar units as demonstrations in seven counties of southwestern Michigan during the early 1930's. The Foundation's assistance continued for about 15 years. During this time, gradually increasing responsibility was placed upon each local community for operation of its program. Primary attention was given to closing the gap between what was known and what was actually practiced (1126). In order to do this, more trained health administrators were needed. Kellogg supported the training of public health practitioners for a number of years.

The Kellogg Foundation probably has made its greatest impact on the evolution of hospitals and related health facilities. Stemming from interest in the needs of Michigan's rural population for access to hospital care, the Foundation organized a Southwestern Michigan Hospital Council even before the better-known one of Rochester, New York, came into being. An outgrowth of this project was the establishment of the Committee on Professional and Hospital Activities and the Professional Activity Study, which it operates. Through grants made to rural communities for construction and equipment or modernization of hospitals, Kellogg was interested not only in demonstrating "the importance of the hospital in a community health program," but also in indicating that "such modern facilities could be economically maintained and still provide adequate patient care" (1126).

In communities too small to support a hospital, experimental health centers were erected with assistance from the Foundation. It was hoped that these units would attract physicians, dentists, and other health personnel to isolated rural areas by providing adequate office space and treatment facilities, and that they would become the agent for coordinating the areas' health services. In some instances these health centers housed the local public health department and provided a limited number of hospital beds. One innovative aspect of several of the health centers was their affiliation with a regional hospital whereby the resources of the larger institution, such as professional and administrative consultation, group purchasing services, and the interchange of patients were made fully available to the health center. These efforts were the subject of continuing study by the communities involved and others, principally the University of Michigan. Funds for the studies were provided by the Foundation.

For 20 years (mid-30's to mid-50's), the Foundation assisted hospitals in Michigan and northern Wisconsin in making available x-ray and laboratory diagnostic services to physicians for the diagnosis and treatment of both in-hospital and office patients. Through these demonstrations the concept of shared services was generated. In some instances, several small communities combined their resources to employ specialists in radiology and pathology which none could have afforded singly. In others, specialist services were obtained on a part-time basis from a nearby larger hospital. As an outgrowth of this experience, the Foundation extended its assistance to State hospital authorities of Colorado, Illinois, Minnesota, and Mississippi for employment of coordinators to work intensively in the improvement of their diagnostic services. The pioneering work of the Kellogg Foundation in the hospital field provided valuable guidance to the nationwide hospital survey and construction program made possible by the passage in 1946 of P.L. 725, the Federal Hospital Survey and Construction Act (Hill-Burton Act).

With the new national program on the horizon, Kellogg was impressed by the need for improvement in hospital administration. This required more trained administrators. Through the Foundation's efforts, this problem was specifically addressed by the Commission on Hospital Care, to which it gave substantial support. Kellogg implemented the recommendations of the Commission and established training programs in hospital and health administration. By deliberate policy these programs were based in Schools of Public Health. It has continued to provide direct support to such programs. In 1972, the Foundation established a national commission to study education in health care administration (1127).

As the functions of the nurse changed, research was directed to the problems of nursing service administration. Beginning in 1951, the W. K. Kellogg Foundation provided support for 14 educational programs in nursing service administration. Also during the 1950's, the Foundation turned its attention and support to community action aimed at reduction of hospital costs. Experiments in hospital group purchasing and accounting services were supported. Results of these experiments were inconclusive, but promising.

The ultimate goal of the Kellogg Foundation has always been achievement of community action to solve local problems—"helping people to help themselves." Research and studies have been secondary to that purpose, but recognized as essential to its attainment. Several major research efforts to which it contributed support, along with other foundations, have already been noted. Two additional studies, financed solely by Kellogg, are worthy of special mention here, although they were cited in Chapter I. The first of these is McNerney and Riedel's study of regionalization and rural health care—an experiment in three communities (251). The second is the ambitious 5-year study by McNerney, et al., of the University of Michigan for the Governor's Study Commission on Prepaid Hospital and Medical Care Plans. The two-volume report of this study, entitled *Hospital and Medical Economics—A Study of Population, Services, Costs, Methods of Payment, and Controls* (163), has become a classic in health services research literature.

The Foundation's current areas of interest continue to be agriculture, health, and education. In each broad area, specific programs reflect current concerns. In health, these are: innovations in health care delivery to increase accessibility, control costs, and improve quality. Expanded roles for health manpower are of particular concern. Examples of the variety of innovative health care delivery projects currently supported are: a primary care center developed by Health, Inc., a private nonprofit organization, to serve a population of 10,000 in Boston; a prepaid group practice initiated by Georgetown University to deliver primary health care to 30,000 persons at three sites in Washington, D. C.; an ambulatory health care outreach center established by a community general hospital in Dearborn, Michigan; a merger of four small inner-city Detroit hospitals to provide comprehensive ambulatory care for a population of nearly 200,000 with previously inadequate access to health care services.

Philosophically, the Foundation continues to be oriented to the application of knowledge rather than to research, per se (1127,1128). It is especially interested in projects that, if successful, may be emulated by other communities, institutions, or organizations with similar problems. It will continue to support pioneering and innovative programs rather than operating phases of established programs.

THE ROCKEFELLER FOUNDATION

The Rockefeller Foundation, with far greater financial assets than any of those previously described, has also covered a much wider range of activity in its program. Its international efforts have been worldwide in scope, and have included support of the agricultural sciences, arts and humanities, biomedical sciences, natural and environmental sciences, and social sciences. Traditionally, the Rockefeller Foundation has been academically oriented, and has placed great emphasis on basic research. Prior to 1925, the Foundation's contributions to health services research were an outgrowth of its programs for the control of such infectious diseases as hookworm, malaria, and yellow fever. In his 50-year history of the Rockefeller Foundation (1129), Shaplen states, "As hookworm slowly disappeared from the South, it became apparent that the Foundation's contribution lay less in its clinical work than in establishing patterns of public health—among them, full-time health officers, well staffed laboratories, state appropriations—patterns which became prototypes for public health work around the world."

The Foundation's broad programs for the study and control of specific diseases created a vital interest in and need for the training of health personnel. This led to its support of the development of schools of medicine, public health, and nursing and to direct aid to individuals to enable them to attend such institutions under fellowships, or to work under grants. In 1916 the Foundation subsidized the building and endowment of the School of Hygiene and Public Health at Johns Hopkins University. It was opened in 1918, and became the country's first complete training center for public health officers. Other schools and institutes were developed and subsidized. Harvard University School of Public Health, beginning in 1921, was the second.

By 1920 there were only 11,000 public health nurses in the United States. This was estimated to be only a fifth of the number required, and their training was very uneven. In 1923 the report of a study supported by the Rockefeller Foundation, *Nursing and Nursing Education in the United States,* was published (694). This study emphasized the need to establish nursing schools with proper academic programs in universities which had hospital affiliations and could be used as teaching centers at both the graduate and undergraduate levels. As a result of the survey, the Foundation endowed a new school of nursing at Yale University, the first of several so aided. Provision of fellowships for nurses as well as assistance to the schools was included in the Foundation's program. As these educational institutions developed, they began to produce graduates trained for research as well as for practice.

Some of the early studies of State and local health organizations were made by staff of the Rockefeller Foundation (182,183).

One of the most direct and lasting influences the Rockefeller Foundation has had upon health services research has been through its support of a number of fellowships for medical care studies during the late 1940's and early 1950's. Recipients of these were such people as Drs. Cecil Sheps, Leonard Rosenfeld, and John Grant, whose contributions to the field have already been noted. This Foundation's support of medical care activities is attributed largely to the interest and backing of Dr. Alan Gregg, then director of its Medical Sciences Division. Dr. Gregg was responsible for the Foundation's moving into new areas of research, including broad studies of human behavior. The Foundation contributed support to the work of the American Public Health Association's Committee on Medical Care and its predecessor Subcommittee on Medical Care, of the Committee on Administrative Practice. These groups had a profound influence on the thinking of their time, and helped shape the position and policies of APHA with respect to a national health program. The staff of these committees was headed by Dr. Milton Terris. The Foundation also gave a few grants to a Special Committee on Medical Care for medical care studies, and supported the chair of Dr. Henry E. Sigerist at the Johns Hopkins University School of Medicine. This was a significant factor in the advancement of health services research because Dr. Sigerist had established a comprehensive framework for understanding health care as a social enterprise. Later, again influenced by Dr. Gregg, the Rockefeller Foundation provided financial aid to the research program of the Health Insurance Plan of Greater New York.

The Institute of Research and Service in Nursing Education, Teachers College, Columbia University was established in 1953 with Rockefeller support. This was the first formalized mechanism within a university to carry out nursing research.

Currently, the Foundation is supporting experimentation in new ways of delivering health care to the inner-city poor and of meeting health manpower shortages in rural areas. Grants have been made to Harvard, Yeshiva, Columbia, and Johns Hopkins Universities for innovative community health care projects. All of these efforts have provided useful information about possibilities for financing medical care, training people in the health professions, and organizing total community resources in the field of medicine (1130). Duke University's physician's assistant program and program for establishment of health services in rural areas have also received support from the Rockefeller Foundation.

OTHER FOUNDATIONS

During the 1930's, the Julius Rosenwald Fund supported the studies of Dr. Michael Davis and Dr. Rufus Rorem for a time, following termination of the work of the Committee on the Costs of Medical Care. It also sponsored the work of the Commission on Hospital Service, of which Dr. Rorem was full-time director. The work of this Commission eventually led to establishment of the Blue Cross Association (see p. 31 for intermediate steps). About the same time the Twentieth Century Fund supported the Committee on Research in Medical Economics and some of the work of Dr. Nathan Sinai.

The Russell Sage Foundation is best known in health services research for its role in the 1950's in bringing discipline-oriented social scientists into key health settings such as medical and public health schools. This was accomplished by arranging entree for the social scientists to this new environment, by subsidizing their initial work, and by publishing the experiences of social scientists in the health services milieu.

Although not a philanthropic foundation, the Health Information Foundation has also contributed importantly to the evolution of health services research. This Foundation was chartered in 1950 for the specific purpose of supporting and conducting studies to help solve social and economic problems in the delivery of medical care. Its work was underwritten by the American drug industry. A few grants were awarded by HIF, but its influence was exerted principally through work of its own competent investigators in collaboration with the research staff of the National Opinion Research Center. This work is discussed in Chapter I, p. 37.

Clearly, philanthropic foundations have been a powerful stimulus to studies, demonstrations, and assessment of various forms of health services over the years. Their involvement diminished, however, once Federal funds became available for activities they had initiated. According to the most recent *Foundation Directory* (1131), "Health used to vie with Education for first place in foundation expenditures. It is now narrowly in third place, with an average of $81 million, and 14 per cent of the 10-year total." This decline is consistent with the basic pattern of foundation operation: to point the way, by financing highly selective exploratory efforts until other resources become available for extending support more broadly.

There are some indications that private initiative may again exert vital leadership in the health field. The newly established Robert Wood Johnson Foundation, second only to the Ford Foundation in assets, has decided to devote all of its resources to the health field in the United States.

Net sums available in other foundation treasuries are greater than ever before. The new president of the Rockefeller Foundation has a rich background of innovative effort for improvement of health services. The National Foundation Council is expected to encourage better programming by the member foundations. As yet, however, no grand strategy has emerged to show where health affairs, and specifically health services research, will rank in the total scheme. But after a decade of strong Federal initiative in health care innovation, the times now seem to call for a resurgence of private initiative.

PROFESSIONAL ORGANIZATIONS

Several leading professional organizations in the health field have strongly influenced the development of various components of health services research. Most prominent among them are the American Hospital Association, American Medical Association, American College of Surgeons, American Academy of Pediatrics, American Nurses' Foundation, American Dental Association, and American Public Health Association.

AMERICAN HOSPITAL ASSOCIATION

The American Hospital Association has long been interested in plans for meeting the cost of hospitalization. As early as 1933, the Board of Trustees approved the principle of hospital insurance as a practicable solution to distribution of the cost of hospital care (1132). That same year, a special study of the trend toward hospital care insurance in the United States and abroad was authorized. During the next decade, the American Hospital Association became increasingly active in the development of group hospitalization plans. The Commission on Hospital Service, previously mentioned, was financed by the Julius Rosenwald Fund at the request of the Association, with offices located at its headquarters. Functions of the Commission were: (1) to provide information and advice to hospitals or communities contemplating the establishment of voluntary hospital service plans; (2) to serve as a clearinghouse of information for the executives of existing hospital service associations; (3) to study other related problems of hospital administration and finance.

In 1938 the Board of Trustees of AHA established the Council on Hospital Service Plans to supplement the work of the Commission on Hospital Service in coordinating the movement throughout the United States. One of the first acts of the Council was to initiate a program of research and information. Funds to support this program were subscribed by the approved plans. In 1941 the Council was discontinued and the Commission (with the title changed to "Hospital Service Plan Commission") was officially established within the Association (1132).

The role of the American Hospital Association in establishing the Commission on Hospital Care and the Commission on the Financing of Hospital Care was discussed in Chapter I. The work of these two commissions during the latter half of the 1940's and the first half of the 1950's has served as a benchmark for the provision of more effective hospital care.

In 1944, the Association established the Hospital Research and Educational Trust as its research arm. Its chief research interests have centered on hospital utilization and methods of improving hospital administration and operation, including cost finding and control.

When the Public Health Service initiated a health facilities research grants program in 1955, the American Hospital Association collaborated in identifying priority areas of research need. In 1966, the journal *Health Services Research* was launched under the sponsorship of the Hospital Research and Educational Trust. This was the first professional periodical devoted exclusively to the publication of reports of health services research.

More recently, again through its Hospital Research and Educational Trust, the American Hospital Association has collaborated with the National Center for Health Services Research and Development (NCHSRD) in developing guidelines for a common data set for hospital management (177a). Association staff also served in an advisory capacity to the Chicago Health Services Research Center in developing similar guidelines for NCHSRD on hospital mergers and shared services (174,175).

Currently, the AHA is establishing a hospital data clearinghouse that will supply standardized data readily usable by a variety of health organizations.

American Medical Association

The American Medical Association made an imprint on the quality of health care early in the century, as its Council on Medical Education worked with the Association of American Medical Colleges to upgrade medical education. The most potent instrument for change was the Flexner report (13), published in 1910. Mr. Flexner's survey of medical schools in the United States and Canada was supported by the Carnegie Foundation for the Advancement of Teaching, but it was stimulated by the American Medical Association. This report was a significant milestone in the development of medical education because it called attention to the many inadequacies of programs then in existence. Research in medical education is not included within the purview of the present history of health services research. However, the Flexner report spoke indirectly to problems of health services as well as to medical education. Inadequately prepared physicians could not provide medical care of high quality. The importance of reassessing the role of the teaching hospital and the need for better facilities were emphasized, along with the necessity of establishing defined educational standards. Following this survey, the AMA became the accreditation body for medical schools, and only graduates of approved schools were licensed by the several States.

Also prior to 1920, a committee of the AMA studied the need for compulsory health insurance at the State level. Methods of health care financing and forms of organization of medical care have been of central concern to the AMA over the years. The studies of group practice by its Bureau of Medical Economics are illustrative of this interest. The most ambitious undertaking was the study of the Commission on the Cost of Medical Care, authorized by the AMA in 1960. The Commission's report (1133) is contained in four volumes. Volume I — *The General Report,* published in 1964 — contains chapters on: *The Economics of Medical Care, The Medical Care Price Index, Demand for Medical Care,* and *Solo and Group Practice.* There are also summary chapters of studies on *Professional Review Mechanisms, Significant Medical Advances,* and *Changing Patterns of Hospital Care.* Volumes II, III and IV give a full report of the study of the last three subjects.

The AMA played an important role in events leading to the establishment of the Commission on Chronic Illness. Beginning in 1946, it had representation on the antecedent Joint Committee on Chronic Disease, along with the American Hospital Association, American Public Health Association, and American Public Welfare Association. This committee developed a set of recommendations, *Planning for the Chronically Ill,* which was adopted by the four associations. When the 1948 National Health Assembly recommended that the existing

Joint Committee on Chronic Disease be continued and constituted a national commission, and that its membership be expanded, the AMA took the initiative to accomplish this. The Joint Committee became the Interim Commission on Chronic Disease for the sole purpose of creating a national commission. This took place in 1949. The AMA bore 70 per cent of the expense of maintaining the Interim Commission.

In 1970, the American Medical Association established a Center for Health Services Research and Development. This Center conducts and encourages socioeconomic research on the environment within which medicine is practiced. The research efforts are organized to:
  • evaluate experimental delivery systems
  • identify cost/effectiveness models for the financing, organization, and delivery of health services
  • provide AMA with research reports and data to assist in its decision-making
  • facilitate participation by medical societies in health services research and development
  • provide an interface between AMA and the health services research community.

To accomplish its objectives, the Center engages in survey research, social and economic research, and health systems research and evaluation. This is one of few health services research centers in the country today with such breadth of program.

The evolution of AMA's research program has mirrored the evolution of the entire health services research field. The emergence of the modern concept of HSR can be traced through the history of the research program of this one organization.

AMERICAN COLLEGE OF SURGEONS

The American College of Surgeons, like the American Medical Association, engaged in early activity aimed at upgrading the quality of medical care. Formed in 1913 as an accrediting organization for surgeons, the American College of Surgeons in 1916 obtained a grant from the Carnegie Corporation for a survey of hospitals similar to Flexner's earlier survey of medical schools (1134). The data obtained were to serve as a baseline for the upgrading of hospital and surgical practice. The conditions found were so poor, however, that the findings concerning individual institutions were never released. Instead, the ACS embarked upon a hospital standardization program in which the cooperation of the hospitals was sought in attainment of minimum standards. A long-range program of training surgeons through graduate education and of organizing hospital medical staffs and boards in accordance with their respective responsibilities and functions, was substituted for the more direct medical audit, based on assessment of end results.[1]

The hospital standardization program was administered by the American College of Surgeons from 1918 to 1952. The indices of quality adopted were: medical staff organization, qualifications for medical staff members, rules and policies governing the professional work of the hospital, medical records, and diagnostic and therapeutic facilities. They were given quantitative expression in the Point Rating System employed from 1948 to 1952 (1134). Thus, for three decades the ACS financed from its own dues a pioneering effort at evaluation of the surgical programs of hospitals. Thereafter, the ACS was succeeded by the Joint Commission on Accreditation of Hospitals in carrying out this function.

AMERICAN ACADEMY OF PEDIATRICS

The American Academy of Pediatrics has contributed outstandingly to health services research through two important studies. The first (1135) indicated where pediatric services were particularly deficient and identified the lack of education for pediatricians in the nation's medical schools as the primary cause. Both the U. S. Public Health Service and the U. S. Children's Bureau collaborated with the Academy in carrying out this comprehensive study.

Twenty years later, the Academy pointed the way to more effective utilization of health manpower. Its 1967 nationwide survey of pediatricians determined how they utilize their own time and that of other health workers in the performance of specific tasks in providing ambulatory pediatric care (43). This

---

[1] The latter method had been developed by Codman prior to 1915, but seemed to be too threatening for general acceptance.

was the opening wedge to both broader and more intensive study of the use of substitutive personnel for other categories of health manpower in short supply.

As a result of these studies, the Academy helped define the appropriate role of pediatric nurse practitioners and developed the essentials needed for approved programs of training. In these efforts, it collaborated with the American Medical Association and the American Nurses' Association.

American Nurses' Foundation

The American Nurses' Foundation, a center for research supported mainly by the American Nurses' Association, was established in 1955. It serves as a receiver and administrator of funds and as a donor of grants for research in nursing. It also conducts programs of research in nursing and provides consultation services to nursing students, research organizations, and others engaged in nursing research. A review of studies sponsored by the American Nurses' Foundation and the American Nurses' Association (1950-1957) was reported by Hughes, Hughes, and Deutscher in 1958 (1136).

American Dental Association

The first major contribution to health services research by the American Dental Association came in its collaboration in 1933 with the Public Health Service in a study of the dental needs of school children. This survey helped lay the groundwork for a formal public health dental program in the Service, that was initiated four years later. In 1957, after some preliminary work of its own, the ADA requested the American Council on Education to appoint a Commission to undertake a survey of dentistry in the United States. As noted previously, the ADA—jointly with three foundations—financed the survey by grants made to the Council. The Commission's report (1137), published in 1961, covered four major areas: dental health, dental practice, dental education, and dental research.

Several years later, the Bureau of Economic Research and Statistics of ADA reported on a survey of dental partnerships (1138). In 1965, with the cooperation of the American Nursing Home Association, two councils of ADA (Council on Dental Health and Council on Hospital Dental Service) conducted a survey of the availability of dental care for residents of nursing homes (1139). The Association initiated an experimental dental health care plan for its own employees and their dependents in 1965. Two reports (1140,1141) were issued on use of the plan. The second report also described changes made in the plan as a result of experience in its operation during the first few years.

American Public Health Association

The American Public Health Association—the professional organization at the center of public health service reform, extension, and expansion—has a long history of involvement in studies and research designed to improve the availability and quality of health services. Some of these activities led to the development of policy statements on important health service issues, which were then adopted as the official position of the organization. Others provided the base for establishment of standards and recommended public health practice. As early as 1920, the APHA established a Committee on Municipal Health Department Practice, which studied the health departments of cities with 100,000 or more population (180,181). Between 1925 and 1943, the Committee on Administrative Practice developed a series of appraisal forms, evaluation schedules, and performance indices for assessment of local public health work. The same committee sponsored the Emerson and Luginbuhl report *Local Health Units for the Nation* (195), issued in 1945.

The work of APHA's Committee on Medical Care and its predecessor Subcommittee on Medical Care (of the Committee on Administrative Practice) developed the base for the Association's position on medical care in a national health program. The official statement was adopted in 1944. More recently, a two-volume *Guide to Medical Care Administration* (1142) has been published by the Program Area Committee on Medical Care Administration. The first volume deals with concepts and principles; the second, with appraisal of the quality and utilization of medical care.

In 1962 the American Public Health Association and the National Health Council jointly sponsored the establishment of a National Commission on Community Health Services. This

Commission, a private corporation which existed for four years, conducted a nationwide study of community health needs, resources, and practices. The results of its studies and its recommendations are contained in a series of task force reports and the summary volume *Health is a Community Affair* (1143). Since the beginning of the century, the *American Journal of Public Health,* the official publication of APHA, has been an important medium for communicating the results of health services research to the community of health professionals.

THE FEDERAL GOVERNMENT

Prior to the 1950's, the Federal Government contributed to the growth of health services research through direct conduct of studies (intramural research), staff assistance to various committees and commissions, and publication of the work of others. Illustrative of studies conducted by Public Health Service staff during the 1930's and 1940's are: analyses of the incidence of illness and the type and volume of medical services among the 9,000 families surveyed by the Committee on the Costs of Medical Care; studies of State and local health services—including their financing, staffing, organization, and methods of evaluation; the National Health Survey of 1935-36; analyses of the distribution, characteristics, and financial support of hospital facilities; studies of medical care provided by tax-supported agencies; and studies of medical group practice. The Division of Nursing Resources, U. S. Public Health Service, in 1949 pioneered in carrying out state-wide surveys and developing manuals and tools for nursing research (1144).

Grants for the support of extramural research and research training in hospital administration and nursing were first made available by the Public Health Service in 1955. Grants for health services research as a federally identified program did not become available until 1963. (See Chapter VI for further discussion of this point.) Study sections and advisory councils serving these programs have played an important role in laying out areas of needed research and emphasizing the need for a single federal focus for this activity.

Section 304 of P.L. 90-174, a part of the 1967 amendments to the Comprehensive Health Planning Act, greatly strengthened this thrust, paving the way for combining and coordinating previously fragmented health services research grant and demonstration programs. In 1968 the National Center for Health Services Research and Development was established as the principal organization responsible for designing and directing a strategic program of research and research and development (R&D) aimed at improving the Nation's health care delivery system. Problems given priority in the National Center's initial program were the: rising cost of medical care; unequal distribution and utilization of health services; inadequate data for health services planning and management at local and national levels; and relative shortages or maldistribution of professional health personnel.

Not all health services research programs of the Federal Government were brought under the umbrella of the National Center, however. The Maternal and Child Health Services (MCHS), a sister agency within the Health Services and Mental Health Administration, continued to support separate research and training grants. This program originated in 1963, when MCHS was a part of the Children's Bureau. The immediate research concern was to find ways to reduce infant mortality and prematurity. The program began by focusing on the study of ways of intervening in health situations, and the way these methods of intervention, coupled with use of basic knowledge, could be infused into new forms of health delivery systems. Among the priorities established for this research program were: health delivery systems for mothers and for children; special needs of the pregnant adolescent girl; health issues in group care facilities for very young children; utilization of paraprofessional personnel; development of family planning as a component of comprehensive maternal health services; and evolvement of methodology and strategy for evaluation of health programs (1145). While the goals and priorities of the research programs of MCHS and NCHSRD are similar, the main difference is that MCHS resources are directed to a selected population group, while NCHSRD is concerned with the total population.

Another major program of health services research that remained independent of the National Center for Health Services Research and Development was that conducted by the

Office of Research and Statistics of the Social Security Administration (1146). The focus of research there over the years has been the financing of health services, expenditures, and costs.

Other federal agencies with substantial health services research activities are the Veterans Administration and the Department of Defense. Both of these agencies are responsible for providing health services to large populations. Although operating within closed systems, they face—to a lesser extent—the problems of organization, financing, staffing, and evaluation of their services which have troubled the country at large.

REPORTS OF NATIONAL COMMISSIONS

The impact of national commission reports on the growth and character of health services research has been quite variable. Some commissions are official instruments of government, appointed by the President or at his request. Others are established by voluntary organizations or private citizen groups in response to concern about a particular problem.

The reports of commissions generally are not research products, per se. Rather, they are an assembly of current thinking and arguments—pro and con—around identified issues, with data to support particular positions. Little new information is developed or presented by most commissions. There are exceptions, of course, if no data exist to answer a question addressed. Then special studies must be made to obtain the information needed. An example of such original research is the material on economic consequences of illness, disability, and premature death arising from cardiovascular diseases and cancer, developed by Dorothy Rice and associates for the President's Commission on Heart Disease, Cancer, and Stroke (1147). Perhaps the chief value of national commissions, committees, or conferences lies in giving coherence to trends, clarifying thinking, developing consensus, and proposing strategies. Frequently, the strategies advocated identify areas, problems, or questions on which further research is needed. Thus, commissions become a factor in determining future directions of the field.

Reports of several officially established national groups

which have influenced the development and priorities of health services research are cited here.

In 1966 the President established the National Advisory Commission on Health Manpower to "develop appropriate recommendations for action by government or by private institutions, organizations, or individuals for improving the availability and utilization of health manpower." The Commission considered manpower questions broadly, as they related to the provision of health services, not as isolated problems. Indeed, the Commission's report, published in 1967 (1148), devoted more space and attention to requirements for improving the health care system than to the education and supply of health professionals. It was one of the first official reports to emphasize the importance of all elements of health care — primary physicians, referral specialists, hospitals, nursing homes, etc. — functioning as a well-articulated, adequately coordinated, system. Gaps in quality of care were noted with suggestions for improving peer review procedures and licensing programs. Possibilities for improving hospital efficiency and controlling utilization were pointed out. Absence of the right kind of data for sound decision-making was observed as a basic weakness.

Among the Commission's recommendations was, "A national program of research and demonstration in the delivery of health services is urgently needed, and should be developed by the Federal Government." When the National Center for Health Services Research and Development was established some six months later, it was strongly influenced by the Commission's report in its selection of program priorities.

In June of 1967, the Secretary of Health, Education, and Welfare established the Secretary's Advisory Committee on Hospital Effectiveness, with Dr. John Barr of Northwestern University as its Chairman. The Secretary asked the Committee to examine the evidence and advise him in four principal areas of health services involving hospitals. These were:

• Ways to improve internal efficiency of the hospital

• The extent to which the hospital should serve as the organizing focus of a new and more effective system for the delivery of health care

• Considerations of the community mix of all health care facilities

• The formula for reimbursement to hospitals and other health care institutions by third-party payers

The Committee's report (1149), known as the "Barr Report," was completed in 1968.

Several months after the Secretary's Committee on Hospital Effectiveness began its work, the President established the National Advisory Commission on Health Facilities. Boisfeuillet Jones, President of the Emily and Ernest Woodruff Foundation, was Chairman of this Commission. The Commission submitted its report to the President in December 1968 (1150). This Commission, like the National Advisory Commission on Health Manpower, strongly endorsed the concept of comprehensive health care systems. Excerpts from its report are challenging to health services research. "If tomorrow's health facilities are to meet people's changing health needs, they must reflect a coherent strategy for the organization and delivery of health services." The Commission's concept of comprehensive health care systems included such characteristics as:

• Combined private and public responsibility
• Assurance of appropriate entry points and continuity of health care services
• Ready access to quality health care for every citizen
• Interdependence of all levels of health care

These are all statements of general principles. How to apply them is still debated, but their enunciation by a national commission encourages research addressed to each.

The *Report of the Task Force on Medicaid and Related Programs* (302) has had a similar effect in generating research. This group was initially requested by the Secretary of HEW to examine deficiencies in operation of Medicaid and related programs, but its charge was broadened to include considerations involved in long-term methods of financing the Nation's health care. In the process, problems requiring research were identified. For example, the Task Force states, ". . . to the best of our knowledge, no State has yet established an effective system of reviewing and controlling utilization from the standpoint of appropriateness, quality, or timeliness of services." Other deficiencies mentioned which are now receiving priority attention through research or research and development (R&D) activity are methods of professional review to assure quality of care and State health personnel licensing laws and their influence on the utilization of manpower. In addition, the report states specifically, "All appropriate sources of Federal funding, in particular the National Center for Health Services Research and Development and the Partnership for Health Programs, should be encouraged to give high priority to development, support, and demonstrations of model health-care-delivery systems."

SUMMARY

The field of health services research has evolved in response to deliberate actions and influences of the private and public sectors. In the early years, financial support by the leading foundations provided both intellectual stimulation and financial support. With the Federal Government assuming a more active role since the early 50's, the foundations' interest tapered off. However, within the past year, the potential for a significant role for private foundations has again increased. Perhaps the time has come when private and public partnership can function in a new balance, more adequately representing the American public's interests in medical care.

Chapter III
Politics and Health Services Research: A Cameo Study of Policy in the Health Services in the 1930's

Duncan W. Clark

To a remarkable degree, 1930–1939 was a pivotal decade in health services in the United States: alliances were formed, decisions made, and opportunities lost that profoundly affected the size and structure of medical practice in the years that followed—and continue to do so even today. The focus of this case portrait is that of interorganizational struggle against the backdrop of applied research. Among others, the figures in the portrait include investigators and reformers, medical practitioners and public health physicians, economists and statisticians—in a nonpejorative sense, politicians all. They are locked in the now familiar struggle that is set off whenever a proposal to apply research findings rationally threatens the *status quo*. The irony in the portrait is the meaningfulness of findings and associated recommendations on the one side and the obstacles to their immediate or early application as professional or public policy on the other.

In the 1930's, the responsibility of government for the protection of the health of all individuals first began to take on the stature of a national issue, one worthy of serious consideration

University and subsequently Secretary of the Interior, was elected chairman. Dr. Harry H. Moore was appointed Director of the full-time Study Staff, and Dr. I. S. Falk was made Associate Director of Study in charge of research. In various ways staff of the Committee were assisted by professional organizations, State and local health departments, and the U. S. Public Health Service. The activity of the last was largely that of tabulation and analysis of data from the Committee's community surveys of illness in families. The Service was not involved in the study and analysis of costs.

The productivity of the Committee staff was such that a "veritable library of medical economics" was produced: 25 major staff reports and 15 "miscellaneous contributions" (1152). Collaborating agencies published 33 additional reports. Research approaches were broad in scope and in the types of questions addressed. The findings of the field studies were of national importance because representative communities were studied. More than just a factual profile emerged. The staff analyzed the meanings of findings and translated them into conclusions which were outlined in Publication Number 27, *The Costs of Medical Care* by I. S. Falk, C. Rufus Rorem, and Martha D. Ring (467). The four main conclusions were:

1. Medical service should be more largely furnished by groups of physicians and related practitioners, so organized as to maintain high standards of care and to retain the personal relations between patients and physicians.
2. The costs of medical care should be distributed over groups of people and over periods of time.
3. Methods of preventing disease should be more extensively and more effectively applied, as measures of both service and economy, and should be so financed as to minimize the economic deterrents to their extension.
4. The facilities and services for medical care should be coordinated by appropriate agencies on a community basis (467).

Of all CCMC field study findings that offended the conscience of the American public and the medical profession itself, the amount of recognized illness that was not attended ranked first (1153). The popular myth that "the poor and the rich both get good health care" might well have been laid to rest under the overwhelming factual documentation. The proportion of families consulting a physician showed a consistent rise with income. Less than half the families with low annual incomes received some dental care while 80 percent of the more affluent families consulted dentists.

In the Committee's review of the experience of a sample of white families (in 130 localities in 18 States), neither the rich nor the poor received medical care in the home, at the physician's office, or in the hospital as extensively or as often as their true needs and the dictates of sound medical procedure were thought to warrant. Economic barriers were considered to be largely responsible for the sharp contrast between the estimate of true need and the care actually received. For each index used, the gap was consistently greater among those having the smaller annual incomes.

In its specific way of employing professional judgments to derive standards for assessing true need, the Committee staff made an important methodological contribution to research (27). Subsequently, the formulas for ascertaining true need were used for many years by the Public Health Service as a guide to policy in estimating hospital bed-population requirements.

From its review of the evidence of the many staff reports, and in the light of differing personal beliefs, the Committee of nearly fifty members could hardly be expected to agree on all policy recommendations. As a result, majority, minority, and other personal reports were produced as part of Publication Number 28, *Medical Care for the American People* (October 31, 1932) (757).

Matters on which there was little disagreement within the Committee concerned public health, coordination of services, and professional education. The analysis of public health need by CCMC staff and the urgency of strengthening public health services had wide Committee support. The subsequent authorization of federal grants-in-aid to the states, under the Social Security Act of 1935, for improving and expanding their public health services, is credited in part to the evidence assembled and reported by the Committee in 1932. Coordination of services received particular attention and the recommendation was made that State and local agencies be formed to study, evaluate, and coordinate services. Improvement in professional education was one of the five major recommendations. But the Committee itself did not study the subject in any extensive or systematic way, partly because the Association of American Medical Colleges was engaged at the time in a national study of medical manpower.

Two areas wherein the Committee was sharply divided had to do with recommendations on the methods of payment for medical care and the organization of medical services. In urging the development of voluntary health insurance and group medical practice, authors of the Majority Report were ideologically committed to voluntarism in the private sector. However, eight of its members held that, eventually, legally required health insurance would be necessary. Furthermore, they thought it unnecessary and perhaps even undesirable to encourage a voluntary system. To a substantial degree their view was based on the experience of European countries which had gone from a voluntary to a required system of insurance. Five other authors of the Majority Report, while endorsing the dominant view that there be the broadest sympathy for experimentation with insurance, urged that this include required as well as voluntary insurance. In 1932 there was no anticipation of intervention by the Federal Government, and any legally compulsory system was expected to be operated as a State program.

Mr. Walton H. Hamilton, Professor of Law at Yale, while approving much of the CCMC final report, was critical of its lack of clean-cut, even uncompromising, alternative programs. His dissent, in the form of a personal statement, held to the view that compulsory health insurance was the very minimum that the Committee should have recommended. Dr. Edgar Sydenstricker, a prominent public health physician and a proponent of health insurance, recorded his personal view that the Committee had not dealt adequately with the fundamental economic question which the Committee was formed to study.

Even the first Minority Report (nine signatories), which was unenthusiastic about health insurance, contained the view of two members to the effect that compulsory health insurance was worthy of a trial. The authors of this Minority Report emphasized that they were not "opposed to insurance but only to the abuses and evils that have practically always accompanied insurance medicine," a position based on their interpretation of European experience, since health insurance was only just beginning in the United States at the time. This Minority Report went on to specify that any insurance plan must be under the control of the medical profession, guarantee free choice, and be open to all physicians.

Although the Majority Report had not classed hospital-type insurance as one of its five major recommendations, its endorsement of group payment and the insurance principle is credited with arousing the interest of many hospitals in sickness insurance. The Great Depression was then at its peak. Hospitals were failing financially and many had to close. Emergence of insurance at this time enabled many hospitals to survive. The combination of the endorsement of hospital insurance by the American Hospital Association in 1933 (1132) and the insistence of organized medicine on professional control of insurance plans, assured to providers of services the initiative and the leadership of the health insurance movement. Given the size of the incentives facing the providers of care, the original hope of members of the Committee's Majority Report, that initiative would come from consumers, was not to be realized and probably was not to be expected. Lessons to be learned from the Committee's Reports were first studied and understood by the health professions and, in the absence of legislation, hospital administrators led the way in the move toward the development of a system of private health insurance. The public and its leaders were much slower to react. Not until the late 1930's did organized consumer groups, more representative of the general public, begin to contest the conservative leadership of the American Medical Association.

Members of the first Minority Report were closer to the mark in anticipating the dominance of providers as sponsors of health insurance. None of the reports anticipated the role of commercial insurance. That so little comprehensive health insurance has emerged from the private insurance movement, so little in the way of payment toward the total cost of health care, so little on the control of costs, and so ambiguous an effect on the quality of care—these consequences have combined to reopen the case originally urged by some members of the Committee and its staff, namely a system of prepaid health insurance tied to a system of group medical practice. This is one meaning of present-day consideration of health maintenance organization legislation now before Congress.

It is to the credit of the Committee that the organization of medical services received prime attention and was the object of the first recommendation of the Majority Report. It was seen as "the Committee's most fundamental specific proposal." The Committee recommended that

> ". . . medical service, both preventive and therapeutic, should be furnished largely by organized groups of physicians, dentists, nurses, pharmacists, and other associated personnel. Such groups should be organized, preferably around a hospital, for rendering complete home, office and hospital care. The form of organization should encourage the maintenance of high standards and the development or preservation of a personal relation between patient and physician.
>
> "By an 'organized group' the Committee understands a group which is so organized that each professional person in it is responsible to the group for the quality of his work rather than solely to himself."

Although the Committee drew upon more than one staff publication in deriving its recommendations on the organization of medical practice, the key study was Publication Number 8, *Private Group Clinics,* by C. Rufus Rorem (209). This was a descriptive study of the administrative and economic aspects of group medical practice manifest in the policies and procedures of 55 private associations of medical practitioners. The report considered factors that enabled groups of physicians to work together and the incentives necessary to physicians to engage in such practice. The monograph concluded that "Private group clinics, through their available equipment and their coordination of medical specialists, are in a position to fulfill the basic requirements of good medical care with economies from which either or both the clinic members and the public may benefit."

In response to this recommendation, the first Minority Report was adamant in its condemnation of group medical practice and saw the recommendation of the Majority as "far-fetched and visionary." Specific objections included the expectation of difficulty with, if not loss of, the physician-patient relationship, competition among medical centers, and the establishment of a medical hierarchy in every community to dictate who might practice medicine there.

Subsequently, the first Minority Report received the formal endorsement of the House of Delegates of the American Medical Association. AMA spokesmen publicly took a harsh, critical view of the Majority Report for its endorsement of voluntary health insurance and group practice (1154). The net effect was to draw battle lines, remnants of which endure to the present day, and to begin to move the competing sets of recommendations to a position of increasing prominence on the nation's agenda of public policy issues.

At the time, in 1932, there was no organized countervailing force to the AMA, none among health, labor, or consumer groups. But there was the Great Depression, which was in process of changing the political climate and the expectations of the public and its leaders. While there was no follow-up organization to pursue the recommendations of the CCMC, as had been planned at its inception, not a few of those identified with the staff of the Committee eventually moved to key federal positions of great influence. In the years that followed they continued to champion change in organization and financing of health care such as had been advocated in the Majority Report. Among them were: I. S. Falk, Margaret C. Klem, Louis S. Reed, and Agnes Brewster.

THE DEPRESSION AND SOCIAL SECURITY

Prior to the Great Depression, American political leaders generally had opposed federal intervention in matters of personal economic security, health included. The Depression changed all this. Inability on the part of local communities to cope with massive unemployment and destitution, coupled with the exhaustion of the resources of voluntary agencies, led to pressure of localities on State governments. In turn, the States demanded federal assistance. In 1931, a few States established emergency relief programs and many more were stimulated to do so with passage of the Emergency Relief and Construction Act in July 1932. In his campaign for the presidency that fall, Franklin Roosevelt advocated federal participation in relief programs, public works, and unemployment insurance, and his election was seen as a mandate to act on these campaign promises. Within a few weeks of his taking office the Federal Emergency Relief Act (FERA) of 1933 was passed and thus, as a matter of national policy, relief of the destitute became a responsibility of the Federal Government. Under Harry Hopkins, first administrator of FERA, a wide range of programs was launched. Federal funds were made available for direct relief as well as work relief (1155).

Within two years there was a broad consensus that favored governmental responsibility for all types of relief. Many national leaders began to urge a comprehensive federal program of social insurance or public assistance or both. The very success of FERA led to the view that the beneficial parts of certain of its programs should be transferred from an emergency to a permanent form. Since each State had set up or had improved its State welfare department under FERA, the machinery had thereby been established for the regular receipt of federal grants and their administration by a single State agency.

In June 1934, the President appointed a five-member (Cabinet) Committee on Economic Security, chaired by Secretary of Labor Frances Perkins, to conduct studies and to recommend legislation to improve the economic security of the individual. Edwin E. Witte, Professor of Economics at the University of Wisconsin, was appointed Executive Director. The Committee's Technical Board was chaired by Arthur J. Altmeyer, Assistant Secretary of Labor, who was destined to become first Chairman of the Economic Security Board and then Commissioner for Social Security. Dr. Edgar Sydenstricker served as Chairman of the Technical Committee on Medical Care, with Dr. I. S. Falk as his assistant. Each had been prominent in the work of the CCMC and both were advocates of health insurance.

Within the span of a few months, the Committee on Economic Security completed the most comprehensive analysis of economic security ever attempted in the United States, and its recommendations were reported in January 1935. In the realm of health the Committee advocated the extension of public health services and noted that it was still studying the question of health insurance. From the very beginning, the medical societies had strongly opposed any consideration of compulsory health insurance. According to Professor Witte, Director of the Technical Study Staff, the medical societies immediately misrepresented and maligned the Committee when it announced that it was studying health insurance. The subject was seen as so controversial that not even study on it could be proposed, much less legislation. As a consequence, some members of the Committee on Economic Security and the President as well, are reported to have been of the belief that pressing for the inclusion of compulsory health insurance would have endangered passage of the rest of the program. Only one member of the Committee, Harry Hopkins, is credited with warmly supporting health insurance. A second limiting factor was the very speed at which the Committee had to move. When the due date for Committee submission of the final recommendations on health insurance was postponed because of the level of disagreement within the Medical Advisory Committee, virtually all hope for consideration of health insurance, except as a later amendment, was lost (1156).

Early in 1935, Senator Robert F. Wagner had introduced, in the Senate, the Administration's bill for economic security, and Representatives Lewis and Doughton introduced it in the House of Representatives. The bill contained the proposal that a Social Insurance Board be created to make recommendations on health insurance, among other matters. However, the House Ways and Means Committee voted unanimously to omit any reference to health insurance in bringing a revised bill to the floor of the House, viz., the Social Security Act, the first to have such title in the legislation of any country. The President signed the bill on August 14, 1935. However, a successful filibuster led by Senator Huey Long prevented an appropriation of funds, and so the President countered by drawing upon funds from other sources and borrowing personnel from other agencies until the next session of Congress (1155).

Passage of the Social Security Act did not end the fight

against it. Not until 1937 was the constitutionality of the Act upheld both at the level of unemployment insurance and old age pensions. In the Supreme Court decision, Justice Benjamin Cardozo cited the general welfare clause of the Constitution in support of the Social Security Act. He asserted the doctrine that changing conditions demand changing programs. The problems of certain groups (the aged) were seen as "plainly national in area and dimensions" and "the laws of the separate States cannot deal with it effectively." The Court reasoned that Congress may "spend money in and for the general welfare" (and) "only a power that is national can serve the interests of all" (1155).

With the Supreme Court decision, the United States established personal economic security as an important national goal and in so doing entered upon an entirely new phase of its history, one marked by new or continually expanding programs through successive amendments to the Social Security Act.

ADMINISTRATION PROPOSAL FOR A NATIONAL HEALTH PROGRAM

In 1935, President Roosevelt appointed an Interdepartmental Committee to Coordinate Health and Welfare Activities among the various federal agencies that were assuming new or expanded responsibilities under the Social Security Act. The Committee consisted of assistant secretaries from half of the President's Cabinet. Josephine Roche, Assistant Secretary of the Treasury, and a supporter of health insurance, was made Committee Chairman. It was the Committee's function to review matters where cooperation and coordination were required and to suggest improvements. In 1937, it was proposed that the Committee examine the health needs of the nation and the possible development of a national health program to serve this need.

Accordingly, a Technical Committee on Medical Care was appointed consisting of Dr. Joseph W. Mountin, Mr. George St. J. Perrott, Dr. Clifford E. Waller, representing the U. S. Public Health Service, Dr. I. S. Falk, then Director of the Bureau of Research and Statistics of the Social Security Board, and Dr. Martha Eliot of the U. S. Children's Bureau as Chairman. This body can be credited with the first governmental effort to try to design a national health program for this country.

THE NATIONAL HEALTH SURVEY

Of particular help in documenting the case of widely known deficiencies in medical care were preliminary findings from the National Health Survey conducted by the U. S. Public Health Service in the winter of 1935-1936 (1157). This Survey represented the second major research effort of the decade in defining the nation's medical needs and resources. Together with the benchmark CCMC field studies, it was to serve as the main source of information about medical care in the United States until the 1950's. The National Health Survey was directed by Mr. George St. J. Perrott with Clark Tibbits, the Field Director, and Rollo H. Britten in charge of analysis. Prominent among the consultants and/or serving as authors of some of the specific research reports were Dr. Selwyn Collins, Dr. W. M. Gafafer, Dr. Joseph Mountin, Miss E. Evelyn Flook, Dr. Dorothy Holland, Dr. Harold Dorn, and Dr. Barkev S. Sanders. In all, approximately 135 research reports were published from the National Health Survey.

In brief, the National Health Survey was a large-scale study of the prevalence of illness and the associated social and economic factors conducted on a survey population, representative of cities of the United States, according to size and region. The approach was that of an 18-State house-to-house canvass of 703,092 urban families residing in 83 cities and 36,801 families residing in certain rural areas. Included as well, were special studies of the health and medical facilities in the counties involved in the house-to-house canvasses; a special study of hearing loss in a sample survey population; and transcripts of records of industrial sick benefit organizations. A communicable disease survey was conducted in 32 cities.

While findings of the CCMC had demonstrated the large burden of unattended illness, the National Health Survey documented the magnitude of chronic illness and disability. This removed any lingering doubt as to the need for improving the availability of medical care.

REPORT OF THE TECHNICAL COMMITTEE
ON MEDICAL CARE

Drawing upon the National Health Survey and other sources, the Technical Committee on Medical Care completed its final report entitled *The Need for a National Health Program,* a program scheduled to be developed over a span of 10 years, if enacted by Congress (1158). The health needs or deficiencies summarized by the Technical Committee fell into the following broad categories: Preventive services for the nation as a whole were grossly inadequate; hospital institutional facilities were inadequate in many communities, especially in rural areas; financial support for hospital care and professional services in hospitals were both insufficient and precarious, especially for services to people who could not pay the costs of the care they needed; one-third of the population, including persons with income, was receiving inadequate or no medical service, and an even larger fraction of the population suffered from economic burdens.

The five principal recommendations in the Report of the Technical Committee were:

1. Federal-State cooperation for general public health services and for maternal and child health services under the Social Security Act should be expanded and strengthened through the device of more adequate grants-in-aid to the States.
2. Federal grants-in-aid should be provided for the construction of needed hospitals together with temporary maintenance grants for the first three years.
3. Federal grants-in-aid should be assigned to the States to help meet the costs of medical care programs for recipients of public assistance and for other persons with low incomes able to meet the ordinary costs of living but not the extraordinary costs of illness. (At that time it was estimated that 20 million people were receiving public aid and another 20 million were in families with incomes of $800 or less).
4. Federal grants-in-aid should be made to the States to enable them to set up a general program of medical care by the use of taxation or by State health insurance pro-

grams or by a combination of the two. (The role advocated for the Federal Government was to be limited to that of technical and financial aid).

5. Federal action should be taken to develop compensation for disability in the form of insurance against the loss of wages due to nonindustrial sickness or accidents. (This was expected to involve complementary insurance systems, one for temporary disability and one for permanent disability. It differed from the first four recommendations in its greater dependence upon federal participation.)

This set of recommendations was described later by C-E.A. Winslow as more than ". . . a program for public health expansion, a program for the extension of medical service, a program for health insurance. It is a complete, coordinated, interlocking, dove-tailing health program for the nation in which all these objectives have their just and proper part" (1159).

The report of the Technical Committee was approved by the Interdepartmental Committee in February 1938, and submitted to the President, who suggested that it be reviewed at a national invitational conference to ascertain the level of public support. Miss Roche convened the National Health Conference on July 18 in Washington, D. C., to present the five principal recommendations and to invite discussion from spokesmen for the public and the several interested health parties (1160). It is noteworthy that not a single dissent on the question of the need of a national health program was heard. The general reception accorded the recommendations was highly favorable with the exception of strong opposition from American Medical Association spokesmen to the fourth recommendation on State health insurance.

ACTIONS OF THE AMERICAN MEDICAL ASSOCIATION

The following September, the AMA House of Delegates met in special session to take action. While generally approving the other recommendations, the House condemned the fourth; in its place the House gave guarded approval to voluntary health insurance for hospital care and to cash indemnity insurance to cover medical emergencies and prolonged illness, but not for other types of medical care. The Association strongly opposed the concept of governmental subsidy of voluntary health insurance plans and, moreover, it was not willing "to foster any system of compulsory health insurance . . . (because) . . . it is a complicated, bureaucratic system which has no place in a democratic state . . ."(1161).

AMA support of as many as four of the five planks in the National Health Program was aimed at dividing the opposition and isolating the proponents of compulsory health insurance. However, even prior to this, rivalry among the federal agencies themselves had had the result of subordinating the priority assigned health insurance to a secondary level, since it was feared that pressing for its inclusion in the Program might imperil the other measures due to be considered as future amendments to the Social Security Act (1156).

For the second time within the decade the anti-insurance campaign of the American Medical Association had been effective. The Association succeeded in gaining the support of other organizations for its version of the National Health Program and its spokesmen directly contested and countered the advice of the Interdepartmental Committee in negotiating sessions before President Roosevelt. Complicating the resolution of this domestic problem was the imminence of war in Europe and the overriding priority of national preparedness. As a result, little in the way of any major domestic legislative reform was to be proposed by the Administration in the months that followed.

CONGRESSIONAL CONSIDERATION OF A NATIONAL HEALTH PROGRAM

In January 1939, Robert F. Wagner embodied the several features of the National Health Program in a non-administration National Health Bill (S. 1620). With the extensive congressional hearings held by Senator Murray, the issue of governmental health insurance at long last had reached the public domain of the highest legislative forum. However, the opposition to health insurance that had been mobilized by the American Medical Association continued to be effective and Senator Wagner's omnibus bill was not enacted. In the years that followed, all portions of the bill were enacted in principle, with the sole exception of compulsory health insurance for the general population. While other Wagner bills proposing enactment of compulsory health insurance were to follow, only the first dealt with health insurance as a federal-state matter.

CONCLUSION

That a form of national health program composed of interrelated parts could not be adopted as one piece of legislation, as in the 1939 Wagner omnibus bill (S. 1620), but only later in bits and pieces, was a portent of things to come. In democracies, we tend to proceed by small incremental change; we assess the effect and modify accordingly. Throughout its history the United States has continued without a comprehensive health policy or a national health plan, and such national plans of health support as do exist are mainly those addressed to categorical groups.

National health planning is an integral part of general socioeconomic planning, and health is but one of many competing priorities. The necessary factual base for a rational health policy has been provided by health services research supplemented by special surveys. But the translation of research implications into actual policy is a matter of politics. And politics in turn is influenced by larger forces such as economic depressions and wars and changes in national administrations.

It has taken 40 years to arrive at the point where the one remaining, unimplemented recommendation of the CCMC can be seriously considered as a national priority item: "that the costs of care can be placed on a group payment basis, through the use of insurance, through the use of taxation, or through the use of both these methods" (757).

The years since 1932 have heightened our appreciation of the CCMC's enormous intellectual, technical, and professional accomplishments. No other body, before or since, has so clearly documented the status of medical care in its day and, based on that documentation, defined the fundamental issues and formulated comprehensive recommendations that remain valid and applicable to this day.

Chapter IV
Health Services Research
in Academia:
A Personal View

Robert J. Haggerty

What is the state of health services research in universities? What are its history, its present problems, and its future? Although this chapter attempts to answer these questions, it falls short of a fully satisfactory answer. As in impressionistic painting, I have tried to capture the essence without documenting all the details. My information is based largely on review of large numbers of grant requests and site visits, as well as reading the literature for the past decade. I have not systematically sampled universities for their research programs and may very well have left out key areas, especially those supported by private money or by the universities themselves and where publications have been in journals other than the health services area.

THE EARLY DAYS—WHY SO LITTLE?

There was little that could be called health services research in universities until the 1950's. This late development occurred for a variety of reasons. First, there was no national data available for analysis until recently. Nationwide registration of births did not occur until 1933, and only in 1956 with the Health Interview Survey out was there any national morbidity data. In addition, university researchers did not have access to smaller systems of care where data could be produced until after World War II when the H.I.P. in New York and the Kaiser prepaid programs on the West Coast began to yield such data. Secondly, there was little general public recognition of any problem in medical care. Most people thought the need was only to produce more biomedical research miracles. But with growing public knowledge of the so-called miracles that medical care now had to offer, combined with frustration over lack of access to such medical care at the same time that costs were rising rapidly, problems began to be publicly voiced in the 1950's and 1960's. Academic interest often needs a publicly visible problem before it enters a field. Thirdly, there were few available methods and few research workers until recently. Physicians were generally busy providing care or doing biomedical research, and social scientists were not yet interested in the professions. Household surveys were not widely developed until the 1950's. Finally, as a few individualistic physicians and social research workers began to study the area in the 1950's, resources from private foundations became available. Prior to that there was little support for such work. The picture has now changed. Third parties, who are increasingly paying for the care, demand some social accounting. This stimulated research, and social and medical scientists have begun to study applied problems. With people, resources, and visibility of problems, the field of health services research has emerged as a legitimate area of inquiry for universities.

EARLY GROWTH AND DEVELOPMENT: A PICTURE OF THE INCREASING ACTIVITY

While two decades ago, there was very little health services research in universities, today there is a considerable amount. Where has this increase in activity occurred? As documented in Chapters I and II of this monograph, most of the early research in health services in the United States was done by public health departments, by officers of the Public Health Service, or by special commissions.

In the 1950's, schools of public health entered the field, especially in evaluation of public health programs. In the late

1950's and early 1960's, other sectors of universities came on
the scene. Behavioral scientists, especially sociologists, became
interested in differential utilization of health services by
different social classes, in studies of organizations such as
group practices providing health care, and in the sociology of
patients. Some of this work was done by sociologists in schools
of public health as well. Cultural anthropologists also began
studies of cross-cultural health care. Research on health facilities and financing attracted workers from university departments of economics, and the field of health economics arose as
a vigorous specialty area of economics departments. Last on
the scene were the rather new departments of preventive and
community medicine and the traditional clinical departments
in medical schools. Their main interest concentrated on medical care research, mostly micro-studies such as problems in
emergency rooms, outpatient departments, referral patterns,
use of new manpower, etc., with a few small-scale controlled
clinical trials.

But even this vigorous initial burst of interest in health
services research by a small number of faculty of universities in
the late 50's and the 60's has been followed by some decline in
the actual performance in the early 70's (as measured by a rise
of applications to the Health Services Research Study Section
of the P.H.S. in the mid-60's, followed by a fall in the early
70's).

PROBLEMS ENCOUNTERED

Yet, with this activity, there are considerable problems in
realizing the goal of developing a vigorous new field of academic endeavor.

WHAT DISCIPLINE, WHAT DEPARTMENT, WHAT SCHOOL?

The major problem with health services research in the
university is that it is not a separate discipline. There are no
departments devoted to it, and therefore, it is not too visible. It
has no graduate students of its own. Universities are organized
by departments of separate disciplines. Any other way of trying to do business in a university has been difficult. Since
health services research is not a discipline and yet is being
done in universities, who does it? Practically all health services

research is done by workers who belong to one of the established disciplines: medicine (especially epidemiology), sociology, anthropology, psychology, economics, political science, systems analysis, public policy, etc. The relationships between the disciplines and health services research are discussed in Chapter V.

Yet this field usually requires an interdisciplinary team, always a difficult task to accomplish. This is particularly difficult in universities, which have yet to solve problems of interdepartmental and interschool programs. In other fields, universities have made attempts to create, through institutes, centers, programs, etc., interdisciplinary programs. Such activities are just beginning in the health services research field with the establishment of some 12 to 15 health services research centers about the nation. It is much too early to render a judgment on the results of such efforts. In other fields, such centers have been in existence for a generation before a new discipline has arisen. For instance, radiation biology, now a respected discipline, arose from the atomic energy — toxicology programs of World War II out of biochemists, pharmacologists, and biophysicists working together. Only after 20 years did the new discipline of radiation biology really start to produce its own kind.

Most of the current workers in health services research argue that good research can only be done by those thoroughly trained in a traditional parent discipline. To shortcut this and try to make a single multi-potential research worker who can work in all of the fields required — sociology, economics, and medicine — would be futile, argue most academics. Individual initiative and creativity by single-discipline workers has to date been more productive than large team efforts. This has limited knowledge of the interrelations and understanding of the whole system of health care in favor of more narrow studies, although it has yielded a great deal of new knowledge in special and separate fields.

Without an organizational base for interdisciplinary individuals that is recognized by universities, it has required a maverick quality in those who have persisted in this work. But all too often even these leaders have rarely persisted for very long in the field, due to lack of stable support from their

departments or research grants and to fairly rapid promotion
of many of the early leaders to positions of administrative
responsibility. With these changes came an inevitable decline
in their research productivity. A strong second and third generation of such research workers has yet to emerge. To date
health services research in universities has been more the
result of individual interest, effort, and ability than of universities' collective interdisciplinary organizational efforts, interest, or ability.

Practical Versus Theoretical Problems

A second problem is the conflict between theoretical and
practical problems. Most of the questions that the public and
the national decision-makers are asking (Administration and
Congress) of health services researchers are very practical
(e. g., does co-insurance control over-use without resulting in
an excess barrier for those in need?). These are very important
questions, but are not the type which are likely to stimulate the
interest of academic scholars. On the other hand, the more
general question of "what influences human behavior in use of
health services" might ultimately produce an answer to this
practical problem and many more in the future. This latter
question is a more general type of research and is more often
what university scholars are interested in and for which they
are rewarded. Traditionally, most research done by university
faculty promotes the career of the individual more than it
directly influences policy. Administrators of public programs
have frequently been frustrated, therefore, when they turned
to university faculty for answers to their questions. This type
of individualistic research has led to disconnected,
non-cumulative knowledge with less application to real-life
problems than is needed. Another problem resulting from the
nature of this research is that much of what is now called
health services research is done as operations research in business (e.g., defining markets, use, resistances, and satisfactions
in telephone, automobile, or supermarket industries). This
operational research and development is not what universities
want to do, for it does little to advance an individual's career
or to develop theory. Health services research is being asked to
supply answers today to complex problems with great political

ramifications. The university is unlikely to be very effective in this cauldron of political controversy of the day-to-day decision-making that characterizes these public policy questions. But there is still hope that the basic type of research, which is what university faculty do, can enrich the field. Without it the applied research field may never yield much that is generalizable. Clearly the need is to combine more basic with applied research in ways that stimulate and enrich each other.

RESEARCH WITHOUT RESPONSIBILITY?

A third problem is the lack of an appropriate setting for doing the research on community health care delivery. It is only 50 years or so since any university took responsibility for managing its own teaching hospitals; but since that time research on diseases seen in such hospitals has flourished. It is tempting to make the analogy to this new field that only with responsibility for some sector of community health care will the stimulus for research in health services be persistent and compelling among university faculty. But there are problems of scale to the undertaking of community health service responsibilities that cause most universities to be wary of such commitments.

This wariness is not limited to academic medical centers, but goes to the heart of some of the current conflict in universities. The degree to which they should engage in a whole variety of human services (welfare, law, business, politics, etc.) in order to be able to do significant and relevant research and, even more important, to educate tomorrow's leaders in how to solve problems, is not settled. It is easy to argue for the remote, contemplative, pure life as more likely to lead to significant research, but there is a considerable amount of evidence that this does not lead its students (its product) to be able later to work successfully on these. Most of the products of medical schools (and other health science disciplines) end up giving care to people in trouble, not in doing research. If they are to be taught how best to render today's care and to work effectively in new organizations of care tomorrow, they and their teachers need to study the effectiveness of various ways of organizing, financing, and delivering care and of knowing what the significant problems are to study. Even more important, faculty will not have access to data if they do not have considerable responsibility for the organization, for this data will be controlled by the organization providing care. Nor can they have any influence in changing the care to conduct experiments. The argument should no longer be whether the university needs involvement in the delivery of care to the community, but how to most effectively do its job.

More than casual access to delivery systems will be needed if universities are to carry out systematic long-term studies, but, with too great a degree of responsibility for management of these delivery systems, there is the danger that there will be too little time, energy, or resources to do the research. In addition, there is the question of how objective can a university remain in its research if it is responsible for running the programs as well. The problem of "coupling without contamination" will remain. If universities elect to remain out of the field, they will forfeit the role of significant research and teaching of this new field. To some degree this is already occurring with research workers moving to the site of delivery systems in order to have continuing access to data and to influence the design of care. If this should occur throughout the country, it is questionable from where the next generation of research workers will come. Like the church of the Middle Ages, the university may cease to offer society what it wants and needs unless it learns the proper method of engagement with the community and with delivery systems.

Inconsistent Funding of Research

The source of funds for health services research has played an important role in universities' on-again, off-again romance with the field. During the 50's, there was very little money for health services research, and the few people who got into the field at that time were highly motivated, usually supported from private foundations, and turned out some very significant work. In retrospect, it may be that the work seemed so significant because it was the first, like the first describers of bacteria in the golden age of bacteriology, but I believe that the initial group of researchers were especially competent and excited by the belief that they were creating a new field. In the mid-60's, federal funds began to flow into universities, although only in small amounts compared to biomedical research. These funds, together with the awakening of medical schools that there was indeed a problem in the delivery of health care, resulted in many young people moving into the health services research field. Many of these young people were motivated more by an interest in changing the organization and in actual delivery of care than by research interests, and the initial relative ease of funding of many of these people undoubtedly resulted in a diminished quality of the research, even though the quantity increased. As the decade came to a close, federal support for research, in general, began to level off. Although there were modest increases each year for health services research, the rate of growth was not as great as had been anticipated. Many universities which had apparently been ready to move into health services research became disenchanted and withdrew their enthusiasm. Many of the young people beginning to go into the field also withdrew, becoming discouraged about the potential for support. This was paralleled by the number of research grant applications submitted to the Health Services Research Study Section, initially relatively small numbers in the early 60's, followed by a large increase in the late 60's and a rapid drop in 1970–72.

THE FUTURE

Crystal ball gazing is always difficult and hazardous. Where health services research will go in universities is not clear. Academic institutions will have difficulty supporting people who are doing short-term applied type research, since the pace and the need for immediate answers will not be compatible with most university structures. However, I believe a few universities should put together a new type of organization where policy analysis can be carried out and where response to public need for information can be fairly quick. In addition, such units will need links to the community of real world delivery systems and to basic science departments where new methods and ideas are developed.

One may ask, if rapid response to policy questions is to be the function, why have it in a university? The major reason is that it is unlikely that most free-standing institutes could attract high caliber people for long unless they are attached to a university. In this setting new scholars can be produced by the mix of graduate students and research. The university needs the stimulus of facing practical problems combined with methodological and theoretical studies to produce a new generation of researchers.

In addition, there is a need to support a few long-range research centers which will focus on development of methods, training of research workers, and long-range problems without concern for policy issues. Both these types of research groups need coupling with community settings of care. I suspect a spectrum of various degrees of attachment to universities would be best—with those engaged in operational research in organized delivery systems and in government only very loosely connected to universities, with a few policy institutes more closely affiliated, and a few theoretical, methodological, and training programs fully integrated in the university. My plea is that the university needs to reach out along this spectrum as far as possible if it is to remain vital. Finally, there must be stable support for the bright individual from whatever discipline who wants to work in this field, for some even as solo endeavors, for from this group are likely to come the few geniuses we can hope for.

What is needed for a university to be successful in health services research? First and foremost—leadership. One or two good people who are recognized research workers and who can draw a group of other people around them are absolutely essential. One key necessity for unlocking the door to productive health services research in the future is the training of such outstanding people. Development and stable support of training grants and career development awardees is then a necessary first step. Stable funding of research projects over at least five years is a second essential. Given the tightness of most university budgets today and the limited alternatives, a reasonably stable budget for such a research program could attract a few outstanding people. Funding sources, private or public, should be prepared to work with these research groups rather than let them drift. The Nuffield Trust in Britain has demonstrated a successful way to provide stable funding and yet maintain responsibility through continued stewardship.

Third, there should be a research group comprising a "critical mass." While research pursued by investigators working individually should be encouraged, there will have to be groupings to provide the necessary back-up of library, computer facilities, data base, and multiple disciplines, each contributing its skills to the same problem. Where this is located in the university makes less difference, but it should pull together people from several departments, such as economics and sociology with clinical medicine and public health. Finally, funding agencies must be prepared for a long time-lag before achieving results and not expect precise answers to their daily practical problems. The university is not the best place for seeking answers to those questions. The university should be the place where investment for the future occurs.

Chapter V
Academic Disciplines and Health Services Research

Robert L. Eichhorn and Thomas W. Bice

WHAT IS HEALTH SERVICES RESEARCH?

Health services research (HSR) is concerned with understanding the planning, organization, staffing, financing, management, operation, maintenance, and use of the health services delivery system.[1] HSR also includes evaluation and analysis of the system's efficiency, effectiveness, and efficacy. HSR is not a discipline, as traditionally defined by academics, characterized by an integrated body of theory, a set of preferred methodological approaches, and a cadre of professionals alike in background, training, and motivation. Instead, it is primarily defined by the substantive problems and questions with which it deals. At the most global level, HSR addresses the questions: How are organizational arrangements, financing, staffing patterns, and costs related to access to needed services? What are the elements of the quality of care

---

[1] The health services delivery system includes personnel, facilities, economic resources, knowledge, equipment, and structural arrangements for treating patients, paying bills, and training staff. It is concerned with the delivery of personal health services whether they be preventive, diagnostic, therapeutic, or rehabilitative. A physician is, therefore, central to the health services delivery system. Factors in the environment which also influence health, such as housing and air pollution, and those public health workers concerned with them, are peripheral to the system discussed here.

136

and how are these influenced by the foregoing? What factors contribute to unit and aggregate costs? More concretely, there are studies of the impact of deductible and co-insurance provisions in health insurance plans upon the use of services; physician remuneration and productivity; hospital mergers; geographic distribution of health manpower; and information systems for the management of delivery systems.

The field is purposive in its orientation, even normative, and strongly "applied" in the sense that its ultimate goal is the improvement of health care and health. This means that health services research is concerned with improving access to care (effectiveness), assuring its quality (including efficacy), and improving efficiency. Implicit in the minds of many researchers is the desire to do something about segments of the population that have difficulty in entering the delivery system or obtaining good care at prices that they can afford. Public policy today holds that serious inequities should not exist. HSR seeks to provide knowledge necessary for correcting the flaws in present arrangements, and it also analyzes the factors that determine whether, and how, important findings are implemented in public policy. It also seeks to determine whether the full therapeutic potential of medical care is realized. In this way, intended improvements of health services delivery based on HSR are subjected to validation by criteria independent of the normative judgments of investigators or providers of care.

Unlike clinical medicine, HSR is concerned generally with populations and systems of care rather than with individuals. The distribution of morbidity in the aggregate must be known so that scarce resources can be organized and distributed to achieve the best results in terms of care and cure. But in research on efficacy, the outcomes of care must be determined for highly selected medical conditions in individual patients. These in the aggregate are only a sample, and not necessarily a representative one, of the general population.

HSR is necessarily multidisciplinary. Its coherence stems from its concern with a set of real world problems or dependent variables, such as the utilization of services. But it borrows its theoretical perspective, including its explanatory variables, and methods for research from medicine and epidemiology, operations research and systems analysis, psychology, economics, and sociology.[2]

Although HSR borrows from these disciplines the concepts and methods it employs for the analysis of the delivery system, a theoretical and methodological synthesis that is shared by all health services researchers has failed to materialize. This is due, in part, to the nature of academic disciplines and, in part, to the character of the phenomena being studied.

WHAT IS A DISCIPLINE?

The social sciences upon which HSR so importantly rests are modelled on physics. The universe is assumed to be orderly and capable of being comprehended. Real events are defined as concepts; concepts are related to one another as hypotheses; and hypotheses are fitted into theory, which mirrors the order that is initially assumed to exist. Theories define the range of problems that are studied, the characteristic mode of conceptualizing variables, and notions of cause and effect. Thus a psychologist may well study health attitudes as they relate to health behavior to satisfy his scientific curiosity about affective processes.

Associated with each of the disciplines is a favored methodological approach, including tools for data collection, analytic techniques, and research settings. The approach is influenced by theory, substantive interests, and tradition. Thus, the psychologist referred to above might well administer a questionnaire in the local schools to determine students' attitudes toward preventive health measures, transform the answers to Likert scales, and run a multiple regression to reach his conclusions.

Members of a particular discipline share common life experiences and futures. They are selected into a discipline, a process that involves family background, personality, and available opportunities. Once in training, students are taught the content of the discipline and its associated values. Once in academic positions, they are subject to peer review and re-

---

[2] Health services research also employs concepts, theoretical frameworks, data, and methods from the other health professions (nursing, dentistry, pharmacy, etc.), political science, applied social science (social work, business and hospital administration, etc.), engineering, law, biostatistics, demography, and geography.

warded for contributions that advance their discipline qua discipline.

The psychologist, sociologist, or economist does not escape his discipline when he enters health services research. Instead, he brings to the set of problems that constitute HSR (utilization of health services, costs, organizational arrangements, manpower, etc.) theories, methods, and values that are often not suitable for understanding the health services delivery system. For the investigator, this can result in frustration; for HSR, this can slow the development of a body of knowledge upon which policy decisions can be based.

TENSIONS BETWEEN THE DISCIPLINES AND HEALTH SERVICES RESEARCH

Relationships between the disciplines and HSR vary from cooperative and facilitating interdependence to outright conflict. Although one could point to instances of either extreme, it is likely that the usual situation is one of tension. This tension results from the fundamental interests of each, which, as we have noted, are often at odds. The disciplines contend that their research is "objective"; HSR is explicitly normative when studying structure and process, but empirical and scientific when relating these to outcomes. The disciplines aim to advance theory and, therefore, prefer to view events in the concrete empirical world as indicators of abstract concepts; HSR aims to change organizational patterns, financial arrangements, and the like within a single sector of society. Therefore, HSR is apt to concentrate on phenomena that are seen as directly relevant to the health services system, and at a level of concreteness that often precludes generalizing the findings to other parts of society. On the other hand, by studying a societal subsystem with a set of defining attributes to serve as validating criteria, HSR is able to test its results more in the manner of physics than of the social sciences.

In this section we will analyze the various sources of tensions. Specifically, we will point out (1) some of the problems encountered by social scientists who do applied research; (2) the difficulties and hazards in adapting the intellectual styles of the disciplines to HSR and in developing a synthesis of the disciplines that would increase the power of HSR; and (3) the difference between the research styles of the disciplines and of HSR that diminishes the relevance of discipline-oriented research to policy.

Social Science of Health and Social Science in Health

The basic values and perspectives of the disciplines and of health services research are incompatible. The disciplines are oriented toward independent variables: they seek to show the relevance of their theoretical frameworks to a range of empirical events (e.g., health, crime, consumer behavior, etc.). HSR and other applied research areas are oriented toward dependent variables: they endeavor to understand why events and variations occur within subsystems of society and to determine how these might be brought under control through social policy. The disciplines thus begin with independent variables and search for dependent variables; HSR reverses the process.

These differences are recognized by researchers in both camps. Indeed, sociologists, who are more likely than other academics to do HSR, honor the distinction between traditional sociology *of* medicine and sociology *in* medicine. This divides sociologists into those who accept the discipline's view that sociology should use the medical and health arena as a testing ground for general theories of human, social, and organizational behavior (i.e., sociology *of* medicine), and those who adopt the normative perspectives, concepts, and research strategies of clinicians, health services administrators, and policy makers (i.e., sociology *in* medicine). The distinction is not only descriptive, it is also evaluative and prescriptive. Those who insist that the camps should be clearly demarcated are firmly entrenched in the sociology *of* medicine and, therefore, view sociology *in* medicine as perhaps useful but not true sociology. Some outside the entrenched discipline find the distinction overdrawn, elitist, and shot through with assertions about intellectual autonomy and identity that have never been verified.

The practical implications of this dichotomy are manifest in the choices of problems and the selection of variables to be studied. Those engaged in the sociology of medicine are prone to study relationships among physicians and nurses, health attitudes and knowledge, social stress, and the like. They avoid conceptualizing their research problems in terms of the managerial, operational, and policy concerns of providers and administrators in the health system. Therefore, they do not subject their theories to the tests of predictive validity. It is left to those who practice sociology in medicine to conduct research on the use of health services, the social epidemiology of medically defined diseases, and the effectiveness of neighborhood health centers. The assumptions made by most sociologists of medicine is that their interests and efforts will have long-term consequences and will inform the sociologists in medicine. While a few instances have proven this true, especially with respect to research methods, it is our impression that the division of labor has led primarily to fragmented jurisdictions and a minimum of exchange.

Although the other disciplines would probably agree that the intellectual and methodological strategies of pure and applied research are in fact different, there are structural and ideological grounds for expecting sociologists more than others to distinguish orthodoxy from revisionism. To identify oneself as a sociologist is to convey one's intellectual approach as well as one's occupation, namely, a college- or university-based teacher and/or researcher. Other disciplines, such as economics, operations research, psychology, and epidemiology, explicitly recognize their dual natures through educational, occupational, and reward structures. Economics, for instance, is a pure science analogous to sociology. Business administration, economics' applied cousin, has left the family to fraternize with organizational theory and industrial psychology among others. Those in business administration and public administration generally enjoy autonomy from their cognate disciplines. They exist as separate schools or departments; they have their own journals, intellectual styles, and career channels; and they recruit students who presumably are aware of these differences. In contrast, sociology is more monolithic: those steeped in orthodoxy control academic appointments, journals, standards of scholarship, career channels, and the recruitment of students, whose applied orientations are discouraged.

Social scientists, especially sociologists, are thus trained that their role models should be selected from among the purists. Lost to the student are forgotten bits of the biographies of many who are held up for emulation. These bits often include periods spent in government service, responsibility for administration, and first-hand experience in affairs that generated the unique perspectives which in turn made their works no less scholarly, more encompassing, and more significant. To eschew involvement removes the researcher from responsibility for his acts and leads to irrelevance beyond his own disciplinary audience.

THEORETICAL ISSUES

A major source of tension between the disciplines and HSR as well as among the disciplines themselves is the necessarily different intellectual predilections of their theoretical perspectives. The disciplines prefer to demonstrate that the structures of their abstract explanatory models contribute to the understanding of events within isolated systems. HSR, in contrast, attempts to account for variations in concretely conceptualized phenomena, usually within open systems. These differences lead the disciplinarian to favor internal consistency and conceptual purity over predictive power and practical relevance; the health services researcher sacrifices parsimony to gain increments of explained variance and the broadest possible coverage of sources of variance.

As we have noted, the rationale for the division of the social sciences into separate disciplines is that each makes special and unique contributions to the whole of knowlege. This leads investigators to omit from their models not only the variables of other disciplines, but also those that common sense suggests should be considered. Thus, the disciplines are content to seek only partial explanations of the problems they study.

The research literature on the use of health services provides illustrations of this point (461). Psychologists typically deal with the effects of attitudes and beliefs on the use of specific types of services. Sociologists examine relationships with socio-demographic variables, especially social class and indicators of social structure. Economists examine the effects of income and prices. Furthermore, each discipline uses its characteristic criteria when conceptualizing its dependent variables, a practice which is recommended by logic once one has accepted the premise that explanation is intended to be only partial. No single discipline deals explicitly with all sets of independent variables nor the various operational definitions of dependent variables, except to allow that they exist and that they may have something to do with the phenomena under investigation. For instance, none of the social sciences gives illness a prominent place in its models, despite its obvious influence on the use of health services.

A special case is the concept of "health." Although no one has satisfactorily solved the elusive and philosophical problems in defining and measuring health, there are identifiable differences in the meanings and uses of the concept. Since the disciplines are analysis-oriented, health and illness (when referred to at all) are employed as predictors of behavior. Hence, the disciplines prefer to use subjectively defined indicators of health because, as the usual caveat notes, behavior is motivated by what is believed to be true more than by what is objectively true. While it is difficult to argue with this assumption (which is an especially convenient one for researchers who use household surveys to collect data), it should be recognized that such measures are of little value to health services researchers charged with the responsibility for evaluating programs. The health services researcher cannot rely on either the partial conceptions or the global all-encompassing formulations of health advanced by the disciplines. The social psychologist's perceptions and the sociologist's sick role have not been shown to co-vary strongly with the ills and concerns that kill and cripple people. At the other extreme, those who conceive of health as a blissful compatibility with a benign nature (i.e., those who do not try to measure it) sweep so much under the concept that nothing could possibly affect it.

In the context of HSR, changes in health are the ultimate test of the efficacy of health services. What is needed, therefore, are valid and reliable indicators of health that can be used as evaluative criteria. The definitions and measures should be as broadly or narrowly conceived as the objectives of the specific interventions under investigation. This implies that HSR requires a store of indicators, not a single GNP-like expression that purports to tell it all, nor a series of conveniently construed and vague operational definitions.

RESEARCH STYLES

Since testing of theory implies the use of analytic research strategies, the disciplines assign the lowest of priorities to description. HSR, however, has rarely succeeded in moving beyond this level of research. As a consequence, we inherit two types of literature: one over-analyzing the relatively trivial and traditional concerns of the social sciences; the other attempting to describe, in all their detail, bits and pieces of health care and health services. Between these literatures is the sparsely inhabited region where social science theory and methods are applied to meaningful problems in a manner that produces better social science as well as more socially useful results. Examples of such research include Purola and his associates' evaluations of the national pensions plans in Finland (1162), Andersen, Smedby, and Anderson's comparison of the use of medical care in Sweden and the United States (1163), Andersen and Anderson's analyses of national trends in health services utilization (443), Bush's attempts to quantify health levels and outcomes (1164), and Klarman's cost/benefit analyses of intervention (365).

Research by those working in the interstices between the disciplines and those who "let the facts speak for themselves" has several commendable features. It is *problem-focused:* the research is addressed to social needs, which determine its scope, and is focused on problems that call for scientifically informed action (1165). The researcher draws his dependent variables and their operational definitions from the world of experience and attempts to grapple with them in the context of formulated or anticipated policy questions. His criteria for the selection of independent variables stress (a) their relevance to the problem under investigation rather than their systemic meanings within particular frames of reference, (b) their ability to identify populations and specific instances where the problem is most severe, and (c) their ability to be changed if the results of the research are to be implemented. Finally, the inferences and conclusions drawn from problem-focused research point to specific hypotheses and hunches to be tested with controlled experimental designs. Thus, problem-focused research leads to more delimited investigations that validate conclusions suggested by the more global and less controlled research. National studies on the use of health services, for instance, lead to speculations about effects of payment mechanisms on consumption but usually cannot provide conclusive evidence (456). Such speculations, however, can provide impetus for more localized experiments to measure effects of co-payments and the like.

Such research is multidisciplinary and, therefore, necessarily multivariate. As discussed by Bice and White (1166), it encounters all of the conceptual, methodological, and organizational problems identified by those who have realistically examined the difficulties that presently plague multidisciplinary research. Nevertheless, the development of conceptual and methodological tools and research settings and careers for problem-focused HSR will ultimately produce larger payoffs for society as well as for the disciplines themselves.

A GENERAL THEORY AND METHOD FOR HEALTH SERVICES RESEARCH

Since HSR is normative, the optimizing sciences are most compatible with the field. These include economics, operations research, and systems analysis, and their specialized techniques of linear programming, the Planning-Programming-Budgeting System, cost/benefit analyses, and mathematical models. According to Olson (1167), these sciences are essentially problem-solving approaches. Alternative courses of action are compared in terms of desired outcomes, subject to the constraints of resources and value preferences.

However, the optimizing sciences must simplify the "real world" in order to construct predictive equations. For instance, the market is assumed to be competitive and consumers to be motivated by only economic gain. Both assumptions distort what we know about health behavior. In HSR, sociology and psychology have contributed concepts that complicate this picture and make the model more credible. The sociologist's concerns with values, power, and hierarchy, like the psychologist's concepts of satisfaction and knowledge, intrude upon economic theory.

In addition to these conceptual frameworks, the academic disciplines have contributed the research methods used by health services researchers. Sociology, psychology, and epidemiology contribute to the development of the household survey, sampling techniques, questionnaire design, and statistics for analysis. The life-table and the techniques for geocoding data are derived from demography. Multivariate statistics and quasi-experimental designs were refined by psychologists. Finally, information science has given impetus to the development of standardized terms that make feasible a national health information system for planning, evaluation, and management.

Although scholars from several disciplines contribute to HSR, it is naive to suggest that they have greatly advanced the cause of a theory of health services. Indeed, we contend that those who hold that grand theory is the hope for HSR are captives of their disciplines' ideology and are pursuing outmoded, analytic models at a time when others should be considered. We agree with Ben-David's advice (1168) to the social sciences that they should adopt the models of clinical medicine and engineering rather than those of physics when thinking about health services. The clinical-engineering model borrows concepts and methods from a variety of disciplines. The researcher who employs it should regard himself as "a re-constructor of social structures and processes, working on the borderline of science and literature, as a clinician or engineer works on the borderline of science and art."

Attempts to structure multidisciplinary research teams to achieve theoretical or methodological syntheses have not been marked by success. Either one discipline dominates, negating the notion of an interdisciplinary framework, or, as noted by Dubin (1169), if interdisciplinary thinking is mandated, the lowest common denominator in theory and method is adopted.

However, we agree with Haggerty (Chapter IV) that research conducted in settings where researchers share responsibility for operations (patient care, fiscal management, etc.), is sobering and desirable. From settings in which economists, sociologists, physicians, and others sharing concern for a set of problems are permitted to function according to the tenets of their disciplines, there is evidence that terms such as "price elasticity" begin to creep into the language of the sociologist, and the economist humanizes his definition of demand. While a direct quest for the theory that unifies HSR or the single most productive method of investigation is futile, disciplines are malleable through time.

The problems in health services are multi-faceted, and current theories are vague and limited in application. Thus, social science would be well advised in the foreseeable future to attempt to explain particular events with the aid of general principles rather than search for the general rules that govern events. Therefore, the economist should apply what he knows about economies of scale in industry to labor-intensive, non-profit group practices and hospital conglomerates. Conversely, administrators, policy makers, and health services researchers should borrow concepts and methods that help them understand the problems at hand.

RESEARCH AND POLICY FORMULATION

Health services research conducted by university-based disciplinarians has had little impact on policy formulation in government and in the health services industry. Academics argue that managers and government officials cannot state objectives with sufficient clarity to make research possible; furthermore, academics contend that they are unduly impatient for results. On the other hand, academics are considered to be cavalier about deadlines, speciously precise about experimental conditions, and generally disinterested in the relevance of their findings to policy. Consequently, leaders of the health services industry and government question the value of social science research as an aid to decision-making, while academics grow wary of the intentions of decision-makers and feel misused and misunderstood.

The failure of the disciplinarian and the health services practitioner to communicate is exceedingly unfortunate. With national health insurance in the offing and vague outlines of a national health policy beginning to take shape, one searches the disciplinary literature in vain for a body of findings upon which to base decisions. Productive working arrangements between policy-makers and academics are fragile and few in number. One available mechanism for strengthening these relationships is to direct HSR to large-scale social experiments now under way. For example, the Experimental Health Services Delivery Systems program (see p. 174) offers new and exciting possibilities for research and evaluation to the disciplines. (1170)

Programs such as this, fostering the development of innovative solutions to problems of access, quality, and cost within a systems framework, represent a fundamental departure from federal initiatives of the past. They state a series of goals to be attained (equity of access, cost containment, acceptable standards of quality for all persons residing in a defined locale). They establish local boards which broadly represent the community and charge them with the responsibility for attaining these goals and for establishing mechanisms to monitor progress. Research and evaluation are not tacked on after the program has become operational, but are an integral part of decision-making from the outset. Furthermore, policy is not stated at the inception of the program, except in the most general terms; rather it emerges from successive stages of implementation and evaluation.

Programs that fit this model are springing up in many agencies of the Federal Government. In the health services field, they include the Experimental Medical Care Review Program (see p. 168), and the Medex and Primex programs (see p. 162). Such programs offer the disciplines opportunities to study authority and accountability, interorganizational conflict and coordination, the emergence and establishment of new professions and paraprofessions, incentives and productivity, value hierarchies, social indicators, directed social change, and the like. However, these programs should not be viewed simply as new research settings for traditional disciplinary interests. What is now required of the disciplinarian are concessions in the selection of his concepts, the elegance of his design, and the character of his evidence. Because of the complexity of major social interventions, he may be required to work with researchers from other disciplines, since a single discipline is seldom adequate. Settings more conducive to multidisciplinary research than those currently found on university campuses must be developed.

Problem-focused research will not supplant traditional disciplinary research, but it may well transform it to such an extent that the distinction between "basic" and "applied" research becomes less invidious, and the tensions between them less obstructive. The academic disciplines will then have an arena in which to test their ideas, and the policy makers will have research findings upon which to base their decisions.

Chapter VI
Federal Health Services R&D Under the Auspices of the National Center for Health Services Research and Development

Paul J. Sanazaro

ORIGINS

Federal health services research and demonstrations began in 1955. In that year, Congress appropriated funds to implement the authority in the Hill-Burton Act to support and conduct demonstration projects for the purpose of improving the design and operation of hospitals and related services. Also in the late 1950's, the National Institutes of Health supported a small number of noncategorical health services research projects under the general research authority of the Public Health Service. In 1963, these scattered research efforts were brought together in the Bureau of State Services, which began the first organized federal program of extramural research in community health services.

At the White House Conference on Health in 1965, Dr. Kerr L. White urged that "this Conference should consider advocating the establishment of a National Institute of Community Health Services to be set up in similar fashion to the other Institutes of NIH" (1171, p. 299). In 1966, the Department of Health, Education, and Welfare began to plan for the consolidation of all federally supported health services research in a "center for health services research." Because this center was also expected to apply the results of the research in the development of improved methods of delivering care, its designation became "National Center for Health Services Research and Development" (NCHSRD).

In his Message to Congress on Health and Education in February 1967, President Johnson stated that he had "directed the Secretary of Health, Education, and Welfare to establish a National Center for Health Services Research and Development." He recommended legislation "to expand health services research" along with appropriation of $20 million for research and development in health services (1172). This action came in response to recommendations contained in the Report to the President on Medical Care Prices (1173). The Report projected a strong role by the proposed National Center in cost containment, encouraging prepaid group practice plans, and developing and evaluating "comprehensive community health care systems." The key function of the Center would be to assure the more efficient use of medical resources.

The Senate Committee on Labor and Public Welfare generally reflected this Report's justification for the new federal program: "In summary, continued increases in the price of medical care, and continued shortages of personnel are inevitable. The question is how far prices will rise and how severe the shortages will be. This new program of health services research and development offers a vehicle through which alternative means for maintaining and increasing the availability of good health care can be achieved; the productivity of health manpower can be increased; better hospitals and nursing homes can be designed, and a full range of alternatives to costly institutional care can be developed. Organizational and administrative practices in the health services industry must be updated and brought into line with the most modern practices in other sections of the economy" (1174).

Authority for the projected program of research, development, demonstrations, and related training in health services was provided in Section 304 of The Partnership for

Health Amendments of 1967 (P.L. 90–174), enacted in December. This authority combined the provisions previously contained in the Hill-Burton Demonstration Grant Authority (hospital and medical facilities) and the Demonstration Authority in community health services originally enacted in P.L. 89–749 in 1966. Expressly intended to be administered by the National Center for Health Services Research and Development, Section 304 authorized support for "research, experiments, or demonstrations. . . relating to the development, utilization, quality, organization and financing of services, facilities, and resources of hospitals, facilities for long-term care, or other medical facilities . . . agencies, institutions or organizations or to development of new methods or improvement of existing methods of organization, delivery or financing of health services . . ." The Act also referred to experimental design and construction of medical facilities; development and testing of new equipment and systems including automation "and other new technology systems or concepts for the delivery of health services"; and "research and demonstration in new careers in health manpower and new ways of educating and utilizing health manpower."

The National Center was officially established by Secretarial order on May 2, 1968. It was initially formed by administrative transfer of ongoing health services research, training, and demonstration programs from the Divisions of Community Health Services, Medical Care Administration, Hospital and Medical Facilities, and from portions of other HEW units. The entire first year was devoted to organizing a balanced and comprehensive program in health services research and training and to assessing the projects that had been transferred from other units.

The Center had a dual mandate: to support research and training but also to produce tangible results on a national scale. So the first order of business was to determine whether and how national improvement in health services could be achieved through HSR and health services demonstrations. As described in Chapters I, IV and V, the purpose of HSR has been the accumulation of new knowledge and understanding to test hypotheses and formulate theories, regardless of their relevance to contemporary problems. Also, by definition, the end product of any health services research project is not known at the outset and is not intended to be immediately useful to the policymaker (see Chapter IV).

In assessing health services demonstrations as potential instruments of change, it was noted that they have been conducted formally and informally for many decades whenever a new method of providing services was attempted under either public or private auspices. They have also involved testing tried methods in a new setting. Evaluations of these demonstrations were almost invariably retrospective, including the attempt to determine whether the demonstration had met its objectives. Potential implementation on a national scale was of secondary importance to improving some aspect of health services locally.

Considering these facts, staff of the Center found it necessary to question the generally held view of how research findings in health services come to be widely applied. In this view, "research" is seen as producing knowledge which, when effectively communicated to decision-makers, leads to a "development" phase which, if successful, is in turn followed by a controlled "demonstration" which is carefully evaluated. If the demonstration is judged successful, the research finding or improved technique is expected to be implemented on a large scale. But no clear instance of this sequence occurring in a short time frame was found in the field of health services, outside the technical and scientific areas of medicine (e.g., new drugs) and public health (e.g., immunization). And the lessons of the past 40 years were discouraging, specifically the difficulties of achieving implementation of the research-based, rational recommendations of the Committee on the Costs of Medical Care (see Chapter III).

In the judgment of the National Center's staff and its consultants, no discernible combinations of HSR and demonstrations could in themselves bring about substantial predictable progress toward improving the delivery of health care nationally in the near future. On the other hand, both were indispensable in their own right, as was training in HSR. Accordingly, HSR, HSR training, and demonstrations were funded on their merits and at higher total amounts than previously.[1] These programs will not be further described here. A parallel "R&D" approach was begun in 1969[2] (9,1175,1176). The setting up of a focused R&D program, and many other decisions as to administration of the Center, were in keeping with confidential recommendations issued in 1967 by a Joint Task Force (American Rehabilitation Foundation and DHEW) under the direction of Dr. Paul Ellwood.

RATIONALE FOR DESIGN OF R&D PROGRAM

The problems in health care which have received so much publicity recently are not of recent origin. The reports of the Committee on the Costs of Medical Care documented the need for increased services to the poor, better distribution, improved quality, elimination of inefficiency, overcoming fragmentation of care, more adequate financing, more adequate dental care, more early diagnosis, cost containment, improved planning, better organization, and more emphasis on preventive services (757). All of these were reiterated in various forms in the reports of the National Health Conference of 1938 (1160), the National Health Assembly of 1948 (1177), the President's Commission on the Health Needs of the Nation of 1952 (1178), and the White House Conference on Health of 1965 (1171).

Though these problems are not new, they are widely discussed in part because the general public now places a higher value on health services. The public, as reflected in the views of Congress, has varying but high expectations of practical payoffs from the heavy investments made in basic and biomedical research in the 1950's and 1960's. The splurge of health care legislation in the mid-1960's was a clear-cut political response to the popularization of the issues of unmet needs of the poor, the elderly, mothers and children; the mentally ill; victims of heart disease, cancer, and stroke; the mentally retarded; and the plight of the migrants. As a consequence, virtually all legislation was addressed to categorical groups.

---

[1] Robert R. Huntley, M.D., while serving as Associate Director of the NCHSRD, organized and directed the initial program of HSR supported by the Center.

[2] Key staff contributing to the formulation of the R&D approach included Thomas McCarthy, Ph.D., Robert L. Eichhorn, Ph.D., Robert R. Huntley, M.D., Gilbert Barnhart, Ph.D., and E. Evelyn Flook.

The sole and major exception was the Comprehensive Health Planning and Public Health Services Amendments of 1966 (P.L. 89-749). This Act was intended to facilitate rational planning and allocation of resources to assure a proper balance and distribution of services, manpower, and facilities at State and local levels.

This Act had additional historical significance in that it established equity of access for everyone as a federal policy goal. But in explicitly identifying the goal of assuring "comprehensive health services of high quality for every person," the law expressly prohibited "interference with existing patterns of private, professional practice of medicine, dentistry, and related healing arts."

The very duration of major problems in health care; their deep historical, social, and political roots; the multiplicity of federal laws directed to these problems; and the commitment to the preservation of pluralism in health care delivery, all combined to make imperative an explicit, comprehensive rationale to guide the design of the R&D program. On the one hand, the rationale had to respect the organizational and historical integrity of the major organizations and agencies involved in the pluralistic system (i.e., organized medicine, private insurance companies, hospital associations, Medicare, Medicaid, health departments, etc.). On the other, it had to quickly lead to innovations which, while acceptable to these several independent agents, bring about definite and continuing change in the direction of the national goals for health services improvement: improved access, cost containment, and assurance of quality.

The rationale had to be based on an accurate and adequately comprehensive analysis of the presently existing structural and functional barriers to the attainment of these goals. One major barrier was the lack of a comprehensive health policy. The goal of equity of access was adopted while endorsing preservation of the private-public mix of health services. Even prior to this, Titles XVIII and XIX (Medicare and Medicaid, respectively) had been enacted to provide financial entitlement to the elderly and the categorically poor and near-poor of all ages. These two financing programs were intended in part to enable these groups to purchase medical and hospital care from private sources as an alternative to the use of clinics and hospitals as public patients. But financial entitlement, combined with the declaration of intent of equity, fell short of constituting formal health policy. Later, in its White Paper of 1971, the Department of HEW described its strategy for responding to existing health care problems based on the Administration's general policy of "New Federalism" (1179). Formal health policy must await future passage of laws which will stipulate how goals, needs, resources, and financing are to be interrelated.

A second barrier to improving health care nationally was the lack of effective health services planning (1180). At the federal level, the Congress and the Executive Branch each has its separate and distinctive responsibilities. Partisan political considerations often influence decision-making. Compounding this lack of central coordination of policy is the instability and lack of continuity stemming from changes introduced by successive administrations. Because policy makers in the Executive Branch are political appointees, policy guidance may fluctuate sharply when administrations change. Another related obstacle was the absence of a single agency at the federal level charged with responsibility for bringing together the information needed for systematic planning for health care on a national scale. Even if such a unit existed and functioned well, the problem would remain of how to translate faithfully the identified requirements for manpower, facilities, services, and financing into legislation which could be enacted.

At the State and local levels, the newly created Comprehensive Health Planning Agencies were slow in clarifying their scope of responsibility. They were hampered in developing competence in planning by underfunding and the shortage of qualified leadership and technical staff. A fundamental technical deficiency in health services planning was the lack of a health services data system which accurately describes the status of health services in the United States. The absence of such a system, and the inability to combine those data that were available, also explain why health care planning had been relatively ineffective.

A third barrier existed as a direct consequence of the plethora of federal programs enacted in the 1960's (1181). These categorical programs tended to have vocal and effective constituencies. However rational the intent, attempts to remove categorical boundaries were not popular and therefore not successful. The end result was the much bemoaned overlap and conflict of jurisdictions, authorities, and responsibilities; the multiple federal sources of funds for similar purposes, each imposing differing requirements; the lack of central coordination of related programs; and substantial and often justifiable resentment of the federal bureaucracy.

A fourth barrier to systematic improvement in the distribution of health services was the uneven and incomplete coverage of the people by private insurance (1182) and by public programs. This was one part of the central dilemma as this country tried to move toward a comprehensive health care policy. Undoubtedly, unevenness of benefits in both public and private programs could only be eliminated by federal legislation. However, despite a strong consensus on this point, the enactment of general entitlement did not, in 1969, appear to be an immediate prospect because of the widely held conviction that there must also be substantial changes in the organization and delivery of health services, in parallel or in tandem with any major change in financing. But this view ran counter to the federal position which supported pluralism and, in effect, the existing patterns of delivery. The immediate implication for health services R&D was that major change in the mechanisms for financing care in the United States must await a new political climate. In the interim, means had to be found to contain the more undesirable effects of existing methods of financing.

Given the foregoing considerations, the technical task of a federal program of health services R&D was defined as accelerating improvement in health services planning and management, more efficient resource development and distribution, while operating within a pluralistic system during a period of shifting public policy on health services. The improvement was to be measured against the widely endorsed goals of improving access, containing cost increases, and assuring quality.

In addition to its technical aspects, the R&D rationale incorporated the principle that the specific deficiencies which were to be the targets of health services R&D be defined within the framework of a "system." This had been recommended by a number of advisory committees and commissions (302,1148,1150). Such a systems approach was not to be equated with constructing a uniform monolithic national system nor even with creating a small number of standard systems for wide implementation. Rather, the term denoted creation of *system properties* within the existing health care enterprise.

Creating "system properties" meant that our existing delivery system would be modified through selective innovations without fundamentally changing its organization and financing. As a result of these innovations, specific components within the health care enterprise would perform more dependably and predictably in providing the appropriate level, quality, and duration of services, regardless of the organization and the source and method of financing.

Deriving from the overall rationale just described, the original strategy of the National Center's R&D program had three identifiable elements:

1. Identifying the requirements for conducting actual "R&D" in health services (the R&D process).
2. Identifying, designing, and producing prototypes of "real world" improvements in health services which could be introduced on a national scale (R&D components).
3. Designing and developing "real world" prototype community health services delivery systems committed to the goals of facilitating access to needed care, while moderating cost increases, and assuring an acceptable level of quality.

THE R&D PROCESS

R&D, as formulated by the NCHSRD, was the process of identifying, designing, developing, introducing, testing, and evaluating new methods that meet specified performance criteria under realistic operating conditions. It was to be a direct analogue, albeit in a social system (health services), of the R&D used by NASA in the physical system and by industrial engineering to achieve specified goals. R&D in health services was to bring about targeted technological, organizational, and functional innovations. Likely to be multidisciplinary, each project was to draw upon relevant knowledge and methods derived from earlier research, but the selection of these and the makeup of each R&D team would depend upon the specific objectives of the particular project. The success of the R&D would depend upon the adequacy of the underlying basic knowledge; correctness and acceptability of objectives and their priorities; technically sound designs and evaluations; management; adequacy and stability of support; freedom from political pressures; and the adequacy of participation by major users.   As the R&D program evolved, it exhibited the following principles and characteristics:

1. It is necessary to anticipate the political, legal, economic, social, professional, and administrative considerations which determine the feasibility of any proposed major innovation on a national scale in health services delivery. All of these forces and factors must be in concordance in order to provide a stable framework within which to design, develop, and install new components of the delivery system.

2. R&D creates new entities, procedures, organization, systems, or operations on a scheduled basis. These innovations fit in with but modify real world settings and functions.

3. Each R&D product performs in accord with criteria which are predetermined.

4. The R&D innovations are generic; that is, they must be capable of national application throughout our pluralistic health care delivery system.

5. Each R&D project is designed in accord with the system concept, so that all resulting major innovations, when combined, fit together structurally and functionally, and produce predictable and measurable changes in the desired directions.

6. R&D predetermines the implementation of the targeted innovation if the innovation proves successful in achieving its objectives. The first step is to assure compliance of the projected innovation with legislative authority and HEW policy. Next comes the formulation of the innovation by consultation with and involvement of the private and public organizations or institutions which must endorse the innovation if it is to be adopted on a large scale.

7. R&D innovations must undergo planned replications and appropriate modifications in deliberately selected adminstrative, geographic, political, and socioeconomic settings, in order to subject the products to the large number of interacting, real world variables. This is necessary if the innovation is to perform predictably when applied more generally.

8. R&D leaves the successfully developed innovation or new arrangements in place in the delivery system. Viewed from this perspective, R&D is a method for orderly, rational social change.

It is to be noted that R&D, as above defined, differs in major respects from "research and development" as recently discussed in England (1183) and Canada (1184).

R&D in health services begins by identifying the "right problems" and assuring necessary cooperation from the public and private sectors. Accordingly, the National Center began by holding extensive consultations to define the specific innovations needed to overcome clearly identified deficiencies in health services. Those consulted represented federal, state and local governments; all major interests in the public sector; the several health professions; third party payers; health-related institutions and institutes as well as universities not directly involved in health professional education; and the technical and management expertise of those in operating settings in health services and in business and industry. Staff of the Center conducted a thorough analysis of Commission reports and reviewed the extensive literature on problems in medical care.

Preliminary statements of objectives and priorities for R&D were presented formally at meetings of an ad hoc advisory group composed of the chief executives and elected leaders of the following organizations: American Hospital Association, American Public Health Association, American Medical Association, National Medical Association, American Osteopathic Association, Association of State and Territorial Health Officers, Association of American Medical Colleges, American Nurses' Association, American Dental Association, American Pharmaceutical Association, Health Insurance Association of America, Blue Cross Association, National Association of Blue Shield Plans, and American Nursing Home Association. The reactions and advice of this group were helpful in refining the R&D strategy. The provisional, unofficial concurrence in the R&D program by these private and public gatekeepers also laid the groundwork for future implementation.

Subsequent to such reviews, each cluster of related R&D projects was formally developed into what were called "R&D components." Each component was assigned a Professional Advisory Group and a Technical Advisory Group. Composed of nationally recognized leaders from the private, public, and academic health sectors, these advisory groups helped assure that the final design of each project fit in with the real world but would yield an innovation producing substantial predictable improvement. Once the projects were launched, these same advisory groups served as steering committees.

R&D COMPONENTS

Priorities were assigned to the various R&D projects in accord with the priorities of the Department of HEW's health services improvement strategy. The Center's initial R&D components were:

1. training and deployment of physician extenders
2. cost containment and financing methods
3. quality of care
4. cost effective technology
5. health services data systems

The intended contribution of each set of projects to the three primary objectives of nationwide improvement in health services is shown in the following table:

R&D Components	Improving Access	Containing Costs	Assuring Quality
1. Physician extenders	++	+	
2. Cost containment and financing	+	++	
3. Quality of care			++
4. Technology	+	++	+
5. Data systems	++	++	++

++ = primary impact
+ = secondary impact

Within each category, one or more major R&D projects were designed, building upon prior or emerging results or methods developed through health services research. The rationale and design of the five R&D components are described in the sections which follow.

PHYSICIAN EXTENDERS[3]

Rationale. Improving access to care required resolution of two technical problems (other than financing): the maldistribution of physicians across medical specialties and geographically, and the decreasing number of primary care physicians. Although medical schools were increasing their enrollment and placing more emphasis on family and community medicine, there is a time lag of about 10 years between enrollment in medical school and entry into active practice. Therefore, if access were to be improved appreciably in this decade, steps had to be taken to improve the productivity of physicians currently providing primary care. Productivity gains through organizational and technological innovation are uncertain because these latter can not yet be applied effectively to physicians' offices. The only remaining alternative was the use of support personnel who, under supervision, could provide physician-equivalent services in primary and continuing care.

The National Advisory Commission on Health Manpower in 1967 had recommended experimental programs to train and use "health personnel at the intermediate professional level" (1148). The most substantial experience with mid-level workers has been in the military services. Medical corpsmen certified for independent duty have long been full-fledged members of the military medical team. The oldest civilian model is the nurse practitioner in the Frontier Nursing Service of Kentucky (1185). Since 1925, properly trained nurses have been performing medical examinations, prescribing medication through "standing orders" of a physician, and delivering many other health services long thought to be the sole prerogative of duly licensed physicians. More recently, public health nurses have performed well in providing medical care to chronically ill patients, using written guidelines (1186). Nurses were being

---

[3] Initially, this R&D program was directed by Douglas A. Fenderson, Ph. D.

trained to function in triage in outpatient clinics (1187). Under combined public-private auspices, a family nurse practitioner was providing primary, emergency, and chronic care to a small community, maintaining a telephone link with supervisory physicians (1188).

By 1969, reports of experience with pediatric and general nurse practitioners were uniformly describing their ability to increase physicians' productivity by performing delegated tasks while maintaining quality and gaining acceptance by physicians and patients alike (47,48,50,54). Balanced against these beginning indications that mid-level workers could make a critically important national contribution, was the simple fact that large-scale deployment of physician's assistants would be a major and highly significant departure from the traditional form of medical care in the United States. The growing publicity surrounding many of these programs and the apparently unsatisfied demand for medical care had combined to create perhaps as yet unwarranted popular acceptance of the mid-level worker concept. Physician's assistant programs of the widest possible range of types had proliferated in the late 1960's, in uncoordinated fashion. Accordingly, the staff of the National Center, in consultation with the major national professional organizations, decided that R&D would be limited to a five-year demonstration of mid-level health manpower (1189).

It was evident that development of an acceptable national policy with respect to mid-level health workers would require satisfactory evidence that (1) they could be distributed to the relatively under-served areas; (2) physician productivity would be increased without sacrificing quality of care; (3) total costs in training are feasible; (4) the widespread introduction of such workers reduces the costs of physician-directed health services; (5) employment will be stable and the career satisfying; and (6) legal and jurisdictional barriers can be removed. Therefore, a prospective evaluation of the demonstration would be carried out to provide cumulative evidence on these issues which would serve as a rational base for public policies on the use of physician's assistants.

Design. The two program goals of the manpower R&D component were, first, the production of a narrow range of mid-level workers to provide, under physician supervision, primary and continuing care in under-served areas, and second, evaluation of the clinical, social, and economic potentials, as well as the limitations, for improving access to primary care in the under-served areas of the United States through the use of such mid-level workers.

The specific program objectives were defined as follows:

1. To replicate sufficient numbers of provisional models of mid-level workers to establish the limits of their usefulness in the United States.
2. To apply evaluation methods required to rationalize functional job relationships in order to assure their appropriate and efficient employment and deployment in private medical practice.
3. To adapt and apply the evaluation methods to complex staffing patterns and requirements of group medical practices.
4. To provide the emerging results of the evaluation of mid-level workers to users such as physicians, clinic managers, hospital administrators, health services planners, public administrators, and health services researchers.

The foregoing rationale, goals, and objectives were contributed to and reviewed by advisory groups composed of practicing physicians, nurses, other health professionals, medical and nursing educators and administrators, representatives of the major national professional organizations, and of other federal agencies concerned with manpower. Technical consultation was obtained from those who had made significant contributions to establishing the mid-level worker as a potentially nationally applicable model. Special attention was given to evaluation techniques using modern methods of task analysis and health services analysis. The entire approach was reviewed by the National Advisory Health Services Council and the Federal Hospital Council of HEW.

Four major and two minor models were included in the R&D design. The first of these was Medex, i.e., former corpsmen who had been qualified and certified for independent duty and who had had practical experience in providing primary and continuing care while in the military (1190). These corpsmen were to be carefully screened prior to their acceptance in a university-based retraining program. The state and local medical societies had to endorse the local project. Primary care practitioners in the geographic area had to accept responsibility for each corpsman.

When these conditions were met, specialized training was provided to complement their military training and experience and equip them to deal with patients in the setting of private practice. At the completion of their retraining, corpsmen were placed with general practitioners in rural or in inner city areas on a one-to-one preceptorship for periods of one year. At the end of that time, preceptors agreed to hire the Medex to assist them in their practice on a regular basis.

The second major physician extender model was the family nurse practitioner, called Primex for "primary care extender" (1191). Five Primex projects were supported which provided nurses with four–six months of classroom training in schools of nursing followed by clinical experience under the supervision of physicians. The goal was to prepare them to work collaboratively with physicians to provide primary and preventive health services in a variety of community settings. Each of the Primex projects was to be evaluated in accord with a uniform protocol. The third model was the pediatric nurse practitioner. Data from surveys by the National Center for Health Statistics showed that the lowest rate of physician visits was in low- and middle-income family members under the age of 15. The need for pediatric mid-level workers was evident. Because ongoing evaluations were indicating general effectiveness and public acceptance (47,48), prospective evaluation was primarily directed to questions of occupational persistence, flexibility of task allocation, long-term productivity, and interpersonal and interprofessional relations.

The fourth model was the school nurse practitioner who, with additional training in physician's assistant functions, would be able to provide routine and regular health care and treatment for children on the scale of a small neighborhood clinic. The final models included in the national evaluation of mid-level health personnel were the nurse midwife and dental auxiliaries.

There was an immediate practical consequence of the physician extender projects, namely, an increase in the volume of primary ambulatory medical care in shortage areas. In the technical sense, however, their major significance was in serving as a laboratory for the application of a nationwide protocol consisting of objective methods for determining their appropriate selection, preparation, clinical performance, supervision, acceptance, and effect on physician productivity and unit costs. Prospective evaluation of the project took the form of a national information and surveillance system into which the total range of observations and experiences of the manpower R&D projects were to be fed (61).

Results. The uniform evaluation was applied in each project using one or more mid-level models. This amounted to over 200 practice settings in 25 states. The data which began to accumulate suggested numerous areas where specific and major task delegations may occur in primary care without impairment of quality and with professional and public acceptance. Preliminary analyses of the costs, services, and charges suggested that introduction of the physician's assistant could be cost/effective, i.e., increase the volume of services without proportionate increase in unit costs.

In February 1971, President Nixon's Health Message explicitly endorsed physician's assistants, nurse pediatric practitioners, and nurse midwives as "one of the most promising ways to expand the supply of medical care and to reduce its cost . . ." Training funds were then authorized and appropriated, and the training programs subsequently administered by the Bureau of Health Manpower Education in the National Institutes of Health.

During 1971, several studies and analyses were published which reinforced the rationale and initial assumptions of the R&D in mid-level workers (1192–1196). In June 1971, the Department of Health, Education, and Welfare recommended that a two-year moratorium be placed on licensure laws for physician's assistants (1197). During this time, it was proposed that guidelines be developed for statutes governing the use of mid-level health workers. In November 1971, a report issued by a broadly representative committee appointed by the Secretary of DHEW provided additional impetus to extending nurses' functions in primary care, acute care, and long-term care (1198).

Active collaboration, formal and informal, was maintained among the Department of Health, Education, and Welfare, the American Medical Association and the other major health professional organizations, in gradually shaping national policy on physician extenders. The current position of organized medicine strongly suggests that certain categories will be incorporated in a timely and orderly fashion into routine medical practice (1199,1200).

COST CONTAINMENT AND FINANCING[4]

The National Center was organizationally separate from the Medicare and Medicaid programs, each of which had its own authorities for experiments and demonstrations. Despite sustained effort, it was not possible to establish effective working liaisons. Consequently, the Center did not direct R&D to prospective reimbursement, although by 1969 this was well recognized as a potentially important mechanism for containment of hospital costs. Nor did the Center address any of the recommendations proposed by the Medicaid Task Force (302), which by consensus would have yielded important savings without curtailing benefits.

Following extensive consultations with knowledgeable individuals from both the private and public sectors, it was concluded that substantial progress could still be made by R&D directed to reducing the operating expenses of hospitals, and developing efficient and acceptable alternatives to institutional care.

Reducing operating costs. Because personnel salaries account for 60–70 percent of hospital budgets, a major effort was made to test the use of an all-inclusive rate reimbursement method which would significantly reduce personnel requirements. Instead of charging for each individual item of service or treatment, hospitals would establish average costs in typical patient categories and bill each patient or third party payer the appropriate standard daily rate. A feasibility study concluded that savings in clerical personnel alone would amount to several hundreds of millions of dollars annually if the plan

---

[4] The R&D in cost containment within health care institutions was directed by David K. Trites, Ph.D. R&D in financing was initiated by David Schenker, Ph.D.

proved to be successful and could be installed nationwide (1201).

Priority was also given to means of moderating the rate of increase of hospital costs through optimizing the scale of hospital operations (1202). One recommended approach was that of mergers and shared services. National survey data were compiled and in-depth local studies were made of the efficiencies and economies resulting from the sharing of medical services and the centralizing of purchasing, laundry operations, food services, computer services, laboratory testing, and other operations. Based upon this information, technical R&D guidelines were issued for institutions and communities desiring to share services (174) or to establish hospital mergers (175). A merged hospital system was evaluated (1203).

Alternatives to Hospital Care. Another approach to reducing total expenditures for hospital care is to reduce unnecessary hospitalization through providing acceptable alternatives in the forms of organized ambulatory health services (1204, 1205). Guiding concepts in this effort were: (1) the use of supervised mid-level workers wherever feasible; (2) automation of procedures when economies of scale permitted and increased productivity was facilitated with reduction in operating costs; (3) development of decision rules for assigning patients to proper sources of preventive, curative, or health maintenance services; (4) integration of the ambulatory services with hospital and other institutional services. The experimental medical care delivery system within the Kaiser plan in Oakland, California embodies these elements. As yet unpublished results indicate this system is more efficient than the traditional Kaiser medical clinics. Beth Israel Hospital in Boston has also applied these principles in devising new ambulatory care services.

QUALITY OF CARE: THE EMCRO PROGRAM[5]

Rationale. The origins of the R&D program in quality assurance lay in the recommendations of the National Advisory Commission on Health Manpower (1148):

---

[5] James S. Roberts, M.D., Richard S. Goldstein, M.D., Dale N. Schumacher, M.D., and Bernard Slosberg, M. D. shared major responsibility for various stages of this program.

1. Peer Review should be performed at the local level with professional societies acting as sponsors and supervisors.
2. Assurance must be provided that the evaluation groups perform their tasks in an impartial and effective manner.
3. Emphasis should be placed on assuring high quality performance and on discovering and preventing unsatisfactory performance.
4. The more objective the quality evaluation procedures, the more effective the review bodies can be. To enable greater objectivity, there should be a substantial program of research to develop improved criteria for evaluation, data collection methods, and techniques of analysis.

Accordingly, from its beginning, the National Center gave priority to research on methods of evaluating the quality of care, in particular the refinement of criteria, development of better methods of measuring health status and outcomes of care, and improved techniques of data collection and analysis.

By 1970, assuring quality care had become a commitment of the major medical professional organizations and an increasing concern on the part of the public. A measure was introduced in Congress[6] to establish "Professional Standards Review Organizations" (PSRO's). Their function would be to control costs while assuring quality. These were to be composed of practicing physicians who would monitor hospital use and the quality of care reimbursed by the Medicare and Medicaid programs. Each PSRO would be responsible for a designated geographic area and, in the aggregate, these would cover the entire United States.

As of 1970, there were no organizations in this country (or any other) whose primary function was to review the quality of medical care in all settings on an ongoing basis. Anticipating that there would be massive technical and organizational problems when such legislation was enacted, the NCHSRD began its R&D program to develop working models which could test new approaches to the objective review of physicians' services, that is, the content and results of medical care. Designated as "Experimental Medical Care Review Organizations" (EMCRO), each such working model was to explore alternative

---

[6] Amendment 851 to H.R. 17550, introduced by Senator Wallace Bennett (R., Utah).

means of conducting systematic ongoing review of medical care on an areawide and statewide basis. The methods of review were to be objective and reliable and to provide data permitting comparison of the quality of care between different geographic areas at the local and State levels as well as nationally. Each model had to be acceptable to the major parties in our pluralistic health care system.

Design. Because quality assessment and assurance must be integral parts of the actual delivery system, the decision was made to begin EMCRO by supporting several well-qualified health professional organizations or institutions. The program was designed in close consultation with a professional advisory group, composed of distinguished representatives of the medical and hospital professions, a technical advisory group, composed of leading investigators in the quality of care, and representatives of the Medicare and Medicaid programs. The technical design incorporated the cumulative findings and techniques of prior research on the quality of care (310, 312,315,322,323,331), especially the necessity to base review on highly explicit criteria. The design also incorporated some principles and methods established by the San Joaquin Foundation for Medical Care in reviewing office care (1101) and by the Professional Activity Study and other organizations collecting and summarizing data on hospital care (176).

There were five basic requirements.

1. EMCRO's must establish suitable working relationships with local physicians, hospitals, health agencies, private and public third party payers, and any existing medical review activities in their area. As organizations, EMCRO's were to have access to and be capable of analyzing data on the content of personal health services being given to patients in hospitals, offices, clinics, and nursing homes. The geographic area was to be coterminous with a medical trade area and could cover an entire State.

2. EMCRO's must base their review of care on explicit criteria for diagnosis, treatment, and overall management (310,323). Criteria were to be established for the common and important diseases, conditions, and procedures.

3. Each EMCRO must arrange for the appropriate participation of representatives of the public in the review of the findings.

4. Any objectively identified deficiencies in care were to be made the basis for local continuing education programs (324,325). Although the available evidence was that most continuing medical education is ineffective (1206), the Williamson-Brown model was reported to be effective in controlling undesirable practices (325).

5. Each EMCRO was to conduct a prospective evaluation of its organization, data system, criteria, cost, and impact. In addition, an independent evaluation of the entire EM-CRO program was to be obtained from a consultant firm (1207).

The above principles and approaches were reviewed by the National Advisory Health Services Council and the Federal Hospital Council. They were incorporated into Guidelines which were mailed to approximately four hundred county and State medical societies and other interested professional organizations. Thirty-two applications were received which were formally reviewed for scientific and technical merit by panels of non-federal physicians and other health professionals and non-federal experts in medical care assessment. Eight of these projects were initially selected for funding and two others were added later in 1971.

Results. The ten EMCRO's included 8,000 physicians serving four million patients in nine states. In their first year, they made considerable headway in meeting the first two requirements. Organizational relationships reflected local political and professional variations but represented viable alternatives. All proceeded to establish and adopt written, explicit criteria for common diseases, disorders, and procedures. Most often criteria were directed to optimal care, but some EMCRO's specified criteria for minimal levels of care and others used criteria to stipulate maximum reimbursable levels. The focus in all but two EMCRO's was the process rather than the outcome of care. Some progressed more rapidly than others in beginning or extending review of hospital care, office care, drug prescribing, and nursing home care. Important technical advances were made in methods for abstracting records and in making the data system more reliable and efficient (1208).

In October 1972, P.L. 92–603 was enacted, establishing Professional Standards Review Organizations (PSRO's) as the bodies responsible for reviewing all hospital and nursing home care to be reimbursed by Medicare and Medicaid. In implementing the PSRO legislation, the EMCRO program provides a base of experience with, and information on, feasible forms of organization and workable methods of data collection and analysis. It also provides a real world laboratory for continuing R&D and special studies to better assure a cost/effective PSRO system in which there is an appropriate balance between cost containment and quality assurance.

Health Care Technology[7]

The promise of technology (hardware and software systems) for increasing productivity is being examined and commented on more critically because it has rarely been realized in health services settings (1209,1210). Although health care technology's potential for increasing productivity and containing costs is a matter of *res ipse loquitur,* its application in direct patient care is said to have added remarkably to the rate of cost increases (530). The National Center's initial R&D projects in technology were based on the research summarized in Chapter I (see pp. 59–66). Subsequently, the task was to identify those settings and conditions under which the application of health care technology can bring about meaningful reductions in the costs of services as well as added savings in the time of expensive manpower.

Emphasis was first given to increasing the capability of computers to assume the monitoring activity in intensive care settings. Based on earlier work (1211), a communitywide computer-assisted electrocardiogram analysis program was supported in Denver to determine whether it would save specialists' time, improve service, reduce costs, and become self-sustaining. Automation of the clinical laboratory was analyzed to assure that its contribution in improving accuracy, speed, and economy of tests is not counterbalanced by disproportionate increase in costs (1212). Automation of the acquisition of medical histories (1213) was supported as was an assessment of automated multiphasic health testing (924). A modular approach to the development of a "hospital information system" was taken, after a special study concluded that global

---

[7] This R&D program was directed by Bruce Waxman, Ph.D.

efforts to create an entire communication system for the hospital have not been productive (1214).

In order to better anticipate future requirements for health care technology, the Center sponsored an invitational conference on this question. The impressive array of perspectives and proposals has been published (1215).

HEALTH SERVICES DATA SYSTEMS[8]

The final R&D component was the standardized health services data system required for planning, managing, and evaluating health services delivery within areas and States or nationwide. Projects were designed and funded to create a system that would ultimately interrelate: vital and health statistics; demographic and socioeconomic characteristics of defined populations, including their health care requirements and their utilization experience; the available health manpower and facilities; and sources and methods of payment for services. Based upon operational definitions of improved access, cost containment, and quality assurance, the data system was to permit objective determination over time of the rates of progress in different areas of the United States towards the goals of improved access, cost moderation, and improvement of quality. The widely recognized problem was that data then currently available lacked uniformity and a mechanism for coordination. This resulted in wasteful duplication on the one hand and great gaps in needed information on the other.

Although hospital care is only one component of the entire health services delivery system, it is a major element. For this reason, definition of the data required and methods for collecting uniform hospital discharge data was chosen as a logical starting point for construction of a total uniform health services data system. An international conference was held in June 1969, to discuss the content, uses, and methods of collecting information on discharged hospital patients (176). Based on the recommendations of this conference, the National Committee on Vital and Health Statistics approved a provisional uniform hospital discharge data set. This became the basis of feasibility R&D projects carried out through the

---

[8] Early responsibility for R&D in this area rested with Bonnie Owen, M.A., Nancy Pearce, M.A., and Warren Schonfeld, M.S.P.H.

Health Services Foundation of the Blue Cross Association and the American Hospital Association (177,177a). These projects were successfully concluded in California, Wisconsin, Pennsylvania, and Maine, involving 33 hospitals that accounted for about 16,510 discharges each month (1216). The projects defined the differing requirements for facilitating the provision of a minimum, uniform set of data, depending upon the existing data systems and the medical record library staff of individual hospitals. Special attention was given to the utility of the data in analyzing hospital costs in relation to the number and types of patients served, and the size and type of hospital. Such data are expected to be useful in more objectively determining a community's needs for hospital and other institutional beds, and in improving their local management capability.

In April 1972, an international conference on Ambulatory Medical Care Records led to comparable recommendations for a minimum basic data set (1217). These recommendations are to be translated into R&D projects as was done with the suggested hospital care data set. A series of health services data manuals has been prepared by Eichhorn and associates for guidance of the Experimental Systems in the use of a household survey (1218), census data (1219), and ambulatory care data (1220).

In 1971, R&D on health services data was incorporated into the R&D directed to the creation of the Cooperative Federal-State-Local Health Information and Statistics System.[9] The purpose of this cost-sharing system is to provide data which will improve planning, management, operations, and evaluation of health services at federal, State, and local levels (1221). This system is to be developed in the next ten years.

EXPERIMENTAL HEALTH SERVICES DELIVERY SYSTEMS[10]

Rationale. The innovations resulting from the R&D components were designed to fit together if installed side-by-side

---

[9] Authorized in Section 210 of P.L. 91-515. The National Center for Health Statistics is now responsible for the development, implementation, and operation of this system.

[10] Gilbert Barnhart, Ph.D., Robert R. Huntley, M.D., and Robert L. Eichhorn, Ph.D., contributed to the initial design of this program.

in the same community. In order to provide settings for simultaneously testing the validity of the systems concept and evaluating the performance of each new component produced through R&D, the sixth category of R&D was established: the Experimental Health Services Delivery Systems (EHSDS). These were to consist of a new form of local management and community organization, combining public and private interests and resources in health services for geographically defined populations in natural trade areas up to an entire State in size. Under such centralized coordination, innovations would be introduced to enhance productivity and improve distribution of health services while maintaining quality. The planned relationship of the health services R&D components and the Experimental Systems is shown schematically in the following diagram:

	Experimental Health Services
R&D Components	*Delivery System*
	Common Objectives
	Local Management
1. Physician Extenders	Physician Extenders
2. Cost Containment	Cost Containment
3. Quality of Care	Quality of Care
4. Technology	Technology
5. Data System	Data System

There have been repeated recommendations to establish and/or study the equivalent of "health services delivery systems" (302,757,1148,1150,1173). The challenge to the National Center was to define those circumstances under which it would be possible to test whether and how far present pluralism could be modified acceptably, so as to exhibit the characteristics of a system, i.e., improve its efficiency and effectiveness, in the absence of a national health service.

In the United States, no one organization or agency is responsible for the health care of defined populations residing in given areas. This fact makes it impossible to apply the system approach to a representative sample of geographically defined populations. For this reason, early in 1970, the decision was

made to establish "community laboratories." The primary purpose would be to establish voluntary local management to
bring about the cooperative actions and innovations needed to
achieve the goals of improving health services delivery.

Design. The first such community laboratory was the State of
Rhode Island. With the approval and support of the Office of
the Governor, the State Health Department, the State medical
society, the State hospital association, Blue Cross Association,
and Brown University, a nonprofit corporation was established. It was called "Rhode Island Health Services Research,
Inc." According to its Articles of Incorporation, it was to be
responsible for considering innovative revisions which would
materially improve access, contain unit costs, and assure quality within the existing delivery system. The corporation was to
influence the Statewide adoption of those innovations selected
for the benefit of all Rhode Island residents.

The Center also worked with a number of other communities, including Livingston, California; Stockton, California;
and the States of Nebraska and Colorado. Based on these
experiences, the National Center gradually formulated the
concept of "Experimental Health Services Delivery Systems"
(EHSDS).

The essential element of EHSDS was local management by a
voluntarily established autonomous corporation with representation from all the major groups, public, voluntary, and for
profit, involved in health services.[11] By "management" was
meant assumption of accountability and responsibility, on be-
half of the entire community, for the design and development
of an integrated delivery program, the allocation of resources,
the rationalization of services, and the measurement of
effectiveness of programs for individuals and the entire population. The corporation's board of directors had to include
effective representation of the "four Ps": the *p*ublic, *p*roviders,
(both individual and institutional), third party *p*ayers (public as
well as private sources), and *p*olitical representation by local
elected governing officials. A function of the latter was to

---

[11] Specific authority for this approach was contained in P.L. 90–515 which provided
for the support of "projects for research, experiments, and demonstrations dealing
with the effective combination or coordination of public, private, or combined public-private methods or systems for the delivery of health services at regional, State or
local levels . . ."

assure direct participation by the State or local health department, the welfare agency, the Comprehensive Health Planning Agency, and the medical assistance program.

One essential purpose of EHSDS was to coordinate, effectively, all federally-supported personal health service programs at the local level. Besides Medicare and Medicaid there were the Regional Medical Programs, Maternal and Child Health Programs, Comprehensive Health Planning, Family Planning Services, Hill-Burton, OEO Neighborhood Health Centers, Community Mental Health Centers, Model Cities health programs, 314(e) Comprehensive Health Centers, formula grant programs, and more. In the EHSDS, the intent was to determine whether the impact and effectiveness of all such publicly-supported programs could be increased by gradually fitting them into a coherent set of locally determined priorities. Further, it was expected that the several federal agencies would give priority in funding to those projects located within Experimental Systems. In turn, it was expected that these communities, through their Boards, would forcefully recommend to the Department of HEW and other agencies how to improve granting procedures so as to increase the local effectiveness of the limited public funds.

The technical design of EHSDS evolved through discussions with the National Advisory Health Services Council, the Federal Hospital Council, representatives of all federal support programs, numerous consultants, and ad hoc professional and technical advisory groups. As a result of these consultations, the following definitions were adopted.

Experimental[12] connotes application of scientific methods, experimental design, and the collection of reliable and accurate data for assessing results.

Health services refer to personal health services provided to individuals by doctors, dentists, and other professionals and assistants for preventive, curative, or rehabilitative purposes in the physical, emotional, and social domains of illness.

Planning within EHSDS was restricted to short-term operational planning for the improvement of personal health ser-

---

[12] This project was experimental in the additional sense of attempting innovation on a scale never before tested in this country, especially the combining of public and private efforts.

vices. It was to be one basis for decision-making and therefore a direct companion to the function of management. This form of planning contrasts with that of Comprehensive Health Planning Agencies which is long-range and directed to all health services, including environmental concerns.

Delivery signified that the Experimental System was expected to bring about change in the type, volume, and distribution of professional and institutional services. This change was to be responsive to the requirements of the local population for health services.

System denoted the creation and maintenance of functional relations among the providers of personal health services, the payers, and the public to assure that needed services would be predictably available and provided in accord with locally specified standards.

In late 1970, Guidelines for prospective applicants were issued. Applications were to describe the methods by which the community would work toward the attainment of a "delivery system." Priority in funding was to be given to applicant communities which proposed to achieve one or more of the following objectives:

1. *Improving primary care* with special attention to appropriate entry points to the system, including outreach, referral, and follow-up procedures to other levels and sites of health care; and to such supporting services as nutrition, welfare services, etc. First priority was to be given to increasing the accessibility of health care services to the medically disadvantaged.

2. *Placement of patients at proper levels of care* through formal arrangements among private physicians' offices, ambulatory care centers, clinics, hospitals, extended care facilities, nursing homes, and organized home care.

3. *Efficient use* of total community health care resources, especially through sharing services among health care institutions.

4. *Development of a stable financial base* for the local personal health services delivery system through adjustments in administrative regulations, financial provisions, and benefit structures of private and public sources of funds. Financial adequacy and stability were expected to be

demonstrated by the end of the period of developmental support.

5. Determination of *local health manpower requirements,* including that of new types of health manpower and the training and deployment of the latter.

6. *Methods for monitoring the quality of care* provided within the system at all service sites, both institutional and ambulatory.

7. *Developing methods for measuring and evaluating the effects of change* on access, costs, and effectiveness within the local health care system.

Full participation by existing Regional Medical Programs and the Comprehensive Health Planning Agencies was required. Another policy decision was to locate Experimental Systems in different geographical and population areas, ranging from rural low density population areas to inner urban and entire metropolitan areas and States. Three stages of evolution were projected for each Experimental System: organizational (formation of the corporation); developmental (setting objectives and priorities on the basis of data); and operational. Because of their scope, these projects were considered to require five to seven years of support before accurate assessment of their utility would be possible.

Results. One hundred and one applications were received. After initial review for technical and professional merit, site visits, and final review, 12 awards were made in June 1971, to applicant organizations representing the following geo-political areas:

Arkansas	Vermont
Philadelphia	Indianapolis
Binghamton	Tucson
Boise	Lubbock, Texas
Mon Valley, Pennsylvania	Avoca, Pennsylvania
Memphis	East Los Angeles

The above Experimental Systems contain 8,600,000 people. They are reasonably representative of the entire U. S. population except for a greater proportion of medically underserved people, that is, more elderly, more in the lower socioeconomic levels, more Negroes. This sample makes possible a first attempt at comprehensive evaluation of personal health services on a nationwide scale.

The experimental rationale for EHSDS imposed three technical requirements:

1. Creating a local management capability for directing the improvement in personal health services for entire communities

2. Developing and applying workable operational measures of the three cardinal objectives: improving access, containing cost, and assuring quality

3. Attributing any measured changes correctly to (1) EHSDS, (2) independent modification of existing community structures, or (3) independent innovations.

The first capability was seen as attainable through a voluntary corporate body effectively representing all parties in personal health services. This body was to be the vehicle for local, voluntary, centralized "management" guided by the objectives cited above. Leadership by an effective manager knowledgeable in health services was thought to be the critical factor. The organizational phase was completed in all the initially funded EHSDS, and it can be said that this basic concept survived its first test. The Rhode Island corporation, the first pilot project, has acquired highly competent leadership and staff and has proceeded to install several major elements of the health services data system. It is now identifying priority problems on the basis of such data.

The second capability, that of operationalizing the three cardinal objectives, was considered a prerequisite to improving the planning, management, and evaluation of personal health services on a communitywide basis. "Access" was defined operationally as the ratio of utilization to disability, the latter measured by "bed days" and "days unable to perform usual activities" (444). Each EHSDS was to set its own norms and to identify which population sub-groups fell below this norm. In so doing, each EHSDS identified its own target population whose access to personal health services was to be increased.

To assist each EHSDS in quantifying any existing deficiency in utilization based upon this ratio, a special household survey for "management" purposes was considered necessary. This was to be a relatively inexpensive yet sufficiently accurate survey to identify the probable number of people, their basic characteristics, level of disability, and reported utilization. Such a survey instrument was designed, tested, revised, and made available to the Experimental Systems (1218). Through its use, reliable information is obtained by combined telephone and door-to-door interview. This can then be related to census tract data. It permits construction of the utilization-to-disability ratios and identification of barriers to access. By repeated surveys, changes in these can be measured over time.

"Cost containment" refers to stable or reduced unit costs while increasing the volume of services so that the rate of increase in total expenditures in the future will be less than at present. In order to monitor unit costs, standard methods would be necessary for analyzing total public and private expenditures for health care at the State and local levels, by source and by method of payment. Such methods are essential to local management and to the evaluation of the local delivery system's performance. After extensive search, it was concluded that such methods do not exist. A protocol was designed to develop this method and contracts were let to qualified organizations for this purpose.

Quality can not be defined in quantitative terms as can utilization and expenditures. Rather, quality assessment requires the creation of specific formal organizations responsible for and capable of objectively reviewing medical care in standardized fashion. This requirement was a consideration in the design of the EMCRO program (see p. 168). It was expected that each EHSDS would install an EMCRO-like organization as the means of assessing and assuring quality. As of this writing, no EHSDS has been given federal support for this component.

The final technical requirement for EHSDS was a method of evaluation sufficiently powerful to attribute any observed changes in access/cost/quality accurately to their cause: changes in already existing arrangements, innovations independent of EHSDS, or EHSDS. Attempts to create this capability in consultation with many knowledgeable individuals and groups made clear how eclectic health services evaluation can be. Consultations were held with political scientists, sociologists, medical care investigators, epidemiologists, economists, survey specialists, statisticians, management experts, and those in administrative science. Each clearly could contribute an important piece to the entire approach. However, it was not possible to amalgamate the separate pieces into a cohesive protocol for the evaluation of EHSDS.

The difficulties of devising a cohesive evaluation method for one large community, much less for all Experimental Systems, led to the conclusion that "evaluation" should be considered to have two related but operationally separate elements. The first was to be the health services data system which would be built in as an integral part of management of the local Experimental System. This system was to be designed so as to yield data on the direction and magnitude of changes in access and costs, and provide information on the relationships of these changes to characteristics of the population, providers, facilities, and financing. Evaluation of these data would enable local managers to conduct operational planning and revise priorities within EHSDS.

The second component of evaluation was visualized as optional special studies directed to important findings which could not adequately be analyzed, or to problems not adequately defined by the data system. These special studies would be initiated upon joint agreement by the National Center and the board of each EHSDS. Depending upon their nature, they could appropriately draw upon universities, institutes, or private firms for social or behavioral scientists, epidemiologists, management experts, statisticians, industrial engineers, or others.

CONCLUSION

The foregoing sections have described the approach taken by NCHSRD in its initial program of health services R&D in 1969, 1970, and 1971. Prototypical R&D components were to be created or modified which would be or could be installed nationally. Individually, and especially when fitted together, these were to predictably improve the function of the delivery system as reflected in operational measures of improved access, cost containment, quality assurance.

R&D on mid-level health manpower, quality assurance (EMCRO), and data systems are the clearest examples of R&D

components which anticipate and make possible more rapid and effective implementation of innovation and legislation on a national scale. To this extent, health services R&D has been tested in the crucible of public policy in health services and found to have properties distinctly different from those of HSR and of demonstrations. The concept of its being analogous to the R&D of NASA has been partially validated. Other nationally applicable prototypes of innovations in cost containment and health care technology have been developed and evaluated. These await more general endorsement by public and professional policy.

But producing and testing prototypes of effective innovations individually, in different parts of the United States, would not likely lead to improvement on the scale which the systems approach theoretically makes possible. The task was therefore to create analogues of entire health services delivery systems on a small scale, that on the one hand would not disrupt present arrangements, yet on the other would permit realization of greater efficiences through better local management of public and private resources. The initial basic assumptions that entered into the design of the EHSDS program have been borne out by the support they have received from their local lay, professional, and political communities.

It is of particular interest therefore that the decentralization of many federal grant programs, and advent of state and local revenue sharing,[13] provide new practical tests of the EHSDS principles. The concept of local management of communitywide health services delivery may be validated, by the extent to which existing EHSDS enable their local areas and states to improve personal health services substantially, without new major federal programs or funding being superimposed.

---

[13] P.L. 92–512, 1972.

Chapter VII
International Health
Services Research

Paul J. Sanazaro

International health services research is of two broad types. The first consists of comparative studies *between* countries of entire health services systems or selected aspects (cross-national studies). The second comprises health services research conducted *within* different countries on their own problems of concern or interest. A recently published series of papers provides a concise overview of the evolution and present status of major issues in international HSR (1222). In this chapter, a brief indication is given of the scope and content of such research. The citations are representative of more recent studies but are in no sense intended to be comprehensive.

CROSS-NATIONAL STUDIES

Cross-national studies have been descriptive for the most part, directed to comparisons of various aspects of the health care systems in question. Examples of this approach are found in the reports by Evang (1223), Abel-Smith (1224,1225), O. W. Anderson (247,1226), Mechanic (1227), Lerner (410), Weinerman (1107), Fry (1228), Hogarth (1229), Roemer (1230), Glaser (551,662), Peterson, et al. (1231), and Liang, et al. (1232). Litman and Robins have suggested a framework for comparative sociopolitical study of national systems (1233).

The most extensive and rigorous cross-national study to date is the International Collaborative Study of Medical Care Utilization under the auspices of the World Health Organization. A feasibility study was conducted in Chittenden, Vermont, in the United States, in Chester, England, and in Smederevo, Yugoslavia, to ascertain whether "valid, reliable and comparable data on the use of doctors' and nurses' services and on hospitalization among a defined population during a given period of time could be collected simultaneously in several settings by standardized epidemiological procedures" (1234). Subsequently, the definitive study was conducted and a preliminary report of this landmark effort in health services research has been published (1235). Some of the research methods and results obtained have been reported (1236,1237) and theoretical frameworks for cross-national comparative research in the utilization of medical services have been proposed by Bice and White (1166).

An important technical development in cross-national health services research was the application of a model for distinguishing systems effects from those attributable to differences in characteristics of the populations (1163). This made possible a more objective analysis of existing differences between two health care systems and the relationships of these to differences in utilization.

In 1966 and 1967, the Health Services Research Study Section of the U.S. Public Health Service sponsored two cross-national studies as part of its program to improve the quantity and quality of HSR in the United States. The surveys were to investigate the state of development of health services research, the use of new methods, the training of investigators, the scope of its application in different countries, and specifically, its relationship to health policy.

Haggerty, Clark, et al. (1238) surveyed health services research in Denmark, Sweden, Norway, and Finland. They were impressed with "the extreme importance of population and disease registers for facilitating health services research." The Study team found that investigators in those countries used large sample sizes in household surveys and noted an "extraordinarily high percentage of compliance . . . with surveys, health examinations, and follow-up studies." The group commented on the unusual degree of cooperation among medical schools, public health authorities, independent institutes, and political bodies. Their report states ". . . the fruits of such collaboration seemed so valuable that every effort to achieve it seems worthwhile. In a very high proportion of research programs visited, the results had been translated into public policy . . ."

A parallel survey was conducted in Great Britain (1239). Important implications for the United States were found in the use of patient record systems that lend themselves to ongoing studies of the content of medical practice; development of record linkage systems; methods for analyzing the care needs of patients confined to hospitals; research in architectural design of hospitals; the organization of "research and intelligence units" linking operating delivery programs and academic research resources; experiments with health services in New Towns; and mathematical models to establish the reliability and validity of screening procedures.

The results of these two surveys had a direct influence on the health services research policies of the National Center for Health Services Research and Development when it was established in 1968.

HEALTH SERVICES RESEARCH
IN OTHER COUNTRIES

Most HSR conducted in other countries has addressed specific subjects or problems unique to that country. Only in exceptional circumstances have investigators had the support, opportunity, and resources necessary to conduct research within theoretical frameworks. The following listing is intended to be illustrative of the range of such research rather than a definitive annotation. Here also the emphasis is on recent studies.

UNITED KINGDOM

Departments of Social Medicine began the study of health services after World War II (1240,1241). This application of epidemiology was popularized by Morris (1242), although in the United Kingdom, as in the United States, the major contributing disciplines were those of the social sciences (1243–1245). In the 1950's and early 1960's, these latter remained descriptive, and, at least in the field of health services, did not pursue quantification, analysis, and theory building to the extent noted in the United States. However, statisticians and epidemiologists very early laid the ground rules for rigor in such studies and pinpointed important problems (1246). HSR in the United Kingdom also included operational research, first applied systematically by Bailey (1247,1248). Initially it was defined as "a collection of disciplines, brought together for the purpose of making a scientific attack on practical problems such as arise in systems embodying a number of interacting parts." A summary of the early formulations and experiences with operational research in the National Health Service was published by the Nuffield Provincial Hospitals Trust (1249). More recently, based on two decades' experience in the health field, operational research is defined as "the science applicable to decision problems in complex and uncertain situations" (1250).

In the United Kingdom, general practice is the arm of the National Health Service which provides direct access to the entire population. Many studies have been made of this system of primary care, including the morbidity statistics from general practice (1251); studies of prescribing (847); variations in tonsillectomy rate (1252); patterns of demand (1253); social class and use of medical care services (1254); attitudes of patients and their doctors (1255,1256); the "epidemiology" of general practice (1257); and the contributions of the nurse (1258).

Research has also been conducted on the problems of long-term care (1259,1260); outcomes of hospital care (337,1261); relationships of hospital and community care (1262); and the demand for hospital care (1263). Brotherston critically reviewed the extensive research conducted in the United Kingdom on the use of the hospital (1264). He also was the first to summarize the status of medical care research and put it in comprehensive perspective in relation to pervasive issues (1265). Acheson made a special contribution in developing a method for beginning medical record linkage (952,1051). Holland developed a population laboratory for prospective epidemiological study of illness and health services utilization (1266). Fletcher contributed importantly to improving survey techniques for respiratory disease (1267).

In Great Britain, emphasis is placed increasingly upon the

need to relate medical care to its demonstrable impact upon health status (1268). Cochrane has summarized the evidence for his view that randomized clinical trials must be given greater support by the National Health Service if health services are to achieve greater effectiveness and efficiency (1269).

The Nuffield Provincial Hospitals Trust in England, under the direction of Gordon McLachlan, has for a number of years sponsored and published special studies of important issues and problems, with the specific intent of providing a more rational base for policy. A few examples of the many that could be cited are the studies of bed requirements (1270), screening (923,1271), and the use of computers in medical services (1272). The respective impacts were that official estimates of the national requirements for hospital beds have been reduced; prescriptive screening is no longer strongly advocated; and a more directive policy guiding the application of computer technology to modules of information systems has been adopted. The Trust publishes a series of reports and essays entitled, "Problems and Progress in Medical Care." Edited by McLachlan, these constitute a cumulative summary of health services research addressed incisively to important scientific, technical, social, or political issues in health services in England.

The potential contribution of HSR to improving health care is explicitly discussed in a unique public document, *Portfolio for Health*. In this, the Department of Health and Social Security has published an overview of such research in 30 areas of particular interest to the Department, along with a listing of ongoing research projects (2). The importance of implementing the significant findings and possible methods for so doing, are discussed.

In the Scottish Home and Health Department, a Research and Intelligence Unit produces research reports based on routinely collected statistics (1273). Through joint appointments, the Department also encourages special studies by investigators holding academic titles (1274).

SCANDINAVIA

The summary by Haggerty, Clark, et al., provides an indication of the ongoing HSR in Denmark, Finland, Norway, and Sweden (1238). The availability of population and disease registers is a distinct advantage in local and national studies of need and health status.

HSR has been applied in Finland systematically to obtain information useful for local and national planning and policy-making (1275–1277). Purola, et al., published the methods, instruments, and results of a national survey of utilization as related to morbidity, health resources, and social factors (1162). Conducted prior to initiation of the National Health Insurance scheme, this is a rigorous national survey in its concepts, methods, and design. Apart from the informative national data and its contribution to refinement of methods, the survey permitted the testing of various hypotheses regarding illness behavior (5). The data were analyzed to provide the most comprehensive formulation to date of the determinants of utilization for an entire population. A subsequent survey was conducted in 1968 to determine what changes had occurred as a result of the institution of National Health Insurance in 1965. This is the only known example of a "before and after" research design of this magnitude (1278).

Screening for disease and laboratory automation has been emphasized in Sweden (1279–1281). An overview of medical care research by sociologists has been published (1282). The National Board of Health and Welfare of Sweden has established RUPRO (the Running Prognosis) whose aim "is to provide responsible authorities and organizations at all levels with statistical data on the present state and trends of development of the services for health and sick care" (1283). This remarkable system "makes it possible to compare different local areas, to add up the services to a total for the whole country and finally to follow the trend of this total over a span of time." Included in RUPRO are statistics on all outpatient and institutional services, personnel, education and training of health personnel, costs, and population of local administrative areas.

Another major national activity is SPRI, the Swedish Planning and Rationalization Institute of Health and Social Services (1284). Supported by public and private funds, this organization conducts and supports a wide range of studies directed to improving the planning and operation of health services.

CANADA

Social science research in medical care in Canada has been briefly reviewed recently (7). Badgley and Wolfe, two pioneers in such research (1285), have recently published the results of an eight-year study of a medical group practice in Saskatchewan (1286). The reports of the Royal Commission on Health Services contain many instances of studies, surveys, and secondary data analyses which constitute an important documentation of the status of health services in Canada (240,1287-1291). A direct observational study of the quality of care in general practice was conducted by Clute in two Provinces and reported in 1963 (321). A recent publication discusses the potential contribution to improved policy- and decision-making by government-directed research and development (1184).

OTHER COUNTRIES

The quality or efficiency of care was studied over a number of years in Amsterdam and brought together in a monograph (8). Although lacking an extensive population base, this series of studies attempted to analyze both process and outcomes and to apply a variety of study techniques to the medical care system in Holland. The quality of medical care in parts of Australia has been studied (1292). The epidemiology of appendectomy in Germany has been reported in careful detail in relation to general patterns of medical care (1293).

The volume of HSR appears to be increasing in other countries. A new periodical, *International Journal of Health Services*, contains papers on policy, concepts, descriptions, and analyses as applied to planning, administration, and evaluation. The admixture accurately reflects the generally practical concerns of health services research in most nations, but with far less of the theoretical emphasis that has characterized HSR in the United States.

References — Chapter I

1. Mainland, D. (Ed.): *Health Services Research.* New York: Milbank Memorial Fund, 1967.

2. *Portfolio for Health. The Role and Program of the Department of Health and Social Services in Health Services Research. Problems and Progress in Medical Care. Sixth Series.* Published for the Nuffield Provincial Hospitals Trust. London: Oxford Univ. Press, 1971.

3. Haggerty, R. J.: "The university and primary medical care." *N. Engl. J. Med.* 281: 416–422, 1969.

4. White, K. L.: "Medical care research and health services systems." *J. Med. Educ.* 42: 729–741, 1967.

5. Kalimo, E.: *Determinants of Medical Care Utilization.* Research Institute for Social Security. Helsinki: 1969. pp. 235–253.

6. McLachlan, G. (Ed.): *Problems and Progress in Medical Care. Second Series.* Published for the Nuffield Provincial Hospitals Trust. London: The Oxford Univ. Press, 1966.

7. Stone, I. J.: "Research in social science and health in Canada." *Milbank Mem. Fund Q.* 49: 177–186, 1971.

8. Querido, A.: *The Efficiency of Medical Care.* Leiden: H. E. Stenfert Kroese N.V., 1963.

9. Sanazaro, P. J.: "Health services research and development." *J. Med. Educ.* 45: 725–730, 1970.

HEALTH MANPOWER RESEARCH

10. Anderson, O. W.: "Influence of social and economic research on public policy in the health field—a review." *Milbank Mem. Fund Q.* 44: No. 3, Part 2, 11–48, 1966.

11. "Midwives of Chicago." *J.A.M.A.* 50: 1346–1350, 1908.

12. Abbott, G.: "The Midwife in Chicago." *Am. J. Sociol.* 20: 684–699, 1915.

13. Flexner, A.: *Medical Education in the United States and Canada: A Report to the Carnegie Foundation for the Advancement of Teaching.* New York: The Carnegie Foundation, 1910.

14. Reed, L. S.: *Midwives, Chiropodists & Optometrists: Their Place in Medical Care* (CCMC Report No. 15). Chicago: Univ. of Chicago Press, 1932.

15. Reed, L. S.: *The Healing Cults: A Study of Sectarian Medical Practice, its Extent, Causes, and Control.* (CCMC Report No. 16) Chicago: Univ. of Chicago Press, 1932.

16. Mountin, J. W., Pennell, E. H., and Nicolay, V.: "Location and movement of physicians—General observations." *Public Health Reports* 57: 1363–1375, 1942.

17. Mountin, J. W., Pennell, E. H., and Nicolay, V.: "Location and movement of physicians—Turnover as a factor affecting State totals." *Public Health Reports* 57: 1752–1761, 1942.

18. Mountin, J. W., Pennell, E. H., and Nicolay, V.: "Location and movement of physicians—Effect of local factors upon location." *Public Health Reports* 57: 1945–1953, 1942.

19. Mountin, J. W., Pennell, E. H., and Nicolay, V.: "Location and movement of physicians." *Public Health Reports* 58: 483–490, 1943.

20. Mountin, J. W., Pennell, E. H., and Brockett, G.: "Location and movement of physicians—Changes in urban and rural totals." *Public Health Reports* 60: 173–185, 1945.

21. Mountin, J. W., Pennell, E. H., and Berger, A. G.: *Health Service Areas—Estimates of Future Physician Requirements.* Public Health Bull. No. 305, Federal Security Agency, Public Health Service. Washington: U. S. Gov't. Print. Off., 1949.

22. Butter, I.: "Health manpower research: A survey." *Inquiry* 4: 5–38, December 1967.

23. Theodore, C. N. and Sutter, G. E.: "A report on the first periodic survey of physicians." *J.A.M.A.* 202: 516–524, 1967.

24. Fein, R.: *The Doctor Shortage: An Economic Diagnosis.* Washington: The Brookings Institution, 1967.

25. Hughes, E. F. X., Fuchs, V. R., Jacoby, J. E., *et al.*: "Surgical work loads in a community practice." *Surgery* 71: 315–327, 1972.

26. Schonfeld, H. K., Heston, J. F., and Falk, I. S.: "Numbers of physicians required for primary medical care." *N. Engl. J. Med.* 286: 571–576, 1972.

27. Lee, R. I. and Jones, L. W.: *The Fundamentals of Good Medical Care.* (CCMC Report No. 22) Chicago: Univ. of Chicago Press, 1933.

28. Klein, H.: "Civilian dentistry in wartime." *J. Am. Dent. Assoc.* 31: 648–661, 1944.

29. Waterman, G. E.: "Effective use of dental assistants." *Public Health Reports* 67: 390–394, 1952.

30. Waterman, G. E. and Knutson, J. W.: "Studies on dental care services for school children: First and second treatment series, Richmond, Indiana." *Public Health Reports* 68: 583–589, 1953.

31. Waterman, G. E. and Knutson, J. W.: "Studies on dental care services for school children: Third and fourth treatment series, Richmond, Indiana." *Public Health Reports* 69: 247–254, 1954.

32. Law, F. E., Johnson, C. E., and Knutson, J. W.: "Studies on dental care services for school children: First and second treatment series, Woonsocket, Rhode Island." *Public Health Reports* 68: 1192–1198, 1953.

33. Law, F. E., Johnson, C. E., and Knutson, J. W.: "Studies on dental care for school children: Third and fourth treatment series, Woonsocket, Rhode Island." *Public Health Reports* 70: 402–409, 1955.

34. Frank, J. E., Law, F. E., Spitz, G. S., *et al.*: "School dental care in a community with controlled fluoridation." *Public Health Reports* 79: 113–124, 1964.

35. Baird, K. M., Shillington, G. B., and Protheroe, D. H.: "Pilot study on the advanced training and employment of auxiliary dental personnel in the Royal Canadian Dental Corps: Preliminary report." *J. Can. Dent. Assoc.* 28: 627–638, 1962.

36. Baird, K. M., Purdy, E. C., and Protheroe, D. H.: "Pilot study on advanced training and employment of auxiliary dental personnel in the Royal Canadian Dental Corps: Final report." *J. Can. Dent. Assoc.* 29: 778–787, 1963.

37. Baird, K. M.. Covey, G. R., and Protheroe, D. H.: "Employment

of auxiliary clinical personnel in the Royal Canadian Dental Corps." *J. Can. Dent. Assoc.* 33: 184–191, 1967.

38. General Dental Council of Great Britain: *Final Report on the Experimental Scheme for the Training and Employment of Dental Auxiliaries, 1966.* London and Colchester: Spottiswoode, Ballantyne & Co., Ltd., 1966.

39. Ludwick, W. E., Schoebelen, E. O., and Knoedler, D. J.: *Greater Utilization of Dental Technicians. I. Report of Training, 1963. II. Report of Clinical Tests, 1964.* U. S. Navy Dental Corps.

40. Bergman, A. B., Dassel, S. W., and Wedgewood, R. J.: "Time-motion study of practicing pediatricians." *Pediatrics* 38: 254–263, 1966.

41. Yankauer, A., Connelly, J. P., and Feldman, J. J.: "A survey of allied health worker utilization in pediatric practice in Massachusetts and in the United States." *Pediatrics* 42: 733–742, 1968.

42. Yankauer, A., Connelly, J. P., and Feldman, J. J.: "Task performance and task delegation in pediatric office practice." *Am. J. Public Health* 59: 1104–1117, 1969.

43. Yankauer, A., Connelly, J. P., and Feldman, J. J.: "Pediatric practice in the United States—with special attention to utilization of allied health workers." *Pediatrics* 45: 521–554, 1970.

44. Yankauer, A., Connelly, J. P., Andrews, P., *et al.*: "The practice of nursing in pediatric offices—challenge and opportunity." *N. Engl. J. Med.* 282: 843–847, 1970.

45. Yankauer, A., Connelly, J. P., and Feldman, J. J.: "Physician productivity in the delivery of ambulatory care." *Med. Care* 8: 35–46, 1970.

46. Silver, H. K., Ford, L. C., and Stearly, S. G.: "A program to increase health care for children: The pediatric nurse practitioner program." *Pediatrics* 39: 756–760, 1967.

47. Silver, H. K., Ford, L. C., and Day, L. R.: "The pediatric nurse-practitioner program." *J.A.M.A.* 204: 298–302, 1968.

48. Schiff, D. W., Fraser, C., and Walters, H.: "The pediatric nurse practitioner in the office of pediatricians in private practice." *Pediatrics* 44: 62–68, 1969.

49. Silver, H. K. and Hecker, J. A.: "The pediatric nurse practitioner and the child health associate: New types of health professionals." *J. Med. Educ.* 45: 171–176, 1970.

50. Lewis, C. E. and Resnick, B.: "Nurse clinics and progressive ambulatory patient care." *N. Engl. J. Med.* 277: 1236–1241, 1967.

51. Lewis, C. E. and Resnick, B.: "The nurse clinic—dynamics of ambulatory patient care—new roles for old disciplines." *Kansas Med. Soc. J.*, 68: 123–124, March 1967.

52. Charney, E., Kitzman, H., Berkow, E., *et al.*: "The child-health nurse (pediatric nurse practitioner) in private practice." *N. Engl. J. Med.* 285: 1353–1358, 1971.

53. Patterson, P. K.: "Time-motion study of six pediatric office assistants." *N. Engl. J. Med.* 281: 771–774, 1969.

54. Patterson, P. K., Bergman, A., and Wedgewood, R.: "Parent reaction to the concept of pediatric assistants." *Pediatrics* 44: 69–75, 1969.

55. Coye, R. D. and Hansen, M. F.: "The doctor's assistant: A survey of physicians' expectations." *J.A.M.A.* 209: 529–533, 1969.

56. McCormack, R., Allen, H. M., and Livers, E. L.: "Family doctors' use of office assistants and opinions regarding nurses in primary care." *Southern Med. J.* 64: 415–418, 1971.

57. Yankauer, A., Jones, S. H., Schneider, J., *et al.*: "Performance and delegation of patient services by physicians in obstetrics-gynecology." *Am. J. Public Health* 61: 1545–1555, 1971.

58. Montgomery, T. A.: "A case for nurse-midwives." *Am. J. Obstet. and Gynecol.* 105: 309–313, 1969.

59. Estes, E. H., Jr.: "Task-oriented vs. degree-oriented training concept of optimizing the use of the most highly skilled with specific personnel." *Military Med.* 134: 386–389, 1969.

60. Yankauer, A., Tripp, S., Andrews, P., *et al.*: "The outcomes and service impact of a pediatric nurse practitioner training program—Nurse practitioner training outcomes." *Am. J. Public Health* 62: 347–353, 1972.

61. Fenderson, D. A.: "A manpower evaluation protocol." *Bull. N. Y. Acad. Med.* 48: 966–973, 1972.

62. Rogers, K. D., Mally, M., and Marcus, F. L.: "A general medical practice using nonphysician personnel." *J.A.M.A.* 206: 1753–1757, 1968.

63. Merenstein, J. H. and Rogers, K. D.: "Tasks of nonphysicians in

primary medical practice." *Pennsylvania Medicine* 75: 47–50, 1972.

64. Riddick, F. A., Jr., Bryan, J. B., Gershenson, M., *et al.*: "Use of allied health professionals in internists' offices." *Arch. Intern. Med.* 127: 924–931, 1971.

65. Gilpatrick, E. G. and Corliss, P. K.: *The Occupational Structure of New York City Municipal Hospitals.* New York: Praeger Publishers, 1970.

66. Shryock, R. H.: *Medical Licensing in America, 1650–1965.* Baltimore: The Johns Hopkins Press, 1967.

67. Roemer, R.: "Licensing and regulation of medical and medical-related practitioners in health service teams." *Med. Care* 9: 42–54, 1971.

HEALTH FACILITIES RESEARCH

68. Mountin, J. W., Pennell, E. H., and Pearson, K.: *Business Census of Hospitals, 1935 — General Report, Supplement No. 154 to the Public Health Reports.* Washington: U. S. Gov't. Print. Off., 1939.

69. Mountin, J. W. and Pennell, E. H.: "Financial support of non-governmental hospitals as revealed by the recent business census of hospitals." *Hospitals* 11: 11–19, Dec. 1937.

70. Mountin, J. W., Pennell, E. H., Flook, E., *et al.*: *Hospital Facilities in the United States. Part I. Selected Characteristics of Hospital Facilities in 1936. Part II. Trends in Hospital Development 1928–1936.* Public Health Bull. No. 243. U. S. Treasury Dept., Public Health Service, Div. of Public Health Methods, Washington: U. S. Gov't. Print. Off., 1938.

71. Mountin, J. W., Pennell, E. H., and Pearson, K.: "Prevailing ratios of personnel to patients in hospitals offering general care." *Hospitals* 12: 42–47, Nov. 1938.

72. Mountin, J. W., Pennell, E. H., and Hankla, E. K.: "A study of the variations in reports on hospital facilities and their use." *Public Health Reports* 53: 17–25, 1938.

73. Mountin, J. W., Pennell, E. H., and Hankla, E. K.: "Summary figures on income, expenditures, and personnel of hospitals." *Hospitals* 12: 11–19, Apr. 1938.

74. Mountin, J. W., Pennell, E. H., and Pearson, K.: "Regional differences in hospital facilities for tuberculosis from the stand-

point of accommodations, sources of financial support, and operating costs." in *Transactions of the 35th Annual Meeting of the National Tuberculosis Association, Boston, Mass., June 26-29, 1939,* pp. 1-15.

75. Mountin, J. W., Pennell, E. H., and Pearson, K.: "The distribution of hospitals and their financial support in southern states." *Southern Med. J.* 33: 402-411, 1940.

76. Mountin, J. W., Pennell, E. H., and Pearson, K.: "Existence and use of hospital facilities among the several states in relation to wealth as expressed by per capita income." *Public Health Reports* 55: 822-846, 1940.

77. Mountin, J. W., Pennell, E. H., and Pearson, K.: "Factors that influence hospital occupancy." *Hospitals* 15: 18-25, March 1941.

78. Mountin, J. W., and Pennell, E. H.: "Financial support of hospitals controlled by state and local governments." *Public Health Reports* 56: 433-445, 1941.

79. Mountin, J. W., Pennell, E. H., and Pearson, K.: "Hospitals existing singly in counties have similar financial structure." *Public Health Reports* 56: 498-509, 1941.

80. Mountin, J. W. and Pennell, E. H.: "Selection of hospitals in small urban areas." *Hospitals* 16: 55-61, Aug. 1942.

81. Mountin, J. W., Pennell, E. H., and Hoge, V. M.: *Health Service Areas—Requirements for General Hospitals & Health Centers.* Public Health Bull. No. 292, Federal Security Agency, Public Health Service, Washington: U. S. Gov't. Print. Off., 1945.

82. Mountin, J. W. and Greve, C. H.: *Public Health Areas and Hospital Facilities: A Plan for Coordination.* Public Health Service Publication No. 42, Federal Security Agency, Public Health Service, Washington: U. S. Gov't. Print. Off., 1950.

83. Commission on Hospital Care: *Hospital Care in the United States.* New York: The Commonwealth Fund, 1947.

84. Ginsberg, E.: *A Pattern for Hospital Care.* New York: Columbia Univ. Press, 1949.

85. Corwin, E. H. L.: *The American Hospital.* New York: The Commonwealth Fund, 1946.

86. Burling, T., Lentz, E. M., and Wilson, R. N.: *The Give and Take in Hospitals.* New York: G. P. Putnam's Sons, 1956.

87. Rosenfeld, L. S. and Makover, H. B.: *The Rochester Regional Hospital Council.* Cambridge: Published for The Commonwealth Fund by Harvard Univ. Press, 1956.

88. Lembcke, P. A., Hermansen, D. R., and Poland, E.: "A proposed standard method for measuring hospital capacity." *Public Health Reports* 74: 674–683, 1959.

89. Thompson, J. D.: "Study of two recovery rooms offers clues to intensive care unit design." *Hospitals* 32: 35 and 51–59, Nov. 1, 1958.

90. Pelletier, R. J. and Thompson, J. D.: "Yale index measures design efficiency." *Mod. Hosp.* 95: 73–77, Nov. 1960.

91. Thompson, J. D. and Pelletier, R. J.: "Privacy vs. efficiency in the inpatient unit." *Hospitals* 36: 53–62, Aug. 16, 1962.

92. Fetter, R. B. and Thompson, J. D.: "Patients' waiting time and doctors' idle time in the outpatient setting." *Health Serv. Res.* 1: 66–90, 1966.

93. Anderson, T. R. and Warkov, S.: "Organizational size and functional complexity: A study of administration in hospitals." *Am. Sociol. Rev.* 26: 23–28, 1961.

94. Connor, R. J., Flagle, C. D., Hsieh, R. K. C., *et al.*: "Effective use of nursing resources." *Hospitals* 35: 30–37, May 1, 1961.

95. Georgopoulos, B. S. and Mann, F. C.: *The Community General Hospital.* New York: The Macmillan Co., 1962.

96. Revans, R. W.: "Research into hospital management and organization." *Milbank Mem. Fund Q.* 44: No. 3, Part 2, 207–248, 1966.

97. Blumberg, M. S.: "Hospital automation: The needs and the prospects." *Hospitals* 35: 34–43 and 90, Aug. 1, 1961.

98. London M. and Sigmond, R. R.: "Are we building too many hospital beds?" *Mod. Hosp.* 96: 59–63, Jan. 1961; "Small specialized bed units lower occupancy." *Mod. Hosp.* 96: 95–100, May 1961; "How week ends and holidays affect occupancy." *Mod. Hosp.* 97: 79–83, Aug. 1961. (A related series of reports.)

99. Roemer, M. I.: "Contractual physicians in general hospitals: A national survey." *Am. J. Public Health* 52: 1453–1464, 1962.

100. Connors, E. J. and Hutts, J. C.: "How administrators spend their day." *Hospitals* 41: 45–50 and 141, Feb. 16, 1967.

101. Drosness, D. L., Reed, I. M., Lubin, J. W., *et al.*: "Uses of daily

census data in determining efficiency of units." *Hospitals* 41: 45–48 and 106, Dec. 1, 1967, and 41: 65–68 and 112, Dec. 16, 1967.

102. Georgopoulos, B. S. and Matejko, A.: "The American general hospital as a complex social system." *Health Serv. Res.* 2: 76–112, 1967.

103. Roemer, M. I. and Friedman, J. W.: "Medical staff organization in hospitals: A new typology (in 2 parts)" Part I. *Hosp. Manage.* 105: 58–61, Apr. 1968, and Part II. *Hosp. Manage.* 105: 41–44, May 1968.

104. Rockart, J. F. and Hofmann, P. B.: "Physician and patient behavior under different scheduling systems in a hospital outpatient department." *Med. Care* 7: 463–470, 1969.

105. Roemer, M. I. and Friedman, J. W.: *Doctors in Hospitals.* Baltimore: The Johns Hopkins Press, 1971.

106. Stimson, R. H. and Stimson, D. H.: "Operations research and the nursing staffing problem." *Hosp. Admin.:* pp. 61–69, Winter 1972.

107. Neuhauser, D.: *The Relationship Between Administrative Activities and Hospital Performance.* Univ. of Chicago, Center for Health Administration Studies, Research Series 28, Chicago, 1971.

108. Neuhauser, D. and Andersen, R.: "Structural-comparative studies of hospitals" in *Organization Research on Health Institutions.* Edited by B. S. Georgopoulos. Ann Arbor: Univ. of Michigan, Institute for Social Research, 1972, pp. 83–114.

109. Trites, D. K., Galbraith, F. D., Leckwart, J. F., *et al.*: "Radial nursing units prove best in controlled study." *Mod. Hosp.* 112: 94–99, April 1969.

110. Trites, D. K., Galbraith, F. D., Sturdavant, M., *et al.*: "Influence of nursing unit design on the activities and subjective feelings of nursing personnel." *Environment and Behavior* 2: 303–334, 1970.

111. Gillette, P. J., Rathbun, P. W., and Wolfe, H. B.: "Hospital information systems." Part I. *Hospitals* 44: 76–78, Aug. 16, 1970. Part II. *Hospitals* 44: 45–48 and 110, Sept. 1, 1970.

112. Jydstrup, R. A. and Gross, M. J.: "Cost of information handling in hospitals." *Health Serv. Res.* 1: 235–271, 1966.

113. Hsieh, R. K. C.: "Evaluation of formal communication systems in a hospital." *Health Serv. Res.* 1: 223–234, 1966.

114. Hanson, R. C.: "The systemic linkage hypothesis and role consensus patterns in hospital community relations." *Am. Sociol. Rev.* 27: 304–313, 1962.

115. Oaklander, H. and Fleishman, E. A.: "Patterns of leadership related to organizational stress in hospital settings." *Admin. Sci. Q.* 8: 520–532, 1964.

116. McCarroll, J. R. and Skudder, P. A.: "Conflicting concepts of function shown in national survey." *Hospitals* 34: 35–42, Dec. 1, 1960.

117. Flagle, C. D., Gabrielson, I. W., Soriano, A., *et al.*: *Analysis of Congestion in an Outpatient Clinic.* Baltimore: The Johns Hopkins Hospital, Operations Research Division, 1961.

118. Beenhakker, H. L.: "Multiple correlation—A technique for prediction of future hospital bed needs." *Operations Res.* 11: 824–839, 1963.

119. Preston, R. A., White, K. L., Strachan, E. J., *et al.*: "Patient care classification as a basis for estimating graded inpatient hospital facilities." *J. Chronic Dis.* 17: 761–772, 1964.

120. Feldstein, M. S.: "Effects of differences in hospital bed scarcity on type of use." *Br. Med. J.* 5408: 561–564, 1964.

121. Rosenthal, G. D.: *The Demand for General Hospital Facilities.* American Hospital Association. Hospital Monograph Series No. 14, Chicago, 1964.

122. Sturdavant, M. and Mickey, H. C.: "An experiment in minimal care" (in 3 parts)—Part I. *Hospitals* 40: 70–79, Feb. 16, 1966; Part II. *Hospitals* 40: 50–54 and 112, Mar. 1, 1966; Part III. *Hospitals* 40: 70–74 and 126, Mar. 16, 1966.

123. Hopkins, C. E. and Harris, J. A.: *Methods of Estimating Hospital Bed Needs.* Los Angeles: Univ. of California, 1967.

124. Gustafson, D. H.: "Length of stay: Prediction and explanation." *Health Serv. Res.* 3: 12–34, 1968.

125. Ginsberg, E. and Rogatz, P.: *Planning for Better Hospital Care.* New York: Columbia Univ. Press, 1961.

126. Hallen, P. B.: "Hospitals branch out. A study of multiple unit operations (in 2 Parts)." Part I. *Hospitals* 37: 38–44 and 132, Aug. 1, 1963, and Part II. *Hospitals* 37: 54–57, Aug. 16, 1963.

127. Souder, J. J., Clark, W. E., Elkind, J. I., *et al.*: *Planning for Hospitals: A Systems Approach Using Computer-Aided Techniques.* Chicago: American Hospital Association, 1964.

128. Drosness, D. L., Reed, I. M., and Lubin, J. W.: "The application of computer graphics to patient origin study techniques." *Public Health Reports* 80: 33–39, 1965.

129. Schneider, J. B.: "Measuring the locational efficiency of the urban hospital." *Health Serv. Res.* 2: 154–169, 1967.

130. Pomrinse, S. D. and Weinstein, B. M.: "Improvement of medical care programs by means of a new type of hospital affiliation." *Am. J. Public Health* 55: 1643–1652, 1965.

131. Rosenberger, D. M.: "How mergers begin and how they work." *Mod. Hosp.* 107: 85–89, July 1966.

132. Kerr, F. H.: "First year proves value of Sioux City's merger of two competing church hospitals." *Mod. Hosp.* 109: 116–118, Oct. 1967.

133. Blumberg, M. S.: *Shared Services for Hospitals.* Chicago: American Hospital Association, 1966.

134. Georgopoulos, B. S.: *Organization Research on Health Institutions.* Ann Arbor: Univ. of Michigan, Institute for Social Research, 1972.

135. Haldeman, J. C. and Abdellah, F. G.: "Concepts of progressive patient care." *Hospitals* 33: 38–42, May 16, 1959, and 33: 41–46, June 1, 1959.

136. Lockward, H. J., Giddings, L. and Thoms, E. B.: "Progressive patient care—A preliminary report." *J.A.M.A.* 172: 132–137, 1960.

137. Abdellah, F. G., Meyer, B. and Roberts, H.: "Nursing patterns vary in progressive care." *Mod. Hosp.* 95: 85–91, Aug. 1960.

138. U. S. Dept. of Health, Education, and Welfare, Public Health Service, Divison of Hospital and Medical Facilities: *Elements of Progressive Patient Care.* Public Health Service Pub. No. 930-C-1, Washington: U. S. Gov't. Print. Off., 1962.

139. U. S. Dept. of Health, Education, and Welfare, Public Health Service, Division of Hospital and Medical Facilities: *Elements of Progressive Patient Care.* Public Health Service Pub. No. 930-C-2, Washington: U. S. Gov't. Print. Off., 1963.

140. Weeks, L. E. and Griffith, J. R. (Eds.): *Progressive Patient Care—An Anthology.* Ann Arbor: Univ. of Michigan, 1964.

141. Griffith, J. R., Weeks, L. E., and Sullivan, J. H.: *The McPherson Experiment: Expanded Community Hospital Service.* Univ. of Michigan, Bureau of Hospital Administration, Research Series No. 5, Ann Arbor, 1967.

142. Feldstein, M. S.: "Hospital cost variations and case mix differences." *Med. Care* 3: 95–103, 1965.

143. Feldstein, M. S.: "Hospital bed scarcity: An analysis of the effects of inter-regional differences." *Economica* 32: 393–409, 1965.

144. Feldstein, P. J.: *An Empirical Investigation of the Marginal Cost of Hospital Services.* Chicago: Univ. of Chicago, Grad. School of Business, Grad. Prog. in Hosp. Admin., Studies in Hospital Administration, 1961.

145. Feldstein, P. J. and Waldman, S.: "Financial position of hospitals in the early Medicare period." *Social Security Bull.* 31: 18–23, Oct. 1968.

146. Berry, R. E.: "Returns to scale in the production of hospital services." *Health Serv. Res.* 2: 123–139, 1967.

147. Carr, W. J. and Feldstein, P. J.: "The relationship of cost to hospital size." *Inquiry* 4: 45–65, June 1967.

148. Carr, W. J.: "Economic efficiency in the allocation of hospital resources: central planning vs. evolutionary development" in *Empirical Studies in Health Economics.* Edited by H. E. Klarman. Baltimore: The Johns Hopkins Press, 1970, pp. 195–221.

149. Cohen, H. A.: "Variations in costs among hospitals of different sizes." *Southern Economic J.* 33: 355–366, 1967.

150. Cohen, H. A. "Hospital cost curves with emphasis on measuring patient care output" in *Empirical Studies in Health Economics.* Edited by H. E. Klarman. Baltimore: The Johns Hopkins Press, 1970, pp. 279–293.

151. Francisco, E. W.: "Analysis of cost variations among short-term general hospitals" in *Empirical Studies in Health Economics.* Edited by H. E. Klarman. Baltimore: The Johns Hopkins Press, 1970, pp. 321–332.

152. Long, M. F. and Feldstein, P. J.: "Economics of hospital sys-

tems: Peak loads and regional coordination." *Am. Economic Rev.* 57: 119–129, 1967.

153. Stevens, C. M.: "Hospital market efficiency: The anatomy of the supply response" in *Empirical Studies in Health Economics.* Edited by H. E. Klarman. Baltimore: The Johns Hopkins Press, 1970, pp. 229–248.

154. Muller, C. F. and Worthington, P.: "Factors entering into capital decisions of hospitals" in *Empirical Studies in Health Economics.* Edited by H. E. Klarman. Baltimore: The Johns Hopkins Press, 1970, pp. 399–415.

155. Mann, J. K. and Yett, D. E.: "The analysis of hospital costs: A review article." *J. Business* 41: 191–202, 1968.

156. Hamilton, J. A.: *Patterns of Hospital Ownership and Control.* Minneapolis: Univ. of Minnesota Press, 1961.

157. Klarman, H. E.: "Characteristics of patients in short-term hospitals in New York City." *J. Health Soc. Behav.* 3: 46–52, 1962.

158. Klarman, H. E.: *Hospital Care in New York City: The Roles of Voluntary and Municipal Hospitals.* New York: Columbia Univ. Press, 1963.

159. Flagle, C. D.: "Operations research in the health services." *Operations Res.* 10: 591–603, 1962.

160. Blumberg, M. S.: "DPF concept helps determine bed needs." *Mod. Hosp.* 97: 75–81, Dec. 1961.

161. Shuman, L. J., Wolfe, H. A., and Hardwick, C. P.: "Predictive hospital reimbursement and evaluation model." *Inquiry* 9: 17–33, June 1972.

162. Belknap, I. and Steinle, J. G.: *The Community and Its Hospitals—A Comparative Analysis.* Syracuse: Syracuse Univ. Press, 1963.

163. McNerney, W. J., *et al.*: *Hospital and Medical Economics—A Study of Population, Services, Costs, Methods of Payment and Controls.* (2 vols.) Chicago: Hospital Research and Educational Trust, American Hospital Association, 1962.

164. Solon, J. A. and Baney, A. M.: "Ownership and size of nursing homes." *Public Health Reports* 70: 437–444, 1955.

165. Solon, J. A., Roberts, D. W., Krueger, D. E., *et al.*: *Nursing*

Homes, Their Patients and Care: A Study of Nursing Homes and Similar Long-Term Facilities in 13 States. Public Health Service Pub. No. 503, Washington: U. S. Gov't. Print. Off., 1957.

166. Winter, K.: *Michigan Nursing Facilities and Their Patients: A Source-Book of State and County Data.* Univ. of Michigan, School of Public Health, Bu. of Pub. Health Economics, Research Series No. 8, Ann Arbor, 1960.

167. Kramer, C. H. and Lessing, J. D.: "Medical care in Illinois nursing homes." *J. Am. Geriatrics Soc.* 10: 983–994, 1962.

168. Spier, H. B.: *Characteristics of Nursing Homes and Related Facilities.* Public Health Service Pub. No. 930-F-5, Washington: U. S. Gov't. Print. Off., 1963.

169. Kelleher, R. P. and Shaughnessy, M. E.: *Fact-Finding Survey of Massachusetts Nursing Homes.* Boston College, School of Nursing, Boston College Press, 1963.

170. Goldmann, F.: "Nursing service in homes for the aged." *Public Health Reports* 75: 1124–1132, 1960.

171. Goldmann, F.: "Personal health services in homes for the aged." *Am. J. Public Health* 50: 1274–1287, 1960.

172. Morris, R.: "How hospitals and nursing homes can work together." *Hospitals* 35: 32–36 and 104, June 1, 1961.

173. Walker, J. E. C., Jessiman, A. F., and Taubenhaus, L. J.: "Problems in hospital-nursing home relationships: A teaching hospital reports." *Hospitals* 40: 72–77, June 16, 1966.

174. Health Services Research Center, Chicago, Illinois: *Guidelines for Health Services R&D: Shared Services.* U. S. Dept. of Health, Education, and Welfare, Health Services and Mental Health Administration, National Center for Health Services Research and Development. DHEW Pub. No. (HSM) 72-3023, 1972.

175. Health Services Research Center, Chicago, Illinois: *Guidelines for Health Services R&D: Hospital Mergers.* U. S. Dept. of Health, Education, and Welfare, Health Services and Mental Health Administration, National Center for Health Services Research and Development. DHEW Pub. No. (HSM) 72-3024, 1972.

176. Murnaghan, J. H. and White, K. L. (Eds.): *Hospital Discharge Data. Report of the Conference on Hospital Discharge Abstracts Systems, June 18–20, 1969. Med. Care* 8: No. 4, Supplement, 1970.

177. Health Services Foundation, Blue Cross Association: *Guidelines for Health Services R&D: Uniform Discharge Data.* U. S. Dept. of Health, Education, and Welfare, Health Services and Mental Health Administration, National Center for Health Services Research and Development. DHEW Pub. No. (HSM) 72-3025, 1972.

177a. Hospital Research and Educational Trust and American Hospital Association. *Guidelines for Health Services R&D: Common Data Set for Hospital Management.* U. S. Dept. of Health, Education, and Welfare, Health Services and Mental Health Administration, National Center for Health Services Research and Development. DHEW Pub. No. (HSM) 72-3026, 1972.

ORGANIZATION AND ADMINISTRATION OF HEALTH SERVICES

Public Programs

178. Chapin, C. V.: *A Report of State Public Health Work, Based on a Survey of State Boards of Health.* Chicago: American Medical Association, 1915.

179. Chapin, C. V.: *History of State and Municipal Control of Disease in a Half Century of Public Health.* New York: American Public Health Association, 1921.

180. American Public Health Association in Cooperation with the United States Public Health Service: *Report of the Committee on Municipal Health Department Practice.* Public Health Bull. No. 136. U. S. Treasury Dept., Public Health Service, Washington: U. S. Gov't. Print. Off., 1923.

181. American Public Health Association in Cooperation with the United States Public Health Service: *Report of the Committee on Administrative Practice: Municipal Health Department Practice for the Year 1923.* Public Health Bull. No. 164. U. S. Treasury Dept., Public Health Service, Washington: U. S. Gov't. Print. Off., 1926.

182. Ferrell, J. A. and Mead, P. A.: *Health Departments of States and Provinces of the United States and Canada.* Public Health Bull. No. 184. U. S. Treasury Dept., Public Health Service, Washington: U. S. Gov't. Print. Off., 1927.

183. Ferrell, J. A., *et al.*: *Health Departments of States and Provinces of the United States and Canada, rev. ed.* Public Health Bull. No. 184,

2d. ed. U. S. Treasury Dept., Public Health Service, Washington: U. S. Gov't. Print. Off., 1932.

184. Mountin, J. W. and Flook, E.: *Distribution of Health Services in the Structure of State Government.* Public Health Bull. No. 184, 3d ed. Federal Security Agency, Public Health Service, Washington: U. S. Gov't. Print. Off., 1943.

185. Mountin, J. W., Flook, E., *et al.*: *Distribution of Health Services in the Structure of State Government.* Public Health Bull. No. 184, 4th ed. Federal Security Agency, Public Health Service, Washington: U. S. Gov't. Print. Off., 1952.

186. Mountin, J. W. and Haldeman, J. C.: "State health organization today and a decade ago." *J.A.M.A.* 151: 35-37, 1953.

187. Mountin, J. W., *et al.*: *Brunswick-Greensville Health Administration Studies, Nos. 1-9: Effectiveness and Economy of County Health Department Practice.* No. 1—Mountin: "Description of study." *Public Health Reports* 49: 1232-1241, 1934, Reprint No. 1654. *NOTE:* Other studies of this series are distributed among the several research categories to which they apply.

188. Mountin, J. W., *et al.*: *County Health Department Studies in Three Selected Areas, Nos. 1-10.* No. 9—Mountin and Flook, E.—"The place of an index in health department record keeping." *Public Health Reports* 55: 387-393, 1940. *NOTE:* As with the Brunswick-Greensville studies, others of the "Three Selected Areas" are distributed as appropriate.

189. *Report of White House Conference on Child Health and Protection.* New York: The Century Co., 1932.

190. Ferrell, J. A. and Mead, P. A.: *History of County Health Organizations in the United States, 1908-1933.* Public Health Bull. No. 222. U. S. Treasury Dept., Public Health Service, Washington: U. S. Gov't. Print. Off., 1936.

191. Mountin, J. W., Pennell, E. H., and Flook, E.: *Experience of the Health Department in 811 Counties, 1908-1934.* Public Health Bull. No. 230. U. S. Treasury Dept., Public Health Service, Washington: U. S. Gov't. Print. Off., 1936.

192. Mountin, J. W. and Norman, N. L.: "Joint City-County Health Units" in *The Municipal Year Book.* Chicago: The International City Manager's Association, 1945, pp. 308-323.

193. Mountin, J. W., Borowski, A. J., and O'Hara, H.: "Variations in the form and services of public health organizations." *Public Health Reports* 53: 523–536, 1938, Reprint No. 1923.

194. Borowski, A. J.: "Positions and rates of pay in public health agencies." *Am. J. Public Health* 28: 1197–1202, 1938.

195. American Public Health Association. Committee on Administrative Practice (Emerson, H. M. and Luginbuhl, M.): *Local Health Units for the Nation*. New York: The Commonwealth Fund, 1945.

196. Walker, W. F. and Randolph, C. R.: *Recording of Local Health Work*. New York: The Commonwealth Fund, 1935.

197. Mustard, H. S.: *Government in Public Health*. New York: The Commonwealth Fund, 1945.

198. Mountin, J. W., Hankla, E. K., and Druzina, G. B.: *Ten Years of Federal Grants-in-Aid for Public Health, 1936–1946*. Public Health Bull. No. 300. Federal Security Agency, Public Health Service, Washington: U. S. Gov't. Print. Off., 1948.

199. Mountin, J. W. and Greve, C. H.: *The Role of Grants-in-Aid in Financing Public Health Programs*. Public Health Bull. No. 303. Federal Security Agency, Public Health Service, Washington: U. S. Gov't. Print. Off., 1950.

200. Mountin, J. W. and Flook, E.: *Devices for Reducing Health Department Records and Reports*. Supplement No. 187 to *Public Health Reports*, 1945.

201. Hiscock, I. V. (Ed.): *Community Health Organization*. American Health Congress Series, vol. 2, part 4, New York: American Public Health Association, 1927; rev. eds. New York: The Commonwealth Fund, 1932, 1939, 1950.

202. Hanlon, J. J.: *Principles of Public Health Administration*. St. Louis: The C. V. Mosby Company, 1950.

203. Griffith, J. R.: "Role of the government in personal health care" in *Hospital and Medical Economics: A Study of Population, Services, Costs, Methods of Payment, and Controls*, vol. 2. Edited by W. J. McNerney. Chicago: Hospital Research and Educational Trust, 1962, pp. 1129–1201.

204. Reed. L. S.: "The Canadian Hospital Insurance Program." *Public Health Reports* 77: 97–106, 1962.

The Private Sector

205. Davis, M. M. and Warner, A. R.: *Dispensaries.* New York: The Macmillan Co., 1918.

206. Davis, M. M.: *Clinics, Hospitals, and Health Centers.* New York: Harper and Bros., 1927.

207. Peebles, A.: *A Survey of Statistical Data on Medical Facilities in the United States* (CCMC Report No. 3). Washington: Committee on the Costs of Medical Care, 1929.

208. Carpenter, N.: *Medical Care for 15,000 Workers and Their Families: A Survey of the Endicott Johnson Workers Medical Service* (CCMC Report No. 5). Washington: Committee on the Costs of Medical Care, 1930.

209. Rorem, C. R.: *Private Group Clinics* (CCMC Report No. 8). Chicago: Univ. of Chicago Press, 1931.

210. Rorem, C. R.: *The "Municipal Doctor" System in Rural Saskatchewan.* (CCMC Report No. 11). Chicago: Univ. of Chicago Press, 1931.

211. Falk, I. S., Griswold, D. M., and Spicer, H.: *A Community Medical Service Organized Under Industrial Auspices in Roanoke Rapids, North Carolina* (CCMC Report No. 20). Chicago: Univ. of Chicago Press, 1932.

212. Falk, I. S.: *Organized Medical Service at Fort Benning, Georgia.* (CCMC Report No. 21) Chicago: Univ. of Chicago Press, 1932.

213. Griswold, D. M. and Spicer, H.: *University Student Services.* (CCMC Report No. 19) Chicago: Univ. of Chicago Press, 1932.

214. Rorem, C. R. and Musser, J. H.: *Private Group Medical Service.* Chicago: The Julius Rosenwald Fund, 1937.

215. Rorem, C. R.: "Patterns and problems of group medical practice." *Am. J. Public Health* 40: 42–56, 1950.

216. Hunt, G. H.: "Medical group practice in the United States. Introduction." *N. Engl. J. Med.* 237: 71–77, 1947.

217. Hunt, G. H. and Goldstein, M.: "Medical group practice in the United States. Survey of five groups in New England and the Middle Atlantic States." *N. Engl. J. Med.* 237: 719–731, 1947.

218. Hunt, G. H. and Goldstein, M.: "Medical group practice in the United States. Report of a questionnaire survey of all listed groups, 1946." *J.A.M.A.* 135: 904–909, 1947.

219. Goldstein, M.: "Medical group practice in the United States. Organization and administrative practices." *J.A.M.A.* 136: 857-861, 1948.

220. Goldstein, M.: "Medical group practice in the United States. Growth of groups." *Lancet* 69: 42-46, 1949.

221. Goldstein, M.: "Medical group practice in the United States. Income of physicians." *J.A.M.A.* 142: 1049-1052, 1950.

221a. Goldstein, M.: "Medical group practice." *J. National Med. Assoc.* 42: 223-228, 1950.

222. Hunt, H. G. and Goldstein, M.: *Medical Group Practice in the United States. Summary Report.* Public Health Service Pub. No. 77, Federal Security Agency, Public Health Service. Washington: U. S. Gov't. Print. Off., 1951.

223. American Medical Association, Bureau of Medical Economics. "Private group practice." *J.A.M.A.* 100: 1605-1608, 1693-1699, 1773-1778, 1933.

224. American Medical Association, Bureau of Medical Economics. *Group Medical Practice.* Chicago: American Medical Association, 1940.

225. Commission on Chronic Illness. *Prevention of Chronic Illness* (vol. 1). Cambridge: Published for The Commonwealth Fund by Harvard Univ. Press, 1957.

226. Commission on Chronic Illness. *Care of the Long-Term Patient* (vol. 2). Cambridge: Published for the Commonwealth Fund by Harvard Univ. Press, 1956.

227. *Public Health Service and Commission on Chronic Illness (A Joint Project). A Study of Home Care Programs.* Public Health Monograph No. 35, U. S. Dept. of Health, Education, and Welfare, Public Health Service, PHS Pub. No. 447, Washington: U. S. Gov't. Print. Off., 1955.

228. Hassinger, E.: "The pattern of medical services for incorporated places of 500-or-more population in Missouri, 1950." *Rural Sociol.* 21: 175-177, 1956.

229. Weinerman, E. R.: "An appraisal of medical care in group health centers." *Am. J. Public Health* 46: 300-309, 1956.

230. Trussell, R. E.: *Hunterdon Medical Center—The Story of One Approach to Rural Medical Care.* Cambridge: Published for the Commonwealth Fund by Harvard Univ. Press, 1956.

231. Boulware, J. R.: "The composition of private pediatric practice in a small community in the South of the United States: A 25-year study." *Pediatrics* 22: 548–558, 1958.

232. Shortliffe, E. C., Hamilton, T. S., and Noroian, E. H.: "The emergency room and the changing pattern of medical care." *N. Engl. J. Med.* 258: 20–25, 1958.

233. Pomrinse, S. D. and Goldstein, M. S.: "The 1959 survey of group practice." *Am. J. Public Health* 51: 671–682, 1961.

234. Balfe, B. E. and McNamara, M. E.: *Survey of Medical Groups in the United States, 1965.* Chicago: American Medical Association, 1968.

235. Bailey, R. M.: "A comparison of internists in solo and fee-for-service group practice in the San Francisco Bay Area." *Bull. N. Y. Acad. Med.* 44: 1293–1303, 1968.

236. Ross, A., Jr.: "A report on physicians' termination in group practice." *Med. Group Manage.* 16: 15–21, July 1969.

237. Aspen Systems Corporation, Health Law Center: *Group Practice and the Law.* Pittsburgh: Aspen Systems Corp., 1969.

238. Kralewski, J. E.: "Group practice of medicine." *Rocky Mountain Med. J.,* 66: 35–41, Feb. 1969.

239. McNamara, M. E. and Todd, C.: "A survey of group practice in the United States, 1969." *Am. J. Public Health* 60: 1303–1313, 1970.

240. Boan, J. A.: *Group Practice.* Ottawa: Royal Commission on Health Services, Queen's Printer, 1966.

241. Donabedian, A.: *A Review of Some Experiences with Prepaid Group Practice.* Univ. of Michigan, School of Public Health, Bu. of Public Health Economics, Research Series No. 12, Ann Arbor, 1969.

242. Donabedian, A.: "An evaluation of prepaid group practice." *Inquiry* 6: 3–27, Sept. 1969.

243. Saward, E. W., Blank, J. D., and Greenlick, M. R.: "Documentation of twenty years of operation and growth of a prepaid group practice plan: A case study." *Med. Care* 6: 231–244, 1968.

244. Feldstein, P. J.: *Prepaid Group Practice: An Analysis and Review.*

Ann Arbor: Univ. of Michigan, School of Public Health, Bu. of Hospital Administration, 1971.

245. Greenberg, I. G. and Rodburg, M. L.: "The role of prepaid group practice in relieving the medical care crisis." *Harvard Law Rev.* 84: 887–1001, 1971.

246. Roemer, M. I.: "The impact of hospitals on the practice of medicine in Europe and in America." *Hospitals* 37: 61-64 and 124, Nov. 1, 1963.

247. Anderson, O. W.: "Health services systems in the United States and other countries: Critical comparisons." *N. Engl. J. Med.* 269: 839–843 and 896–900, 1963.

248. Stevens, R.: *Medical Practice in Modern England. The Impact of Specialization in State Medicine.* New Haven: Yale Univ. Press, 1966.

249. Forsyth, G. and Logan, R. F. L.: "Medical technology and the needs of chronic disease—A review of some British studies on the organization of medical care services." *J. Chronic Dis.* 17: 789–802, 1964.

250. Field, M. G.: *Soviet Socialized Medicine—An Introduction.* New York: The Free Press, 1967.

251. McNerney, W. J. and Riedel, D. C.: *Regionalization and Rural Health Care—An Experiment in Three Communities.* Ann Arbor: Univ. of Michigan, 1962.

252. Freidson, E.: "The organization of medical practice" in *Handbook of Medical Sociology.* Edited by H. E. Freeman, S. Levine and L. G. Reeder. Englewood Cliffs, N. J.: Prentice-Hall, Inc., 1963, pp. 299–319.

253. Bailey, R. M.: "Economies of scale in medical practice" in *Empirical Studies in Health Economics.* Edited by H. E. Klarman. Baltimore: The Johns Hopkins Press, 1970, pp. 255–273.

254. Littauer, D., Flance, I. J., and Wessen, A. F.: *Home Care.* American Hospital Association, Hospital Monograph Series No. 9, Chicago, 1961.

255. Huntley, R. R.: "Epidemiology of family practice." *J.A.M.A.* 185: 105–108, 1963.

256. Hessel, S. J. and Haggerty, R. J.: "General pediatrics: A study of practice in the mid-1960s." *Pediatrics* 73: 271–279, 1968.

257. Walker, J. E. C., Murawski, B. J., and Thorn, G. W.: "An experimental program in ambulatory medical care." *N. Engl. J. Med.* 271: 63–68, 1964.

258. Kovner, A. R., Katz, G., Kahane, S. B., *et al.*: "Relating a neighborhood health center to a general hospital: A case history." *Med. Care* 7: 118–123, 1969.

259. Torrens, P. R.: "A pilot program in coordination of care between an urban teaching hospital and the community's general practitioners." *Am. J. Public Health* 59: 60–64, 1969.

260. Weinerman, E. R.: "Research into the organization of medical practice." *Milbank Mem. Fund Q.* 44: No. 4, Part 2, 104–140, 1966.

EVALUATION AND QUALITY OF HEALTH SERVICES

261. American Public Health Association, Committee on Administrative Practice. *Appraisal Form for City Health Work.* New York: American Public Health Association, 1925.

262. American Public Health Association, Committee on Administrative Practice. *Appraisal Form for City Health Work. (2d. ed.)* New York: American Public Health Association, 1926.

263. American Public Health Association, Committee on Administrative Practice. *Appraisal Form for Rural Health Work.* New York: American Public Health Association, 1927.

264. Platt, P. S.: *The Validity of the Appraisal Form as a Measure of Administrative Health Practice.* New York: American Public Health Association, 1928.

265. American Public Health Association, Committee on Administrative Practice. *Appraisal Form for City Health Work. (3d. ed.)* New York: American Public Health Association, 1929.

266. American Public Health Association, Committee on Administrative Practice. *Appraisal Form for Rural Health Work. Revised.* New York: American Public Health Association, 1932.

267. American Public Health Association, Committee on Administrative Practice. *Appraisal Form for City Health Work. (4th ed.)* New York: American Public Health Association, 1934.

268. American Public Health Association, Committee on Adminis-

trative Practice. *Appraisal Form for Local Health Work.* New York: American Public Health Association, 1938.

269. American Public Health Association, Committee on Administrative Practice. *Evaluation Schedule of the APHA.* New York: American Public Health Association, 1943.

270. American Public Health Association, Committee on Administrative Practice. *Health Practice Indices.* New York: American Public Health Association, 1943.

271. Derryberry, M.: "Contributions of George T. Palmer, Letter to the Editor." *Am. J. Public Health* 62: 130–131, 1972.

272. Palmer, G. T. (Dir. of Study): *Health Survey of 86 Cities.* American Child Health Association, Research Div., New York: J. J. Little and Ives Co., 1925.

273. Palmer, G. T. (Dir. of Study): *Physical Defects—The Pathway to Correction.* American Child Health Association, Research Div., New York: Lenz and Riecker, Inc., 1934.

274. Nyswander, D. B. (Dir. of Study): *Solving School Health Problems—The Astoria Demonstration.* Sponsored by the Dept. of Health and the Board of Education of New York City. New York: The Commonwealth Fund, 1942.

275. Yankauer, A.: "Designs for evaluation needed in the school health field." *Am. J. Public Health* 42: 655–660, 1952.

276. Yankauer, A. and Lawrence, R. A.: "A study of periodic medical examinations (in 4 Parts): I. Methodology and initial findings." *Am. J. Public Health* 45: 71–78, 1955.

277. Yankauer, A. and Lawrence, R. A.: "II. The annual increment of new 'defects.' " *Am. J. Public Health* 46: 1553–1562, 1956.

278. Yankauer, A., Lawrence, R. A., and Ballon, L.: "III. The remediability of certain categories of 'defects.' " *Am. J. Public Health* 47: 1421–1429, 1957.

279. Yankauer, A., Wendt, R., Eichler, H., *et al.*: "IV. Educational aspects." *Am. J. Public Health* 51: 1532–1540, 1961.

280. Sydenstricker, E.: *The Measurement of Results of Public Health Work.* New York: Annual Report of the Milbank Memorial Fund, 1926, pp. 1–35.

281. Dean, J. O. and Pennell, E. H.: "Communicable diseases and

activities for their control in the Brunswick-Greensville area (B-G. Study No. 7)." *Public Health Reports* 51: 991–1013, 1936, Reprint No. 1761.

282. Dean, J. O.: "Tuberculosis control by a small county health department." *Public Health Reports* 52: 597–609, 1937, Reprint No. 1822.

283. Mountin, J. W., Pennell, E. H., and O'Hara, H.: "Relationship of a rural health program to the needs of the area." *Public Health Reports* 52: 1264–1284, 1937, Reprint No. 1858.

284. Mountin, J. W.: "How expenditures for selected public health services are apportioned." *Public Health Reports* 52: 1384–1389, 1937, Reprint No. 1865.

285. Mountin, J. W. and Flook, E.: "The scope of personal service given by representative county health departments." *The Health Officer* 4: 242–250, 1939.

286. Dean, J. O. and Flook, E.: "Neglected opportunities for teamwork in county health department practice." *Public Health Reports* 55: 573–582, 1940, Reprint No. 2150.

287. Mountin, J. W., Pennell, E. H., and Flook, E.: *Illness and Medical Care in Puerto Rico.* Public Health Bull. No. 237. U. S. Treasury Dept., Public Health Service, Washington: U. S. Gov't. Print. Off., 1937.

288. Reed, L. S. and Clark, D. A.: "Appraising public medical services." *Am. J. Public Health* 31: 421–430, 1941.

289. Frost, W. H.: "Rendering account in public health" in *Papers of Wade Hampton Frost, M.D.: A Contribution to Epidemiologic Method.* Edited by Kenneth F. Maxcy. New York: The Commonwealth Fund, 1941. London: Humphrey Milford, Oxford Univ. Press, pp. 553–559.

290. Greenberg, B. G., Harris, M. E., MacKinnon, C. F., *et al.*: "A method for evaluating the effectiveness of health education literature." *Am. J. Public Health* 43: 1147–1155, 1953.

291. Sheps, M. C. and Sheps, C. G.: *Assessing the Effectiveness of Programs in Operation.* Study Group Reports, Committee IV on Research, National Conference on Care of the Long-Term Patient. Baltimore: Commission on Chronic Illness. (Processed). 1954.

292. Glasser, M. A.: "A study of the public's acceptance of the Salk vaccine program." *Am. J. Public Health* 48: 141–146, 1958.

293. James, G.: "Evaluation in public health practice." *Am. J. Public Health* 52: 1145–1154, 1962.

294. Densen, P. M., James, G., and Cohart, E.: "Research, program planning, and evaluation." *Public Health Reports* 81: 49–56, 1966.

295. Densen, P. M.: "Some practical and conceptual problems in appraising the outcome of health care services and programs" in *Outcomes Conference I-II. Methodology of Identifying, Measuring and Evaluating Outcomes of Health Service Programs, Systems and Subsystems.* Edited by C. E. Hopkins. Los Angeles: Univ. of California, 1970. Distributed as Report No. PB196-001, 1970 by National Technical Information Service, U. S. Dept. of Commerce, Springfield, Va. for National Center for Health Services Research and Development. pp. 15–30.

296. Suchman, E. A.: *Evaluative Research. Principles and Practice in Public Service and Social Action Programs.* New York: Russell Sage Foundation, 1967.

297. Kelman, H. R. and Elinson, J.: "Strategy and Tactics of Evaluating Large-Scale Medical Care Programs" in Proceedings of Social Statistics Section, Am. Statistical Assoc. Washington: 1968. pp. 169–191.

298. Hopkins, C. E.: "Outcomes Conference I: Synopsis" in *Outcomes Conference I-II. Methodology of Identifying, Measuring and Evaluating Outcomes of Health Service Programs, Systems and Subsystems.* Edited by C. E. Hopkins. Los Angeles: Univ. of California, 1970. Distributed as Report No. PB196-001, 1970 by National Technical Information Service, U. S. Dept. of Commerce, Springfield, Va. for National Center for Health Services Research and Development.

299. Borgatta, E. F.: "Research problems in evaluation of health services demonstrations." *Milbank Mem. Fund Q.* 44: No. 4, Part 2, 182–200, 1966.

300. Morehead, M. A.: "Evaluating quality of medical care in the neighborhood center program of OEO." *Med. Care* 8: 118–131, 1970.

301. Dreyfus, E. G., Minson, R., Sharbaro, J. A., *et al.*: "Internal

chart audits in a neighborhood health program: A problem-oriented approach." *Med. Care* 9: 449–454, 1971.

302. Task Force on Medicaid and Related Programs (W. J. McNerney, Chairman). *Report of the Task Force.* U. S. Dept. of Health, Education, and Welfare. Washington: U. S. Gov't. Print. Off., 1970.

303. Cabot, R. C.: "Diagnostic pitfalls identified during a study of 3,000 autopsies." *J.A.M.A.* 59: 2295–2298, 1912.

304. Codman, E. A.: "The product of a hospital." *Gynecology and Obstetrics* 18: 491–496, 1914.

305. Codman, E. A.: *A Study in Hospital Efficiency: The First Five Years.* Boston: Thomas Todd Company, 1916.

306. Goldmann, F.: "The adequacy of medical care." *Yale J. Biol. and Med.* 19: 681–688, 1947.

307. Anderson, O. W.: *Administration of Medical Care: Problems and Issues.* Univ. of Michigan, School of Public Health, Bureau of Public Health Economics, Research Series No. 2, Ann Arbor, 1947.

308. Ciocco, A., Hunt, H., and Altman, I.: "Statistics on clinical services to new patients in medical groups." *Public Health Reports* 65: 99–115, 1950.

309. Lembcke, P. A.: "Measuring the quality of medical care through vital statistics based on hospital service areas. I. Comparative study of appendectomy rates." *Am. J. Public Health* 42: 276–286, 1952.

310. Lembcke, P. A.: "Medical auditing by scientific methods: Illustrated by major female pelvic surgery." *J.A.M.A.* 162: 646–655, 1956.

311. Makover, H. B.: "The quality of medical care: Methodological survey of the medical groups associated with the Health Insurance Plan of New York." *Am. J. Public Health* 41: 824–832, 1951.

312. Rosenfeld, L. S.: "Quality of medical care in hospitals." *Am. J. Public Health* 47: 856–865, 1957.

313. Daily, E. F. and Morehead, M. A.: "A method of evaluating and improving the quality of medical care." *Am. J. Public Health* 46: 848–854, 1956.

314. Trussell, R. E., Morehead, M. A., and Ehrlich, J.: *The Quantity, Quality and Costs of Medical and Hospital Care Secured by a Sample of Teamster Families in the New York Area.* New York: Columbia Univ. School of Public Health and Administrative Medicine, 1962.

315. Morehead, M. A., Donaldson, R. S., Sanderson, S., *et al.*: *A Study of the Quality of Hospital Care Secured by a Sample of Teamster Family Members in New York City.* New York: Columbia Univ. School of Public Health and Administrative Medicine, 1964.

316. Lerner, M. and Riedel, D. C.: "The teamster study and the quality of medical care." *Inquiry* 1: 69–80, Jan. 1964.

317. Myers, R. S.: "Hospital statistics don't tell the truth." *Mod. Hosp.* 83: 53–54, July 1954.

318. Myers, R. S., Slee, V. N., and Hoffman, R. G.: "Medical audit." *Mod. Hosp.* 85: 77–83, Sept. 1955.

319. Eisele, C. W., Slee, V. N., and Hoffman, R. G.: "Can the practice of internal medicine be evaluated?" *Ann. Intern. Med.* 44: 144–161, 1956.

320. Peterson, O. L., Andrews, L. T., Spain, R. S., *et al.*: "An analytical study of North Carolina general practice, 1953–1954." *J. Med. Educ.* 31: No. 12, Part 2, 1956.

321. Clute, K.: *The General Practitioner. A Study of Medical Education and Practice in Ontario and Nova Scotia.* Toronto: Univ. of Toronto Press, 1963.

322. Fitzpatrick, T. B., Riedel, D. C., and Payne, B. C.: "Character and effectiveness of hospital use" in *Hospital and Medical Economics: A Study of Population, Services, Costs, Methods of Payment, and Controls,* vol. I. Edited by W. J. McNerney. Chicago: Hospital Research and Educational Trust, 1962. pp. 449–526.

323. Payne, B. C.: "Continued evolution of a system of medical care appraisal." *J.A.M.A.* 201: 536–540, 1967.

324. Williamson, J. W., Alexander, M., and Miller, G. E.: "Priorities in patient-care research and continuing medical education." *J.A.M.A.* 204: 303–308, 1968.

325. Brown, C. R., Jr. and Uhl, H. S.: "Mandatory continuing education, sense or nonsense?" *J.A.M.A.* 213: 1660–1668, 1970.

326. Price, P. B., Taylor, C. W., Nelson, D. E., *et al.*: *Measurement*

and Predictors of Physician Performance: Two Decades of In-termittently Sustained Research. Salt Lake City: LLR Press, 1971.

327. Sanazaro, P. J. and Williamson, J. W.: "Physician performance and its effects on patients: A classification based on reports by internists, surgeons, pediatricians and obstetricians." Med. Care 8: 299–308, 1970.

328. Lewis, C. E., Resnick, B. A., Schmidt, G. et al.: "Activities, events and outcomes in ambulatory patient care." N. Engl. J. Med. 280: 645–649, 1969.

329. Hubbard, J. P., Levit, E. J., Schumacher, C. F., et al.: "An objective evaluation of clinical competence. New technics used by the National Board of Medical Examiners." N. Engl. J. Med. 272: 1321–1328, 1965.

330. Donabedian, A.: "Evaluating the quality of medical care." Milbank Mem. Fund Q. 44: No. 3, Part 2, 166–203, 1966.

331. Donabedian, A.: Medical Care Appraisal—Quality and Utilization. A Guide to Medical Care Administration—Vol. II. New York: American Public Health Association, 1969.

332. Brook, R. H. and Stevenson, R. L. Jr.: "Effectiveness of patient care in an emergency room." N. Engl. J. Med. 283: 904–907, 1970.

333. Brook, R. H., Berg, M. H., and Schechter, B. A.: "Effectiveness of nonemergency care via an emergency room." Ann. Intern. Med. 78: 333–339, 1973.

334. Gonnella, J. S., Goran, M. J., Williamson, J. W., et al.: "Evaluation of patient care: An approach." J.A.M.A. 214: 2040–2043, 1970.

335. Goran, M. J., Williamson, J. W., and Gonnella, J. S.: "The validity of patient management problems." J. Med. Educ. 48: 171–177, 1973.

336. Shapiro, S.: "End result measurements of quality of medical care." Milbank Mem. Fund Q. 45: 7–30, 1967.

337. Lipworth, L., Lee, J., and Morris, J. N.: "Case-fatality in teaching and non-teaching hospitals, 1956–1959." Med. Care 1: 71–76. 1963.

338. Katz, S., Ford, A. B., Moskowitz, R. W., et al.: "Studies of illness of the aged: The index of ADL, a standardized measure of

biological and psychological function." *J.A.M.A.* 185: 914–919, 1963.

339. Katz, S., Vignos, P. J., Jr., Moskowitz, R. W., *et al.*: "Comprehensive outpatient care in rheumatoid arthritis: A controlled study." *J.A.M.A.* 206: 1249–1254, 1968.

340. Sanazaro, P. J. and Williamson, J. W.: "End results of patient care: A provisional classification based on reports by internists." *Med. Care* 6: 123–130, 1968.

341. Thompson, J. D., Marquis, D. B., Woodward, R. L., *et al.*: "End result measurements of the quality of obstetrical care in two U. S. Air Force hospitals." *Med. Care* 6: 131–143, 1968.

342. Williamson, J. W.: "Evaluating quality of patient care—A strategy relating outcomes and process assessment." *J.A.M.A.* 218: 564–569, 1971.

343. Payne, B. C. and Lyons, T. F.: *Episode of Illness Study.* Ann Arbor: Univ. of Michigan, School of Medicine, 1972.

344. Payne, B. C. and Lyons, T. F.: *Office Care Study.* Ann Arbor: Univ. of Michigan, School of Medicine, 1972.

345. Solon, J., Feeney, J. J., Jones, S. H., *et al.*: "Delineating episodes of medical care." *Am. J. Public Health* 57: 401–408, 1967.

346. Falk, I. S., Schonfeld, H. K., Harris, B. R., *et al.*: "The development of standards for the audit and planning of medical care. I. Concepts, research, design and the content of primary physician's care." *Am. J. Public Health* 57: 1118–1136, 1967.

347. Schonfeld, H. K., Falk, I. S., Lavietes, P. H., *et al.*: "The development of standards for the audit and planning of medical care: Pathways among primary physicians and specialists for diagnosis and treatment." *Med. Care* 6: 101–114, 1968.

348. Schonfeld, H. K., Falk, I. S., Lavietes, P. H., *et al.*: "The development of standards for the audit and planning of medical care: Good pediatric care—program content and method of estimating needed personnel." *Am. J. Public Health* 58: 2097–2110, 1968.

349. Bunker, J. P.: "Surgical manpower, a comparison of operations and surgeons in the United States and in England and Wales." *N. Engl. J. Med.* 282: 135–144, 1970.

350. Lewis, C. E.: "Variations in the incidence of surgery." *N. Engl. J. Med.* 281: 880–884, 1969.

351. Bloom, B. S. and Peterson, O. L.: "End results, cost, and productivity of coronary-care units." *N. Engl. J. Med.* 288: 72–78, 1973.

352. Fanshel, S. and Bush, J. W.: "A health-status index and its application to health services outcomes." *Operations Res.* 18: 1021–1066, 1970.

353. Hopkins, C. E. (Ed.): *Outcomes Conference I-II. Methodology of Identifying, Measuring and Evaluating Outcomes of Health Service Programs, Systems and Subsystems.* Los Angeles: Univ. of California, 1970. Distributed as Report No. PB196-001, 1970 by National Technical Information Service, U. S. Dept. of Commerce, Springfield, Va. for National Center for Health Services Research and Development.

354. Roemer, M. I., Moustafa, A. T., and Hopkins, C. E.: "A proposed hospital quality index: Hospital death rates adjusted for case severity." *Health Serv. Res.* 3: 96–118, 1968.

355. Goss, M. E. W.: "Organizational goals and quality of medical care: Evidence from comparative research on hospitals." *J. Health Soc. Behav.* 11: 255–268, 1970.

356. Huntley, R. R., Steinhauser, R., White, K. L., *et al.*: "The quality of medical care: Techniques and investigations in the outpatient clinic." *J. Chronic Dis.* 14: 630–642, 1961.

357. The Committee for the Special Research Project in the Health Insurance Plan of Greater New York. *Health and Medical Care in New York City.* Cambridge: Published for The Commonwealth Fund by Harvard Univ. Press, 1957.

358. Shapiro, S., Weiner, L., and Densen, P. M.: "Comparison of prematurity and perinatal mortality in a general population and in the population of a prepaid group practice medical care plan." *Am. J. Public Health* 48: 170–187, 1958.

359. Shapiro, S., Jacobziner, H., Densen, P. M., *et al.*: "Further observations on prematurity and perinatal mortality in a general population and in the population of a prepaid group practice medical care plan." *Am. J. Public Health* 50: 1304–1317, 1960.

360. Garland, L. H.: "The problem of observer error." *Bull. N. Y. Acad. Med.* 36: 570–584, 1960.

361. Howland, D. and McDowell, W. E.: "Measurement of patient care." "I. Approaches to the system's problem." *Nurs. Res.* 12: 172–174, 1963. "II. Hospital systems model." *Nurs. Res.* 12: 232–236, 1963. "III. A conceptual framework." *Nurs. Res.* 13: 4–7, 1964.

362. Maloney, M. C., Trussell, R. E., and Elinson, J.: "Physicians choose medical care: A sociometric approach to quality appraisal." *Am. J. Public Health* 50: 1678–1686, 1960.

363. Pratt, L., Seligman, A., and Reader, G. G.: "Physicians' views on the level of medical information among patients." *Am. J. Public Health* 47: 1277–1283, 1957.

364. Reader, G. G., and Goss, M. E. W. (Eds.): *Comprehensive Medical Care and Teaching. A Report on the New York Hospital—Cornell Medical Center Program.* Ithaca: Cornell Univ. Press, 1967.

365. Klarman, H. E.: "Present status of cost benefit analysis in the health field." *Am. J. Public Health* 57: 1948–1954, 1967.

366. Andersen, S.: "Operations research in public health." *Public Health Reports* 79: 297–305, 1964.

367. Goodrich, C. H., Olendzki, M. C., and Reader, G. G.: *Welfare Medical Care: An Experiment.* Cambridge: Harvard Univ. Press, 1970.

368. Robertson, L. S., Kosa, J., Heagarty, M. C., *et al.*: *Toward Changing the Medical Care System: Report of an Experiment, 1964–1968.* Springfield, Va.: National Technical Information Service, U.S. Dept. of Commerce, Report No. PB-220-941, 1973.

369. Mather, H. G., Pearson, N. G., Read, K. L. Q., *et al.*: "Acute myocardial infarction: Home and hospital treatment." *Brit. Med. J.* 3: 334–338, 1971.

UTILIZATION OF HEALTH SERVICES

370. Sydenstricker, E.: "The extent of medical and hospital service in a typical small city. Hagerstown Morbidity Studies No. III." *Public Health Reports* 42: 121–131, 1927, Reprint 1134.

371. Collins, S. D.: "Frequency of health examinations in 9,000 families. Based on nationwide periodic canvasses, 1928–1931." *Public Health Reports* 49: 321–356, 1934, Reprint 1618.

372. Collins, S. D.: "Frequency of immunizing and related procedures in 9,000 surveyed families in 18 states (1928–31)." *Milbank Mem. Fund Q.* 15: No. 2, Part 2, 150–172, 1937.

373. Collins, S. D.: "Frequency and volume of doctors' calls among males and females, in 9,000 families, based on nationwide periodic canvasses, 1928–31." *Public Health Reports* 55: 1977–2020, 1940, Reprint 2205.

374. Wiehl, D. G. and Berry, K.: "Maternal health and supervision in a rural area." *Milbank Mem. Fund Q.* 17: 172–204, 1939.

375. Sinai, N. and Paton, D. E.: *Hospitalization of the People of Two Counties.* Univ. of Michigan, School of Public Health, Bureau of Public Health Economics, Research Series No. 6, Ann Arbor, 1949.

376. Meir, I. and Lively, C. E.: *Family Health Practices in Dallas County, Missouri.* Univ. of Missouri, Dept. of Rural Sociology and Agricultural Experiment Station, Research Bull. 369. Columbia: 1943.

377. Kaufman, H. F.: *Use of Medical Services in Rural Missouri.* Univ. of Missouri, Dept. of Rural Sociology and Agricultural Experiment Station, Research Bull. 400. Columbia: 1946.

378. Rosenfeld, L. S., Goldmann, F., and Kaprio, L. A.: "Reasons for prolonged hospital care." *J. Chronic Dis.* 6: 141–152, 1957.

379. Goldmann, F.: "Prolonged stay in general hospitals: A study of 200 patients." *Geriatrics* 14: 789–800, 1959.

380. Odoroff, M. E. and Abbe, L. M.: "Use of general hospitals: Factors in outpatient visits." *Public Health Reports* 72: 478–483, 1957.

381. Densen, P. M., Balamuth, E., and Shapiro, S.: *Prepaid Medical Care and Hospital Utilization.* American Hospital Association, Hospital Monograph Series No. 3. Chicago: 1958.

382. Roemer, M. I.: "The influence of prepaid physician's service on hospital utilization." *Hospitals* 32: 48–52, Oct. 16, 1958.

383. Roemer, M. I. and Shain, M.: *Hospital Utilization Under Insurance.* Chicago: American Hospital Association, 1959.

384. Shain, M. and Roemer, M. I.: "Hospital costs relate to the supply of beds." *Mod. Hosp.* 92: 71–73 and 168, April 1959.

385. Axelrod, S. J. and Patton, R. E.: "The use and abuse of pre-

paid comprehensive physicians' services." *Am. J. Public Health* 42: 566–574, 1952.

386. Ciocco, A., Altman, I., and Truan, T. D.: "Patient load and volume of medical services." *Public Health Reports* 67: 527–534, 1952.

387. Larson, O. F. and Hay, D. G.: "Differential use of health resources by rural people." *New York State J. Med.* 52: 43–49, 1952.

388. McNamara, R. L. and Hassinger, E. W.: *Extent of Illness and Use of Health Services in a South Missouri County.* Univ. of Missouri, Dept. of Rural Sociology and Agricultural Experiment Station, Research Bull. 647. Columbia: 1958.

389. Taubenhaus, L. J.: "A study of one rural practice, 1953." *General Practitioner* 12: 97–102, Sept. 1955.

390. Graham, S.: "Socio-economic status, illness, and the use of medical services." *Milbank Mem. Fund Q.* 35: 58–66, 1957.

391. Darsky, B. J., Sinai, N., and Axelrod, S. J.: *Comprehensive Medical Services Under Voluntary Health Insurance. A Study of Windsor Medical Services.* Cambridge: Harvard Univ. Press, 1958.

392. Freidson, E.: "Specialties without roots: The utilization of new services." *Human Organization* 18: 112–116, 1959.

393. Solon, J. A., Sheps, C. G., and Lee, S. S.: "Delineating patterns of medical care." *Am. J. Public Health* 50: 1105–1113, 1960.

394. Solon, J. A., Sheps, C. G., and Lee, S. S.: "Patterns of medical care: A hospital's outpatients." *Am. J. Public Health* 50: 1905–1913, 1960.

395. Lee, S. S., Solon, J. A., and Sheps, C. G.: "How new patterns of medical care affect the emergency unit." *Mod. Hosp.* 94: 97–101, May 1960.

396. Williams, T. F., White, K. L., Andrews, L. P., *et al.*: "Patient referral to a university clinic: Patterns in a rural state." *Am. J. Public Health* 50: 1493–1507, 1960.

397. Williams, T. F., White, K. L., Fleming, W. L., *et al.*: "The referral process in medical care and the university clinic's role." *J. Med. Educ.* 36: 899–907, 1961.

398. Shanas, E.: *Medical Care Among Those 65 and Over: Reported Utilization of Health Services by the Sick and the Well.* Health

Information Foundation, Research Series No. 16, New York: 1960.

399. Shapiro, S., Williams, J. J., Yerby, A. S., *et al.*: "Patterns of medical use by the indigent aged under two systems of medical care." *Am. J. Public Health* 57: 784–790, 1967.

400. Gaspard, N. J. and Hopkins, C. E.: "Determinants of use of ambulatory health services by an aged population." *Inquiry* 4: 28–36, Mar. 1967.

401. Freeman, H. E. and Richardson, A. H.: "The impact of extended insurance benefits on octogenarian medical experience." *Social Sci. and Med.* 5: 375–390, 1971.

402. Goldmann, F.: "A profile: Residents of homes for the aged." *Geriatrics* 15: 329–337, 1960.

403. Goldmann, F. and Fraenkel, M.: "Patients on home care: Their characteristics and experience." *J. Chronic Dis.* 11: 77–87, 1960.

404. Goldmann, F.: "A profile: Patients in chronic disease hospitals." *Am. J. Public Health* 52: 646–655, 1962.

405. Alpert, J. J., Kosa, J., and Haggerty, R. J.: "Medical help and maternal nursing care in the life of low-income families." *Pediatrics* 39: 749–755, 1967.

406. Alpert, J. J., Kosa, J., and Haggerty, R. J.: "A month of illness and health care among low-income families." *Public Health Reports* 82: 705–713, 1967.

407. Alpert, J. J., Heagarty, M. C., Robertson, L., *et al.*: "Effective use of comprehensive pediatric care. Utilization of health resources." *Am. J. Dis. Child.* 116: 529–533, 1968.

408. Mindlin, R. L. and Lobach, K. W.: "Consistency and change in choice of medical care for preschool children." *Pediatrics* 48: 426–432, 1971.

409. Nolan, R. L., Schwartz, J. L., and Simonian, K.: "Social class differences in utilization of pediatric services in a prepaid direct service medical care program." *Am. J. Public Health* 57: 34–47, 1967.

410. Lerner, M.: *Hospital Use by Diagnosis. A Comparison of Two Experiences.* Univ. of Chicago, Center for Health Administration Studies, Research Series No. 19, Chicago, 1961.

411. Massachusetts Blue Cross, Inc., Office of Research: *1965*

Patient Profiles—Average Stay, 44 Most Frequent Diagnoses. Boston: Mass. Blue Cross, Inc., 1967.

412. Fitzpatrick, T. B., Riedel, D. C., and Payne B. C.: "Appropriateness of admission and length of stay" in *Hospital and Medical Economics: A Study of Population, Services, Costs, Methods of Payment and Controls*—vol. I. Edited by W. J. McNerney. Chicago: Hospital Research and Educational Trust, American Hospital Association, 1962, pp. 471-494.

413. Fitzpatrick, T. B., Riedel, D. C., and Payne, B. C.: "Changing patterns of care" in *Hospital and Medical Economics: A Study of Population, Services, Costs, Methods of Payment, and Controls*—vol. I. Edited by W. J. McNerney. Chicago: Hospital Research and Educational Trust, American Hospital Association, 1962, pp. 593-623.

414. Riedel, D. C. and Fitzpatrick, T. B.: *Patterns of Patient Care: A Study of Hospital Use in Six Diagnoses.* Ann Arbor: Univ. of Michigan, 1964.

415. Hanchett, E. and Torrens, P. R.: "A public health nursing program for outpatients with heart disease." *Public Health Reports* 82: 683-688, 1967.

416. Klarman, H. E.: "Effect of prepaid group practice on hospital use." *Public Health Reports* 78: 955-965, 1963.

417. Densen, P. M., Jones, E. W., Balamuth, E., *et al.*: "Prepaid medical care and hospital utilization in a dual choice situation." *Am. J. Public Health* 50: 1710-1726, 1960.

418. Densen, P. M., Shapiro, S., Jones, E., *et al.*: "Prepaid medical care and hospital utilization. Comparison of a group practice and a self-insurance situation." *Hospitals* 36: 63-68 and 138, Nov. 16, 1962.

419. Densen, P. M. and Shapiro, S.: *Hospital Use Under Varying Forms of Medical Organization. Conference on Research in Hospital Use.* PHS Pub. No. 930E-2, Dept. of Health, Education, and Welfare, Public Health Service, Div. of Hospital and Medical Facilities. Washington: U. S. Gov't. Print. Off., 1963, pp. 14-16.

420. Perrott, G. St. J.: "Federal Employees Health Benefits Program, III. Utilization of hospital services." *Am. J. Public Health* 56: 57-64, 1966.

421. Perrott, G. St. J.: *The Federal Employees Health Benefits Program.*

U. S. Dept. of Health, Education, and Welfare, Health Services and Mental Health Administration, Washington: U. S. Gov't. Print. Off., 1971.

422. Blue Cross Association: "Patterns of repeated hospital admissions, Blue Cross and Blue Shield Federal Employees Program, July 1960–Dec. 1965." *Blue Cross Reports* 6: May 1968.

423. Hill, D. B. and Veney, J. E.: "Kansas Blue Cross/Blue Shield Outpatient Benefits Experiment." *Med. Care* 8: 143–158, 1970.

424. Lewis, C. E.: "The utilization of employee health services in hospitals." *Arch. of Environ. Health* 11: 16–21, 1965.

425. Lewis, C. E. and Keairnes, H.: "Controlling costs of medical care by expanding insurance coverage." *N. Engl. J. Med.* 282: 1405–1412, 1970.

426. McCorkle, L. P.: "Utilization of facilities of a university hospital: Length of inpatient stay in various departments." *Health Serv. Res.* 1: 91–114, 1966.

427. Roemer, M. I.: "Bed supply and hospital utilization. A natural experiment." *Hospitals* 35: 36–42, Nov. 1, 1961.

428. Roemer, M. I.: "Hospital utilization and the supply of physicians." *J.A.M.A.* 178: 989–993, 1961.

429. Rosenthal, G. D.: "Factors affecting the utilization of short-term general hospitals." *Am. J. Public Health* 55: 1734–1740, 1965.

430. Ro, K. K.: "Patient characteristics, hospital characteristics, and hospital use." *Med. Care* 7: 295–312, 1969.

431. Weinerman, E. R. and Edwards, H. R.: "Yale studies in ambulatory medical care: Triage system shows promise in management of emergency department load." *Hospitals* 38: 55–62, Nov. 16, 1964.

432. Weinerman, E. R., Ratner, R. S., Robbins, A., *et al.*: "Yale studies in ambulatory medical care: Determinants of use of hospital emergency services." *Am. J. Public Health* 56: 1037–1056, 1966.

433. Bergman, A. B. and Haggerty, R. J.: "The emergency clinic: A study of its role in a teaching hospital." *Am. J. Dis. Child.* 104: 36–44, 1962.

434. Wingert, W. A., Friedman, D. B., and Larson, W. R.: "The

demographical and ecological characteristics of a large urban pediatric outpatient population and implications for improving community pediatric care." *Am. J. Public Health* 58: 859–876, 1968.

435. Alpert, J. J., Kosa, J., Haggerty, R. J., *et al.*: "The types of families that use an emergency clinic." *Med. Care* 7: 55–61, 1969.

436. Reed, J. I. and Reader, G. G.: "Quantitative survey of New York hospital emergency room, 1965." *N. Y. State J. Med.* 67: 1335–1342, 1967.

437. Torrens, P. and Yedvab, D. G.: "Variations among emergency room populations: A comparison of four hospitals in New York City." *Med. Care* 8: 60–75, 1970.

438. van Dyke, F., Brown, V., and Thom, A. M.: *"Long Stay" Hospital Care.* New York: Columbia Univ., School of Public Health and Administrative Medicine, 1963.

439. Durbin, R. L. and Antelman, G.: "A study of the effects of selected variables on hospital utilization." *Hosp. Manage.* 98: 57–60, Aug. 1964.

440. Rafferty, J. A.: "Patterns of hospital use: An analysis of short-run variations." *J. Political Economy* 79: 154–165, 1971.

441. Anderson, O. W. and Sheatsley, P. B.: *Hospital Use: A Survey of Patient and Physician Decisions.* Univ. of Chicago, Center for Health Administration Studies, Research Series No. 24. Chicago: 1967.

442. Anderson, O. W.: "The utilization of health services" in *Handbook of Medical Sociology.* Edited by H. E. Freeman, S. Levine, and L. G. Reeder. Englewood Cliffs, N. J.: Prentice-Hall, 1963.

443. Andersen, R. and Anderson, O. W.: *A Decade of Health Services: Social Survey Trends in Use and Expenditure.* Chicago: Univ. of Chicago Press, 1967.

444. Andersen, R., Greeley, R. McL., Kravits, J., *et al.*: *Health Service Use—National Trends and Variations, 1953–1971.* Univ. of Chicago, Center for Health Administration Studies, and National Center for Health Services Research and Development. DHEW Pub. No. (HSM) 73-3004, Washington: U. S. Gov't. Print. Off., 1972.

445. Andersen, R.: *A Behavioral Model of Families' Use of Health Ser-*

vices. Univ. of Chicago, Center for Health Administration Studies, Research Series No. 25. Chicago: 1968.

446. Andersen, R. and Benham, L.: "Factors affecting the relationship between family income and medical care consumption" in *Empirical Studies in Health Economics.* Edited by H. E. Klarman. Baltimore: The Johns Hopkins Press, 1970, pp. 73–95.

447. Sheps, C. G., Sloss, J. H., and Cahill, E.: "Medical care in Aluminum City. I. Families and their 'regular doctors'." *J. Chronic Dis.* 17: 815–826, 1964.

448. Altman, I., Kroeger, H. H., Clark, D. A., *et al.*: "The office practice of internists: II. Patient load." *J.A.M.A.* 193: 667–672, 1965.

449. Goodrich, C. H., Olendzki, M., Buchanan, J. R., *et al.*: "The New York Hospital-Cornell Medical Center project: An experiment in welfare medical care." *Am. J. Public Health* 53: 1252–1259, 1963.

450. Rodman, A. C.: "Comparison of Baltimore's utilization rates under two physician-payment systems." *Public Health Reports* 80: 476–480, 1965.

451. Lewis, C. E.: "Medical care for patients with neurological and sensory diseases." "I. Utilization of institutional facilities." *J. Chronic Dis.* 18: 985–996, 1965. "II. Office visits to practicing physicians." *J. Chronic Dis.* 18: 997–1006, 1965.

452. Last, J. M. and White, K. L.: "The content of medical care in primary practice." *Med. Care* 7: 41–48, 1969.

453. Coe, R. M., Goering, J. M., Cummins, M., *et al.*: *Health Status of Low-Income Families in an Urban Area.* St. Louis: Washington Univ., Medical Care Research Center, (Processed) 1969.

454. Richardson, W. C.: "Measuring the urban poor's use of physicians' services in response to illness episodes." *Med. Care* 8: 132–142, 1970.

455. Richardson, W. C.: *Ambulatory Use of Physicians' Services in Response to Illness Episodes in a Low-Income Neighborhood.* Univ. of Chicago, Center for Health Adminstration Studies, Research Series No. 29, Chicago: 1971.

456. Bice, T. W., Eichhorn, R. L., and Fox, P. D.: "Socioeconomic status and use of physician services: A reconsideration." *Med. Care* 10: 261–271, 1972.

457. Roghmann, K. J., Haggerty, R. J., and Lorenz, R.: "Anticipated and actual effects of Medicaid on the medical-care patterns of children." *N. Engl. J. Med.* 285: 1053–1057, 1971.

458. Olendzki, M. C., Grann, R. P., and Goodrich, C. H.: "The impact of Medicaid on private care for the urban poor." *Med. Care* 10: 201–206, 1972.

459. Greenlick, M. R., Freeborn, D. K., Colombo, T. J., *et al.*: "Comparing the use of medical services by a medically indigent and a general membership population in a comprehensive prepaid group practice program." *Med. Care* 10: 187–200, 1972.

460. Metzner, C. A., Shannon, G. W., and Bashshur, R. L.: "The concept of distance as a factor in accessibility and utilization of health care." *Med. Care Rev.* 26: 143–161, 1969.

461. Aday, L. A. and Eichhorn, R. L.: *The Utilization of Health Services: Indices and Correlates—A Research Bibliography 1972.* Dept. of Health, Education, and Welfare, Health Services and Mental Health Administration, National Center for Health Services Research and Development. DHEW Pub. No. (HSM) 73-3003.

ECONOMICS, COSTS, AND FINANCING OF HEALTH CARE

462. Rorem, C. R.: *Capital Investment in Hospitals: The Place of "Fixed Charges" in Hospital Financing and Costs.* (CCMC Report No. 7) Washington: Committee on the Costs of Medical Care, 1930.

463. Sinai, N. and Mills, A. B.: *A Study of Physicians and Dentists in Detroit: 1929.* (CCMC Report No. 10) Chicago: Univ. of Chicago Press, 1931.

464. Rorem, C. R. and Fischelis, R. P.: *The Costs of Medicines: The Manufacture and Distribution of Drugs and Medicines in the United States and the Services of Pharmacy in Medical Care.* (CCMC Report No. 14) Chicago: Univ. of Chicago Press, 1932.

465. Leven, M.: *The Incomes of Physicians: An Economic and Statistical Analysis.* (CCMC Report No. 24) Chicago: Univ. of Chicago Press, 1932.

466. Reed, L. S.: *The Ability to Pay for Medical Care.* (CCMC Report No. 25) Chicago: Univ. of Chicago Press, 1933.

467. Falk, I. S., Rorem, C. R. and Ring, M. D.: *The Costs of Medical Care: The Economic Aspects of the Prevention and Care of Illness.* (CCMC Report No. 27) Chicago: Univ. of Chicago Press, 1933.

468. Williams, P.: *The Purchase of Medical Care Through Fixed Periodic Payment.* New York: National Bureau of Economic Research, Inc., 1932.

469. Rorem, C. R.: *The Public's Investment in Hospitals.* Chicago: Univ. of Chicago Press, 1930.

470. Rorem, C. R. and Musser, J. H.: *Group Payment for Medical Care.* Chicago: The Julius Rosenwald Fund, 1932.

471. Rorem, C. R.: *Hospital Care Insurance.* Chicago: American Hospital Association, 1938.

472. Rorem, C. R.: *Non-Profit Hospital Service Plans.* Chicago: Commission on Hospital Service, 1940.

473. Rorem, C. R.: *Blue Cross Hospital Service Plans: Description and Appraisal of a Nation-wide Program for the Distribution of Adequate Hospital Care on a Non-Profit, Non-Political Basis, 2d. ed.* Chicago: American Hospital Association, 1940.

474. Sinai, N. and Simons, A. M.: *The Way of Health Insurance.* Chicago: Univ. of Chicago Press, 1932.

475. Sinai, N., Anderson, O. W., and Dollar, M. L.: *Health Insurance in the United States.* New York: The Commonwealth Fund, 1946.

476. Sinai, N.: *Disability Compensation for the Disabled Sick.* Univ. of Michigan, School of Public Health, Bureau of Public Health Economics, Research Series No. 5. Ann Arbor: 1949.

477. Davis, M. M.: *Paying Your Sickness Bills.* Chicago: Univ. of Chicago Press, 1931.

478. Davis, M. M. and Rorem, R. C.: *The Crisis in Hospital Finance.* Chicago: Univ. of Chicago Press, 1932.

479. Davis, M. M.: "The American approach to health insurance." *Milbank Mem. Fund Q.* 12: 203–217, 1934.

480. Davis, M. M.: *Eight Years' Work in Medical Economics.* Chicago: The Julius Rosenwald Fund, 1937.

481. Davis, M. M.: *America Organizes Medicine.* New York: Harper and Brothers, 1941.

482. Davis, M. M.: "Health insurance plans under medical societies." *Med. Care* 3: 217–225, 1943 and *Med. Care* 4: 17–36, 1944.

483. Falk, I. S.: "Fundamental facts on the costs of medical care." *Milbank Mem. Fund Q.* 11: 130–150, 1933.

484. Falk, I. S.: *Security Against Sickness: A Study of Health Insurance.* Garden City, N. Y.: Doubleday, Doran, and Co., 1936.

485. Reed, L. S.: *Health Insurance: The Next Step in Social Security.* New York: Harper and Brothers, 1937.

486. Reed, L. S.: "Costs and benefits under prepayment medical service plans." *Social Security Bull.* 3: 13–26, March 1940.

487. Reed, L. S.: *Blue Cross and Medical Service Plans.* Federal Security Agency, Public Health Service, Washington: U. S. Gov't. Print. Off., 1947.

488. Klem, M. C.: "Family expenditures for medical and dental care." *J. Am. Dent. Assoc.* 26: 828–840, 1939.

489. Klem, M. C.: "Prepayment medical care organizations." Social Security Board, Bureau Memo. No. 55, 3d ed., Washington: U. S. Gov't Print. Off., 1945.

490. Klem, M. C.: "Recent State legislation concerning prepayment medical care." *Social Security Bull.* 10: 10–16, January 1947.

491. Goldmann, F.: *Prepayment Plans for Medical Care, New York.* New York: Joint Committee of the 20th Century Fund and the Good Will Fund and the Medical Administration Service, Inc., 1941.

492. Goldmann, F.: *Voluntary Medical Care Insurance.* New York: Columbia Univ. Press, 1948.

493. Goldmann, F.: *Public Medical Care.* New York: Columbia Univ. Press, 1948.

494. Anderson, O. W.: *State Enabling Legislation for Non Profit Hospital and Medical Plans, 1944.* Univ. of Michigan, School of Public Health, Ann Arbor: Univ. of Michigan Press, 1944.

495. Anderson, O. W.: *Prepayment of Physicians' Services For Recipients of Public Assistance in the State of Washington: Problems and Issues.* Univ. of Michigan, School of Public Health, Bu. of Public Health Economics, Research Series No. 4, Ann Arbor, 1949.

496. Mountin, J. W. and Perrott, G. St. J.: "Health insurance programs and plans of Western Europe." *Public Health Reports* 62: 369–399, 1947.

497. Simpson, H. D.: *Compulsory Health Insurance in the United States. An Analysis and Appraisal of the Present Movement.* Evanston and Chicago: Northwestern Univ., 1943.

498. Dickinson, F. G.: *The Cost and Quantity of Medical Care in the United States.* American Medical Association, Bu. of Medical Economics, Research Bull. 66, Chicago, 1948.

499. Anderson, O. W.: "Health insurance in the United States, 1910-1920." *J. History of Med.* 5: 363-396, 1950.

500. Anderson, O. W.: "Compulsory medical care insurance, 1910-1950." *Ann. Am. Acad. Political Social Sci.* 273: 106-113, 1951.

501. Anderson, O. W. and Feldman, J. J.: *Family Medical Costs and Voluntary Health Insurance: A Nationwide Survey.* New York: McGraw-Hill Book Co., Inc. (The Blakiston Div.), 1956.

502. Greenfield, H. J. and Anderson, O. W.: *The Medical Care Price Index.* Health Information Foundation, Research Series No. 7, New York: 1959.

503. Anderson, O. W. and Sheatsley, P. B.: *Comprehensive Medical Insurance—A Study of Costs, Use, and Attitudes Under Two Plans.* Health Information Foundation, Research Series No. 9, New York: 1959.

504. Klarman, H. E.: "Economic aspects of hospital care." *J. Business* 24: 1-24, Jan. 1951.

505. Davis, M. M.: *Medical Care for Tomorrow.* New York: Harper and Brothers, 1955.

506. Klem, M. C.: *Industrial Health and Medical Programs.* Public Health Service Pub. No. 15. Federal Security Agency, Public Health Service, Washington: U. S. Gov't. Print. Off., 1950.

507. Klem, M. C.: *Small Plant Health and Medical Programs.* Public Health Service Pub. No. 215. Federal Security Agency, Public Health Service, Washington: U. S. Gov't. Print. Off., 1952.

508. Klem, M. C.: *Management and Union Health and Medical Programs.* Public Health Service Pub. No. 329. U. S. Dept. of Health, Education, and Welfare, Public Health Service, Washington: U. S. Gov't. Print. Off., 1953.

509. Langford, E. A.: "Medical care in the consumer price index, 1936-56." *Monthly Labor Review,* 1053-1058, Sept. 1957.

510. Commission on Financing of Hospital Care: Vol. 1: *Factors Affecting the Costs of Hospital Care.* Edited by J. H. Hayes. New York: The Blakiston Co., Inc., 1954. Vol. 2: *Financing Hospital Care in the United States—Prepayment and the Community.* Edited by H. Becker. New York: McGraw-Hill Book Co., Inc., 1955. Vol. 3: *Financing Hospital Care in the United States—Financing Nonwage and Low Income Groups.* Edited by H. Becker. New York: McGraw-Hill Book Co., Inc., 1955.

511. Anderson, O. W., Collette, P. and Feldman, J. J.: *Changes in Medical Care Expenditures and Voluntary Health Insurance: A Five-Year Resurvey.* Cambridge: Harvard Univ. Press, 1963.

512. Anderson, O. W.: *The Uneasy Equilibrium. Private and Public Financing of Health Services in the United States, 1875–1965.* New Haven: College and University Press, 1968.

513. Anderson, O. W. and Neuhauser, D.: "Rising costs are inherent in health care systems." *Hospitals* 43: 50–52, Feb. 16, 1969.

514. Reed, L. S.: *The Extent of Health Insurance Coverage in the United States.* Social Security Administration, Office of Research and Statistics, Research Report No. 10, U. S. Dept of Health, Education, and Welfare, Washington: U. S. Gov't. Print. Off., 1965.

515. Reed, L. S.: "Private health insurance, 1968: Enrollment, coverage, and financial expense." *Social Security Bull.* 32: 19–35, Dec. 1969.

516. Reed, L. S. and Carr, W.: *The Benefit Structure of Private Health Insurance, 1968.* Social Security Administration, Office of Research and Statistics, Research Report No. 32, U. S. Dept. of Health, Education, and Welfare, Washington: U. S. Gov't. Print. Off., 1970.

517. Roemer, M. I.: "On paying the doctor and the implications of different methods." *J. Health and Soc. Behav.* 3: 4–14, 1962.

518. Sinai, N., Thomas, B. S., and Wheeler, B. W.: *Disability Insurance in California.* Univ. of Michigan, School of Public Health, Bu. of Public Health Economics, Research Series No. 11. Ann Arbor: 1965.

519. Sinai, N.: *Disability Insurance and Vocational Rehabilitation.* Univ. of Michigan, School of Public Health, Bu. of Public Health Economics, Research Series No. 13. Ann Arbor: 1967.

520. University of Michigan, Bureau of Public Health Economics and Department of Economics: *The Economics of Health and Medical Care: Proceedings of the Conference on the Economics of Health and Medical Care, May 10-12, 1962.* Ann Arbor: Univ. of Michigan, 1964.

521. Straight, B. W.: "Reducing the incidence of office and home visits in a medical service plan by use of coinsurance charges." *Proceedings of the Conference of Actuaries in Private Practice* 11: 73-79, 1961-1962.

522. MacIntyre, D. M.: *Voluntary Health Insurance and Rate Making.* Ithaca: Cornell Univ. Press, 1962.

523. Columbia Univ. School of Public Health and Administrative Medicine: *Family Medical Care Through Three Types of Insurance.* New York: Foundation on Employee Health, Medical Care and Welfare, Inc., 1962.

524. Klarman, H. E.: *The Economics of Health.* New York: Columbia Univ. Press, 1965.

525. Klarman, H. E.: "Approaches to moderating the increases in medical care costs." *Med. Care* 7: 175-190, 1969.

526. Klarman, H. E.: "Reimbursing the hospital. The difference the third party makes." *J. of Risk and Insurance* 36: 553-565, 1969.

527. Klarman, H. E.: "Increase in the cost of physician and hospital services." *Inquiry* 7: 22-36, March 1970.

528. Klarman, H. E. (Ed.): *Empirical Studies in Health Economics.* Proceedings of the Second Conference on the Economics of Health. Baltimore: The Johns Hopkins Press, 1970.

529. Feldstein, M. S.: "The rising price of physicians' services." *Rev. of Economics and Statistics* 52: 121-133, 1970.

530. Feldstein, M. S.: *The Rising Cost of Hospital Care.* Washington: Information Resources Press, 1971.

531. Feldstein, M. S.: "Hospital cost inflation: A study of nonprofit price dynamics." *Am. Economic Rev.* 66: 853-872, 1971.

532. Feldstein, M. S.: *The Welfare Loss of Excess Health Insurance.* Discussion Paper No. 210, Harvard Institute of Economic Research, Cambridge: Oct. 1971.

533. Weisbrod, B. A.: *Economics of Public Health.* Philadelphia: Univ. of Pennsylvania Press, 1961.

534. Weisbrod, B. A. and Feisler, R. J.: "Hospitalization insurance and hospital utilization." *Am. Economic Rev.* 51: 126-132, 1961.

535. Weisbrod, B. A.: "Some problems of pricing and resource allocation in a non-profit industry—the hospitals." *J. Business,* Univ. of Chicago, 38: 18-20, Jan. 1965.

536. Fuchs. V. R.: "The contribution of health services to the American economy." *Milbank Mem. Fund Q.* 44: No. 4, Part 2, 65-101, 1966.

537. Fuchs, V. R.: "The growing demand for medical care." *N. Engl. J. Med.* 279: 190-195, 1968.

538. Reder, M. W.: "Some problems in the economics of hospitals." *Am. Economic Rev.* 55: 472-480, 1965.

539. Reder, M. W.: "Some problems in the measurement of productivity in the medical care industry" in *Production and Productivity in the Service Industries.* Edited by V. R. Fuchs. National Bureau of Economic Research, New York. Distributed by Columbia Univ. Press, 1969, pp. 95-131.

540. Ingbar, M. L. and Lee, S. S.: "Economic analysis as a tool of program evaluation: Costs in a home care program" in *The Economics of Health and Medical Care.* Ann Arbor: Univ. of Michigan, 1964, pp. 173-210.

541. Ingbar, M. L., Whitney, B. J., and Taylor, L. D.: "Differences in the costs of nursing service. A statistical study of community hospitals in Massachusetts." *Am. J. Public Health* 56: 1699-1715, 1966.

542. Ingbar, M. L. and Taylor, L. D.: *Hospital Costs in Massachusetts. An Econometric Study.* Cambridge: Harvard Univ. Press, 1968.

543. Muller, C. F.: "Economic analysis of medical care in the United States. Some significant concepts and aspects." *Am. J. Public Health* 51: 31-42, 1961.

544. Muller, C. F.: "Income and the receipt of medical care." *Am. J. Public Health* 55: 510-521, 1965.

545. Rice, D. P. and Horowitz, L. A.: "Trends in medical care prices." *Social Security Bull.* 30: 13-28, July 1967.

546. Rice, D. P. and Horowitz, L. A.: "Medical care price changes in Medicare's first two years." *Social Security Bull.* 31: 3-11, Nov. 1968.

547. Horowitz, L. A.: "Medical care price changes in Medicare's first five years." *Social Security Bull.* 35: 16–29, March 1972.

548. Feldstein, P. J.: "The demand for medical care" in *Report of the Commission on the Cost of Medical Care* Vol. 1, Chicago: American Medical Association, 1964, pp. 57–76.

549. Feldstein, P. J.: "Research on the demand for health services." *Milbank Mem. Fund Q.* 44: No. 3, Part 2, 128–165, 1966.

550. Garbarino, J. W.: *Health Insurance Plans and Collective Bargaining.* Berkeley and Los Angeles: Univ. of California Press, 1960.

551. Glaser, W. A.: *Paying the Doctor, Systems of Remuneration and Their Effects.* Baltimore: The Johns Hopkins Press, 1970.

552. Knapp, D. A.: "Paying for outpatient prescription drugs and related services in third-party programs." *Med. Care Rev.* 28: 826–859, 1971.

553. Newhouse, J. P.: "Toward a theory of nonprofit institutions: An economic model of a hospital." *Am. Economic Rev.* 60: 64–74, 1970.

554. Piore, N.: "Metropolitan areas and public medical care" in *The Economics of Health and Medical Care.* Ann Arbor: Univ. of Michigan, 1964. pp. 60–71.

555. Scitovsky, A. A.: "Changes in the costs of treatment of selected illnesses, 1961–65." *Am. Economic Rev.* 52: 1182–1195, 1967.

556. Scitovsky, A. A. and Snyder, N. M.: *Effects of the Introduction of a Coinsurance Provision on Physician Utilization.* Palo Alto Medical Research Foundation, 1972.

557. Wirick, G. C., Morgan, J., and Barlow, R.: "Population survey: Health care and its financing" in *Hospital and Medical Economics: A Study of Population, Services, Costs, Methods of Payment, and Controls* — vol. I. Edited by W. J. McNerney, Chicago: Hospital Research and Educational Trust, American Hospital Association, 1962. pp. 61–357.

558. Wolfman, B.: "Medical expenses and choice of plan: A case study." *Monthly Labor Rev.* 84: 1186–1190, 1960.

559. Lave, J. R. and Lave, L. B.: "Estimated cost functions for Pennsylvania hospitals." *Inquiry* 7: 3–13, June 1970.

560. Lave, J. R. and Lave, L. B.: "The extent of role differentiation among hospitals." *Health Serv. Res.* 6: 15–38, 1971.

561. Shanas, E.: *Meeting Medical Care Costs Among the Aging.* Health Information Foundation, Research Series No. 17. New York: 1960.

562. Royle, C. M. and Brewster, A. W.: "The impact of aged persons on hospital use and income." *Public Health Reports* 81: 488–496, 1966.

563. Hall, C., Jr.: "Deductibles in health insurance. An evaluation." *J. of Risk and Insurance* 33: 253–263, 1966.

564. Williams, R.: "A comparison of hospital utilization and costs by types of coverage." *Inquiry* 3: 28–42, Sept. 1966.

565. Buxbaum, R. J.: "Blue Cross provision of coordinated home care benefits." *Inquiry* 4: 69–82, Oct. 1967.

566. Josephson, C. E.: "Family expenditure patterns of Federal employees for covered items of health care services." *Inquiry* 3: 40–54, Feb. 1966.

567. Yett, D. E.: "An evaluation of alternative methods of estimating physicians' expenses relative to output." *Inquiry* 4: 3–27, Mar. 1967.

568. Yett, D.: "Supply of nurses: An economist's view." *Hosp. Progress* 46: 88 ff, Feb. 1965.

569. Yett, D.: "Nursing shortage and the Nurse Training Act of 1964." *Ind. Labor Relat. Rev.* 19: 190–200, 1966.

570. Yett, D. and Mann, J. K.: "Reinterpretation of hospital cost analyses." *Western Econ. J.* 5: 386, 1967.

571. Yett, D.: "Lifetime earnings for nurses in comparison with college trained women." *Inquiry* 6: 35–70, Dec. 1968.

572. Conley, I.: *Federal Employees Health Benefits Program. Highlights of First Decade of Operation, July 1960–June 1970.* U. S. Civil Service Commission, Bu. of Retirement, Insurance, and Occupational Health, Office of the Actuary. Washington: U. S. Gov't. Print. Off., 1970.

573. Hardwick, C. P. and Wolfe, H. A.: "Multifaceted approach to incentive reimbursement." *Med. Care* 8: 173–188, 1970.

574. Hardwick, C. P. and Wolfe, H. A.: *An Incentive Reimbursement/Industrial Engineering Experiment.* U. S. Dept. of Health, Education, and Welfare, Health Services and Mental Health

Administration, National Center for Health Services Research and Development, DHEW Pub. No. (HSM) 72-3003, 1971.

575. Rafferty, J. A.: "Hospital output indices." *Econ. and Bus. Bull.* 24: 21-27, Winter 1971.

576. Berkowitz, M. and Johnson, W. G.: "Towards an economics of disability: The magnitude and structure of transfer and medical costs." *J. Human Resources* 5: 271-297, 1970.

577. Stuart, B. C. and Bair, L. A.: *Health Care and Income: The Distributional Impacts of Medicaid and Medicare Nationally and in the State of Michigan. 2d ed.* Lansing: Dept. of Social Services, State of Michigan, Sept. 1971.

578. Owens, A.: "Inflation closes in on physicians' earnings." *Med. Economics,* 63-71, Dec. 21, 1970.

579. Starkweather, D. B.: "The regulation of health insurance: A review article." *Med. Care Rev.,* 27: 335-371, and 474-493, 1970.

580. Mueller, M. S.: "Private health insurance in 1969: A review." Social Security Administration, Office of Research and Statistics, *Social Security Bull.* 34: 3-18, Feb. 1971.

581. Faulkner, E. J.: *Health Insurance.* New York: McGraw-Hill Book Co., Inc., 1960.

582. Follman, J. F., Jr.: *Medical Care and Health Insurance. A Study in Social Progress.* Homewood, Ill.: Richard D. Irwin, Inc., 1963.

583. Angell, F. J.: *Health Insurance.* New York: The Ronald Press Co., 1963.

584. Dickerson, O. D.: *Health Insurance. 3d ed.* Homewood, Ill.: Richard D. Irwin, Inc., 1968.

585. Health Insurance Council: *Extent of Voluntary Health Insurance Coverage in the United States. New York:*
As of December 31, 1957 — Report published in 1958.
As of December 31, 1958 — Report published in 1959.
As of December 31, 1963 — Report published in 1964.

SOCIAL-BEHAVIORAL ASPECTS OF HEALTH CARE

586. Duncan, O. D.: *Social Research on Health.* New York: Social Science Research Council, 1946.

587. Gordon, G., Anderson, O. W., Brehm, H. P., *et al.*: *Disease, The Individual, and Society.* New Haven: College and University Press, 1968.

588. Lively, C. E.: "Objectives and methods of rural sociological research in health at the University of Missouri." *Rural Sociology* 14: 199–206, 1949.

589. Schuler, E. A., Hoffer, C. R., Loomis, C. P., *et al.*: "Objectives and methods of rural sociological research in health at Michigan State College." *Rural Sociology* 14: 206–212, 1949.

590. Hoffer, C. R., *et al.*: *Health Needs and Health Care in Michigan.* Michigan State College Agriculture Experiment Station, Section of Sociology and Anthropology, Special Bulletin No. 365, East Lansing: 1950.

591. Larson, O. and Hay, D. G.: "Hypothesis for sociological research in the field of rural health." *Rural Sociology* 16: 225–237, 1951.

592. Saunders, L. and Samora, J.: "A medical care program in a Colorado community" in *Health, Culture, and Community.* Edited by B. D. Paul, New York: Russell Sage Foundation, 1955. pp. 377–400.

593. Koos, E. L.: *The Health of Regionville. What the People Thought and Did About It.* New York: Columbia Univ. Press, 1954.

594. Coser, R. L.: "Authority and decision making in a hospital." *Am. Sociol. Rev.* 23: 56–63, 1958.

595. Anderson, O. W. and Seacat, M. S.: *The Behavioral Scientists and Research in the Health Field.* Health Information Foundation, Research Series No. 1, New York: 1957.

596. Anderson, O. W. and Seacat, M. S.: *An Analysis of Personnel in Medical Sociology.* Health Information Foundation, Research Series No. 21, New York: 1962.

597. Freidson, E. and Feldman, J. J.: *The Public Looks at Hospitals.* Health Information Foundation, Research Series No. 4, New York: 1958.

598. Freidson, E. and Feldman, J. J.: *Public Attitudes Toward Health Insurance.* Health Information Foundation, Research Series No. 5, New York: 1958.

599. Freidson, E. and Feldman, J. J.: *The Public Looks at Dental Care.*

Health Information Foundation, Research Series No. 6, New York: 1958.

600. Freidson, E.: *Patients' Views of Medical Practice.* New York: Russell Sage Foundation, 1961.

601. Freidson, E.: *The Hospital in Modern Society.* New York: The Free Press of Glencoe, a Division of the Macmillan Co., Crowell-Collier Publishing Co., 1963.

602. Freidson, E. and Rhea, B.: "Processes of control in a company of equals." *Social Problems* 11: 119–131, 1963.

603. Freidson, E.: *Professional Dominance: The Social Structure of Medical Care.* New York: Atherton Press, Inc., 1970.

604. Freidson, E.: *Profession of Medicine: A Study of the Sociology of Applied Knowledge.* New York: Dodd, Mead and Co., 1970.

605. Jaco, E. G. (Ed.): *Patients, Physicians, and Illness. Sourcebook in Behavioral Science and Medicine.* Glencoe, Ill.: Free Press of Glencoe, 1958.

606. Freeman, H. E., Levine, S., and Reeder, L. G. (Eds.): *Handbook of Medical Sociology.* Englewood Cliffs, N. J.: Prentice-Hall, Inc., 1963.

607. Suchman, E. A.: *Sociology and the Field of Public Health.* New York: Russell Sage Foundation, 1963.

608. Knutson, A. L.: *The Individual, Society, and Health Behavior.* New York: Russell Sage Foundation, 1965.

609. Scott, W. R. and Volkart, E. H. (Eds.): *Medical Care: Readings in the Sociology of Medical Institutions.* New York: John Wiley and Sons, Inc., 1966.

610. Duff, R. S. and Hollingshead, A. B.: *Sickness and Society.* New York: Harper and Row, 1968.

611. Mechanic, D.: *Medical Sociology: A Selective View.* New York: The Free Press, 1968.

612. Coe, R. M.: *Sociology of Medicine.* New York: McGraw-Hill Book Co., 1970.

613. Rosenstock, I. M.: "What research in motivation suggests for public health." *Am. J. Public Health* 50: 295–302, 1960.

614. Rosenstock, I. M.: "Why people use health services." *Milbank Mem. Fund Q.* 44: No. 3, Part 2, 94–124, 1966.

615. Kirscht, J. P., Haefner, D. P., Kegeles, S. S., *et al.*: "A national study of health beliefs." *J. Health Soc. Behav.* 7: 248–254, 1966.

616. Merrill, M. H., Hollister, A. C., Gibbens, S. L., *et al,*: "Attitudes of Californians toward polio vaccination." *Am. J. Public Health* 48: 146–152, 1958.

617. Rosenstock, I. M., Derryberry, M., and Carriger, B.: "Why people fail to seek poliomyelitis vaccination." *Public Health Reports* 74: 98–103, 1959.

618. Hochbaum, G.: *Public Participation in Medical Screening Programs: A Social Psychological Study.* Public Health Service Monograph 572. U. S. Dept. of Health, Education, and Welfare, Public Health Service. Washington: U. S. Gov't. Print. Off., 1958.

619. Rosenstock, I. M.: "Public response to cancer screening and detection programs. Determinants of health behavior." *J. Chronic Dis.* 16: 407–418, 1963.

620. Tyroler, H. A., Johnson, A. L., and Fulton, J. T.: "Patterns of preventive health behavior in populations." *J. Health Soc. Behav.* 6: 128–140, 1965.

621. Elling, R., Whittemore, R., and Green, M.: "Patient participation in a pediatric program." *J. Health Soc. Behav.* 1: 183–191, 1960.

622. Deisher, R. W., Engel, W. L., Spielholz, R., *et al.*: "Mothers' opinions of their pediatric care." *Pediatrics* 35: 82–90, 1965.

623. Kegeles, S. S.: "Why people seek dental care: A review of present knowledge." *Am. J. Public Health* 51: 1305–1311, 1961.

624. Kegeles, S. S.: "Why people seek dental care: A test of a conceptual formulation." *J. Health Soc. Behav.* 4: 166–173, 1963.

625. Tash, R. H., O'Shea, R. M., and Cohen, L. K.: "Testing a preventive-symptomatic theory of dental health behavior." *Am. J. Public Health* 59: 514–521, 1969.

626. Bashshur, R. L., Metzner, C. A., and Worden, C.: "Consumer satisfaction with group practice, the CHA case." *Am. J. Public Health* 57: 1991–1999, 1961.

627. Heinzelman, F.: "Determinants of prophylaxis behavior with respect to rheumatic fever." *J. Health Soc. Behav.* 3: 78–81, 1962.

628. Davis, M. and Èichhorn, R.L.: "Compliance with medical regimens." *J. Health Soc. Behavior* 4: 240–249, 1963.

629. Davis, M.: "Variations in patients' compliance with doctors' orders: Analysis of congruence between survey responses and results of empirical investigations." *J. Med. Educ.* 41: 1037–1048, 1966.

630. Davis, M.: "Predicting non-compliant behavior." *J. Health Soc. Behav.* 8: 265–271, 1967.

631. Davis, M.: "Variations in patients' compliance with doctors' advice: An empirical analysis of patterns of communication." *Am. J. Public Health* 58: 274–288, 1968.

632. Davis, M.: "Physiologic, psychological, and demographic factors in patient compliance with doctors' orders." *Med. Care* 6: 115–122, 1968.

633. Charney, E., Bynum, R., Eldredge, D., *et al.*: "How well do patients take oral penicillin?—A collaborative study in private practice." *Pediatrics* 40: 188–195, 1967.

634. Seligman, A. W., McGrath, N. E., and Pratt, L.: "Level of medical information among clinic patients." *J. Chronic Dis.* 6: 497–509, 1957.

635. Samora, J., Saunders, L., and Larson, R. F.: "Medical vocabulary knowledge among hospital patients." *J. Health Soc. Behav.* 2: 83–92, 1961.

636. Metzner, C. A., Bashshur, R. L., and Worden, C.: *Choice of Health Care Plans. A Survey of Auto Workers' Selection of Blue Cross/Blue Shield or Community Health Association.* Ann Arbor: Univ. of Michigan, School of Public Health, Bu. of Public Health Economics, 1965.

637. Metzner, C. A. and Bashshur, R. L.: "Factors associated with choice of health care plans." *J. Health Soc. Behav.* 8: 291–299, 1967.

638. Andersen, R. and Riedel, D. C.: *People and Their Hospital Insurance: Comparisons of the Uninsured, Those With One Policy, and Those With Multiple Coverage.* University of Chicago, Graduate School of Business, Center for Health Administration Studies, Research Series No. 25, Chicago, 1968.

639. Weeks, H. A., Glass, L., Hubin, D., *et al.*: *Family Spending*

Patterns and Health Care. Cambridge: Harvard Univ. Press, 1961.

640. King, S. H.: *Perceptions of Illness and Medical Practice.* New York: Russell Sage Foundation, 1962.

641. Mechanic, D.: "Perception of parental responses to illness: A research note." *J. Health Soc. Behavior* 6: 253–257, 1965.

642. Watts, D. D.: "Factors related to the acceptance of modern medicine." *Am. J. Public Health* 56: 1205–1212, 1966.

643. Mechanic, D.: "The study of illness behavior: Some implications for medical practice." *Med. Care* 3: 30–32, 1965.

644. Mechanic, D.: "Sociology and public health: Perspectives for application." *Am. J. Public Health* 62: 146–151, 1972.

645. Leventhal, H.: "Fear communications in the acceptance of preventive health practices." *Bull. N. Y. Acad. Med.* 41: 1144–1167, 1965.

646. Haefner, D. P. and Kirscht, J. P.: "Motivational and behavioral effects of modifying health beliefs." *Public Health Reports* 85: 478–484, 1970.

647. Battistella, R. M.: "Limitations in use of the concept of psychological readiness to initiate health care." *Med. Care* 6: 308–319, 1968.

648. Battistella, R. M.: "Factors associated with delay in the initiation of physicians' care among late adulthood persons." *Am. J. Public Health* 61: 1348–1361, 1971.

649. Solon, J., Sheps, C. G., Lee, S. S., *et al.*: "Staff perception of patients' use of a hospital outpatient department." *J. Med. Educ.* 33: 10–21, 1958.

650. Goss, M. E. W.: "Influence and authority among physicians in an outpatient clinic." *Am. Sociol. Rev.* 26: 39–50, 1961.

651. Goss, M. E. W.: "Patterns of bureaucracy among hospital staff physicians" in *The Hospital in Modern Society.* Edited by E. Freidson. New York: The Free Press of Glencoe, a Division of the Macmillan Co., Crowell-Collier Pub. Co., 1963, pp. 170–194.

652. McElrath, D. C.: "Perspective and participation of physicians in prepaid group practice." *Am. Sociol. Rev.* 26: 596–607, 1961.

653. Seeman, M. and Evans, J. W.: "Stratification and hospital care:

I. The performance of the medical interne." *Am. Sociol. Rev.* 26: 67–80, 1961. "II. The objective criteria of performance." *Am. Sociol. Rev.* 26: 193–204, 1961.

654. Seeman, M. and Evans, J. W.: "Alienation and learning in a hospital setting." *Am. Sociol. Rev.* 27: 772–782, 1962.

655. Kendall, P.: "The learning environments of hospitals" in *The Hospital in Modern Society.* Edited by E. Freidson. New York: The Free Press of Glencoe, a Division of the Macmillan Co., Crowell-Collier Pub. Co., 1963, pp. 195–230.

656. Rosengren, W. R. and DeVault, S.: "The sociology of time and space in an obstetrical hospital" in *The Hospital in Modern Society.* Edited by E. Freidson. New York: The Free Press of Glencoe, a Division of the Macmillan Co., Crowell-Collier Pub. Co., 1963, pp. 266–292.

657. Sussman, M. B., Caplan, E. K., Haug, M. R., *et al.*: *The Walking Patient: A Study in Outpatient Care.* Cleveland: The Press of Western Reserve Univ., 1967.

658. Mechanic, D.: "General practice in England and Wales." *Med. Care* 6: 245–260, 1968.

659. Freidson, E. and Rhea, B.: "Physicians in large medical groups." *J. Chronic Dis.* 17: 827–836, 1964.

660. Freidson, E. and Rhea, B.: "Knowledge and judgment in professional evaluations." *Admin. Sci. Q.* 10: 107–124, 1965.

661. DuBois, D. M.: "Organizational viability of group practice." *Group Practice,* 16: 261–270, Apr. 1967.

662. Glaser, W. A.: *Social Settings and Medical Organization: A Cross-National Study of the Hospital.* New York: Atherton Press, Inc., 1970.

663. Elling, R. H. and Roemer, M. I.: "Determinants of community support." *Hosp. Admin.* 6: 17–34, 1961.

664. Suchman, E. A.: "Preventive health behavior: A model for research on community health campaigns." *J. Health Soc. Behav.* 8: 197–209, 1967.

665. Rosner, M. M.: "Administrative controls and innovation." *Behav. Sci.* 13: 36–43, 1968.

666. Colombotos, J.: "Physicians' responses to changes in health care: Some projections." *Inquiry* 8: 20–26, Mar. 1971.

667. Lieberson, S.: "Ethnic groups and the practice of medicine." *Am. Sociol. Rev.* 23: 542–547, 1958.

668. Suchman, E. A.: "Sociomedical variations among ethnic groups." *Am. J. Sociol.* 70: 319–331, 1964.

669. Suchman, E. A.: "Social patterns of illness and medical care." *J. Health Soc. Behav.* 6: 2–16, 1965.

670. Suchman, E. A.: "Social factors in medical deprivation." *Am. J. Public Health* 55: 1725–1733, 1965.

671. Ross, J. A.: "Social class and medical care." *J. Health Soc. Behav.* 3: 35–40, 1962.

672. Macgregor, G.: "Social determinants of health practices." *Am. J. Public Health* 51: 1709–1714, 1961.

673. Lewis, L. S. and Lopreato, J.: "Arationality, ignorance, and perceived danger in medical practices." *Am. Sociol. Rev.* 27: 508–514, 1962.

674. Solon, J. A.: "Patterns of medical care: Sociocultural variations among a hospital's outpatients." *Am. J. Public Health* 53: 884–894, 1966.

675. Ellenbogen, B. L., Ramsey, C. E., and Danley, R. A.: "Health need, status, and subscription to health insurance." *J. Health Soc. Behav.* 7: 59–63, 1966.

676. Bashshur, R. L. and Metzner, C. A.: "Patterns of social differentiation between community health association and Blue Cross-Blue Shield." *Inquiry* 4: 23–44, June 1967.

677. Coe, R. M. and Wessen, A. F.: "Social-psychological factors influencing the use of community health resources." *Am. J. Public Health* 55: 1024–1031, 1965.

678. Kegeles, S. S.: "A field experimental attempt to change beliefs and behavior of women in an urban ghetto." *J. Health Soc. Behav.* 10: 115–124, 1969.

679. Kegeles, S. S.: "Problems of experimental research in the urban ghetto." *Med. Care* 7: 395–405, 1969.

680. Kane, R. L. and Deuschle, K. W.: "Problems in patient-doctor communications." *Med. Care* 5: 260–271, 1967.

681. Korsch, B. M., Gozzi, E. K., and Francis, V.: "Gaps in doctor-patient communication: I. Doctor-patient interaction and patient satisfaction." *Pediatrics* 42: 855–871, 1968.

682. Francis, V., Korsch, B. M., and Morris, M. J.: "Gaps in doc-tor-patient communication: II. Patients' response to medical advice." *N. Engl. J. Med.* 280: 535–546, 1969.

683. Skipper, J. K., Jr., and Leonard, R. C.: "Children, stress, and hospitalization: A field experiment." *J. Health Soc. Behav.* 9: 275–287, 1968.

684. Caplan, E. K. and Sussman, M. B.: "Rank order of important variables for patient and staff satisfaction with outpatient ser-vice." *J. Health Soc. Behav.* 7: 133–137, 1966.

685. Freeman, H. E., Levine, S., and Reeder, L. G. (Eds.): *Handbook of Medical Sociology.* 2d ed. Englewood Cliffs, N. J.: Pren-tice-Hall, Inc., 1972.

686. Jaco, E. G. (Ed.): *Patients, Physicians, and Illness — Source Book in Behavioral Science and Medicine.* 2d ed. New York: The Free Press, 1972.

NURSING HEALTH SERVICES RESEARCH

687. Nightingale, F.: *Notes on Matters Affecting the Health, Efficiency and Hospital Administration of the British Army.* A Report pub-lished at the request of the Secretary of State for War, London, 1858.

688. Abdellah, F. G. and Levine, E.: *Better Patient Care Through Nursing Research.* New York: The Macmillan Co., 1965.

689. Abdellah, F. G.: "Overview of nursing research, 1955–1968 (in three Parts)." Part I. *Nurs. Res.* 19: 6–17, 1970; Part II. *Nurs. Res.* 19: 151–162, 1970; and Part III. *Nurs. Res.* 19: 239–252, 1970.

690. *Research in Nursing, 1955–1968.* Public Health Service Pub. No. 1356, U. S. Dept. of Health, Education, and Welfare, Public Health Service. Washington: U. S. Gov't. Print. Off., 1969.

691. Nutting, M. A. and Dock, L. L.: *History of Nursing.* Vol. II, New York: G. P. Putnam's Sons, 1907.

692. Emerson, H. and Goldmark, J.: *Nursing. Cleveland Hospital and Health Survey, Part 9.* Cleveland: Cleveland Hospital Council, 1920.

693. Lewinski-Corwin, E. H.: "The hospital nursing situation." *Am. J. Nurs.* 22: 603, 1922.

694. Goldmark, J. (Ed.) *Nursing and Nursing Education in the United States.* Report of the Committee for the Study of Nursing Education and a Report of a Survey. New York: The Macmillan Co., 1923.

695. Burgess, M. A.: *A Five-Year Program for the Committee on the Grading of Nursing Schools.* Committee on the Grading of Nursing Schools, New York, 1926.

696. *Nursing Schools Today and Tomorrow.* Final Report of the Committee on Grading of Nursing Schools, New York, 1934.

697. Burgess, M. A.: *Nurses, Patients, and Pocketbooks.* Report of a Study of the Economics of Nursing conducted by the Committee on the Grading of Nursing Schools, New York, 1928.

698. Johns, E. and Pfefferkorn, B.: *An Activity Analysis of Nursing.* Committee on the Grading of Nursing Schools, New York, 1934.

699. Capen, S. P.: "A member of the grading committee speaks." *Am. J. Nurs.* 32: 307–311, 1932.

700. Pfefferkorn, B. and Rottman, M.: *Clinical Education in Nursing.* New York: The Macmillan Co., 1932.

701. Johns, E. and Pfefferkorn, B.: *An Activity Analysis of Nursing.* New York: National League of Nursing Education, 1934.

702. Feyerherm, A. M.: "Nursing activity patterns: A guide to staffing." *Nurs. Res.* 15: 124–133, 1966.

703. Brown, E. L.: *Nursing for the Future.* New York: Russell Sage Foundation, 1948.

704. Reisman, L. and Rohrer, J. H.: *Change and Dilemma in the Nursing Profession.* New York: G. P. Putnam's Sons, 1957.

705. Belknap, I.: *Human Problems of a State Mental Hospital.* New York: McGraw-Hill Book Co., 1956.

706. Simmons, L. W. and Henderson, V.: *Nursing Research: A Survey and Assessment.* New York: Appleton-Century Crofts, Inc., 1964.

707. "Census of public health nurses, 1937." *Public Health Nurse* 29: 648–652, 1937.

708. "A national inventory of nurses." *Am. J. Nurs.* 40: 1246, 1940.

709. *Personnel Practices for General Staff Nurses.* Sponsored by Ameri-

can Hospital Association, National League for Nursing Education. New York: American Nurses' Association, 1944.

710. Montag, M.: *Community College Education for Nursing.* New York: McGraw-Hill Book Co., 1959.

711. White, R. F. and Goldsen, R. K.: "Which nurses join professional organizations?" *Mod. Hosp.* 97: 123–125, 168, Sept. 1961.

712. Rowe, H. and Flitter, H. H.: *A Study on Cost of Nursing Education.* "Part I, Cost of Basic Diploma Education," NLN Code No. 19-1142, 1964. "Part II, Cost of Basic Baccalaureate and Associate Degree Programs," NLN Code No. 19-1174. New York: National League for Nursing, 1965.

713. Olesen, V. L. and Whittaker, E. W.: *The Silent Dialogue.* San Francisco: Jossey-Bass, Inc., 1968.

714. Reiter, F. and Kakosh, M. E.: *Quality of Nursing Care: A Report of a Field-Study to Establish Criteria.* Conducted at Institute of Research and Studies in Nursing Education, Division of Nursing Education, Teachers College, Columbia University, 1950–1954. New York: New York Medical College, Graduate School of Nursing, 1963.

715. Smith, D. M.: "Clinical nursing tool." *Am. J. Nurs.* 68: 2384–2388, 1968.

716. White, R. P., Quade, D., and White, K.L.: *Patient Care Classification: Methods and Application.* Baltimore: Johns Hopkins Univ., School of Hygiene and Public Health, Department of Medical Care and Hospitals, 1967.

717. Wandelt, M. A.: *Uninterrupted Patient Care and Nursing Requirements.* Detroit: Wayne State Univ., 1963.

718. Klaus, D. J., Gosnell, D.E., Marchese, A.C., *et al: Controlling Experience to Improve Nursing Proficiency: Background and Study Plan Report.* Reports Nos. 1–4. Pittsburgh: American Institutes for Research, 1966–1968.

719. Aydelotte, M. K.: "Use of patient welfare as a criterion measure." *Nurs. Res.* 11: 10–14, 1962.

720. Simon, R. J. and Hudson, W. R.: "Experimental study of the relation between nursing care and patient welfare." *J. Applied Psych.* 48: 268–274, 1964.

721. Bryant, W. D.: *Nursing Resources on the Ward and Nurse-Patient Relationships.* Kansas City: Community Studies, 1957.

722. Dumas, R. G. and Leonard, R. C.: "Effects of nursing on the incidence of postoperative vomiting." *Nurs. Res.* 12: 12–15, 1963.

723. Elms, R. R.: *Prediction of Post-Surgical Nursing Needs.* Fort Worth, Texas: Texas Christian Univ., Harris College of Nursing, 1967.

724. Flitter, H.: *Development of a Plan for Testing a Nursing Evaluation Instrument.* NLN Code No. 19-1121. New York: National League for Nursing, 1964.

725. Kinsinger, R. E.: "Technology and imagination-education evolution." *Nurs. Outlook* 11: 252–254, 1963.

726. Chow, R.: "Postoperative cardiac nursing research: A method for identifying and categorizing nursing action." *Nurs. Res.* 18: 4–13, 1969.

727. Meltzer, L. W., Abdellah, F.G., and Kitchell, J.R.: (Eds.): *Concepts and Practices of Intensive Care for Nurse Specialists.* Philadelphia: Charles Press, 1969.

728. Wooden, H. E.: "The family-centered approach to nursing care." *Nurs. Forum* 1: 60–77, 1962.

729. Gladstein, S., Prasatek, G., and Throne, M.: *A Floor Manager Pattern for the Nursing Unit.* Baltimore: Sinai Hospital of Baltimore, Inc., 1959.

730. Brodt, D. E.: "The service manager, innovation for nursing and health organizations." *Hosp. Prog.,* 47: 69, 70, and 74, Sept. 1966.

731. Tucker, K. and Hilbert, H.: *Survey of Public Health Nursing Administration and Practice.* National Organization for Public Health Nursing. New York: The Commonwealth Fund, 1934.

732. McIver, P.: *An Analysis of First Level Public Health Nursing in Ten Selected Organizations.* New York: National Organization for Public Health Nursing, 1935.

733. Mickey, J. E.: "Findings of study of extra-hospital nursing needs." *Am. J. Public Health* 53: 1049–1057, 1963.

734. Smith L. C.: *Factors Influencing Continuity of Nursing Service.* A Study sponsored by National League for Nursing directed by Institute of Research and Service in Nursing Education, Teachers College, Columbia Univ. New York: National League for Nursing, 1962.

735. Johnson, W. L. and Hardin, C. A.: *Content and Dynamics of Home Visits of Public Health Nurses.* 2 vols. New York: American Nurses' Foundation, Part I — 1962, Part II — 1969.

736. Katz, S., Ford, A. B., Downs, T. D., *et al.*: *The Effects of Continued Care: A Study of Chronic Illness in the Home.* Dept. of Health, Education, and Welfare, Health Services and Mental Health Administration, National Center for Health Services Research and Development. DHEW Pub. No. (HSM) 73-3010, Washington: U. S. Gov't. Print. Off., 1972.

737. Holliday, J. (Ed.): *Public Health Nursing for the Sick at Home: A Descriptive Study.* New York: Visiting Nurse Service of New York, 1967.

738. Hirsch, L. V., Klein, M. S., and Marlowe, G. W.: (Principal Investigator, Dorothy Wilson). *Combining Public Health Nursing Agencies: A Case Study in Philadelphia.* New York: Department of Public Health Nursing of the National League for Nursing, 1967.

739. Simon, H.: *The Management of Health Problems of Secondary School Students.* New York: Columbia Univ., Teachers College, Teachers College Press, 1968.

740. Hagen, E. and Wolff, L. V.: *Nursing Leadership Behavior in General Hospitals.* New York: Columbia Univ., Teachers College, Institute of Research and Service in Nursing Education, 1961.

741. Meyer, G. R.: *Tenderness and Technique: Nursing Values in Transition.* Los Angeles: Univ. of California, Institute of Industrial Relations, 1960.

742. Brackett, M. E. and Spaney, E.: "What nurses like and dislike about their jobs." *Mod. Hosp.* 89: 53, June 1957.

743. Dodge, J. S.: "Nurse and doctor relations and.attitudes toward the patient." *Nurs. Res.* 9: 32–38, 1960.

744. Glaser, B. G. and Strauss, A. L.: *The Discovery of Grounded Theory. Strategies for Qualitative Research.* Chicago: Aldine Pub. Co., 1967.

745. Morgan, J. R., Glass, G. V., Stevens, H. A., *et al.*: "An extendor role for nurses." *Nurs. Res.* 14: 330–334, 1965.

746. Bennis, W. G., Berkowitz, N. H., Malone, M., *et al.*: "Problems of measuring patient care in the outpatient department." *J. Health Soc. Behav.* 2: 138–144, 1961.

747. Hardin, C. A. and Johnson, W. L.: *The Professional Nurse in Public Health.* New York: Am. Nurses' Found. (Processed) Sept. 1959.

748. Hassinger, E. W., and Grubb, C. E.: *Role of the Local Public Health Nurse.* Univ. of Missouri, College of Agriculture, Research Bulletin No. 896. Columbia: 1965.

749. Little, D. and Carnevali, D.: "Nurse specialist effect on tuberculosis." *Nurs. Res.* 16: 321–326, 1967.

750. Richardson, E. H., Chandler, V. T. W., and Harvey, L. H.: *Effect of Nursing Care on Selected Aspects of Premature Infant Welfare in the Home.* Alabama, Tuskegee Institute, 1967.

751. Schwartz, D., Henley B., and Zeitz, L.:*The Elderly Ambulatory Patient: Nursing and Psychological Needs.* New York: The Macmillan Co., 1964.

752. Dumas, R. G.: "Utilization of a concept of stress as a basis for nursing practice" in *ANA Clinical Sessions, 1966.* San Francisco, New York: Appleton-Century-Crofts, Inc., 1967, pp. 193–201.

753. Conant, L. H.: "Use of Bales' interaction process analysis to study nurse-patient interaction." *Nurs. Res.* 14: 304–309, 1965.

754. Hammond, K. R.: "Clinical inference in nursing. Part 2, Psychologist's viewpoint." *Nurs. Res.* 15: 27–38, 1966.

755. Walker, V. H.: *Nursing and Ritualistic Practice.* New York: The Macmillan Co., 1967.

756. Pfefferkorn, B. and Rovetta, C. A.: *Administrative Cost Analysis for Nursing Service and Nursing Education.* New York: National League for Nursing Education, 1940.

757. Committee on the Costs of Medical Care. *Medical Care for the American People.* The Final Report of CCMC (No. 28). Chicago: Univ. of Chicago Press, 1932. Reprinted 1970 by the U. S. Dept. of Health, Education, and Welfare, Health Services and Mental Health Administration, Community Health Service.

DENTAL HEALTH SERVICES RESEARCH

758. U. S. Public Health Service, Division of Dental Health. *A History of the Dental Corps of the United States Public Health Service.* Dec. 1961.

759. Klein, H., Palmer, C. E., and Knutson, J. W.: "Studies on

dental caries. Dental status and dental needs of elementary school children." *Public Health Reports* 53: 751–765, 1938.

760. Wisan, J. M.: "Evaluation of dental programs for children." *Am. J. Public Health* 28: 859, 862, 1938.

761. Pickles, T. H.: "The relationship of caries prevalence data and diagnosed treatment needs in a child population." *Med. Care* 8: 463–473, 1970.

762. Waterman, G. E.: "The Richmond-Woonsocket studies on dental caries services for school children." *J. Am. Dent. Assoc.* 52: 676–684, 1956.

763. Messner, C. T., Gafafer, W. M., Cady, F. C., *et al.*: *Dental Survey for School Children Ages 6–14 Years.* (Made in 1933–34 in 26 States.) U. S. Treasury Dept., Public Health Service. Washington: U. S. Gov't. Print. Off., 1936.

764. Klein, H. and Palmer, C. E.: *On the Epidemiology of Dental Caries.* Univ. of Pennsylvania Bicentennial Conference. Philadelphia: Univ. of Pennsylvania Press, 1941.

765. Knutson, J. W.: "An index of the prevalence of dental caries in school children." *Public Health Reports* 59: 253–262, 1944.

766. Smith, Q. M., Fuchsberg, R. R., and Ake, J. N.: *Report on the Dental Program of the ILWU-PMA. The First Three Years.* Public Health Service Pub. No. 894. U. S. Dept. of Health, Education, and Welfare, Public Health Service. Washington: U. S. Gov't. Print. Off., 1962.

767. Schoen, M. H.: "Effect of a prepaid children's dental care program on mortality of permanent teeth." *J. Am. Dent. Assoc.* 71: 626–634, 1965.

768. Rogers, E. S. and Daniels, A. K.: "Attitudes toward group dental care: Survey of consumers and dentists." *J. Am. College Dent.* 25: 174–240, 1958.

768a. Brusseau, L. S., Hoggard, F. M., and Gribble, J. L.: *Group Dental Practice in the United States, 1971.* National Institutes of Health, Bu. of Health Manpower Education, Division of Dental Health, DHEW Pub. No. (NIH) 72-189, Washington: U. S. Gov't. Print. Off., 1972.

769. Division of Dental Health. *A Survey. Dental Services in Project Head Start—Summer 1967.* Public Health Service, National In-

stitutes of Health, Bu. of Health Professions Education and Manpower Training, 1969.

770. Haber, Z. and Leatherwood, E. C., Jr.: "A dental program for Head Start children in New York City: A retrospective study of utilization and costs." *Med. Care* 7: 281–287, 1969.

771. Jong, A. and Leske, G. S.: "Utilization and cost of dental services for preschool children in Boston's Head Start program." *J. Public Health Dent.* 28: 126–134, 1968.

772. Brewster. L. L.: "Tucson Head Start Dental Project (1966)." *Am. J. Public Health* 58: 887–891, 1968.

773. Ross, B. E.: "A comparative study of four dental payment mechanisms in a Head Start program." *Am. J. Public Health* 61: 2176–2187, 1971.

774. Rayner, J. F. and Cohen, L. K.: "School dental health education" in *Social Sciences and Dentistry—A Critical Bibliography.* Edited by N. D. Richards and L. K. Cohen. Federation Dentaire Internationale, The Hague: A. Sijthoff, 1971 pp. 275–307.

775. Stolpe, J. R., Mecklenburg, R. E., and Lathrop, R. L.: "The effectiveness of an educational program on oral health in schools for improving the application of knowledge." *J. Public Health Dent.* 31: 48–59, 1971.

776. Stadt, Z. M., Blum, H., and Kent, G.W.: "Direct mail motivation of parents of three year old children." *Am. J. Public Health* 53: 572–581, 1963.

777. Cohen, L. K.: "Reaching practitioners by mail." *Public Health Reports* 81: 735–741, 1966.

778. Cassidy, R. J.: "Psychological factors in preventive dentistry." *Alabama J. Med. Sci.* 5: 358–369, 1968.

779. Ramirez, A., Wershow, H. J., and Pelton, W. J.: "Prevention for dental health: Its relationship to the value of the individual." *J. Public Health Dent.* 29: 96–107, 1969.

780. O'Shea, R. M. and Gray, S. B.: "Dental patients attitudes and behavior concerning prevention." *Public Health Reports* 83: 405–410, 1968.

781. Kegeles, S. S.: "Some motives for seeking preventive dental care." *J. Am. Dent. Assoc.* 67: 90–98, 1963.

782. Haefner, D. P., Kegeles, S. S., Kirscht, J., *et al.*: "Preventive action in dental disease, tuberculosis, and cancer." *Public Health Reports* 82: 451–459, 1967.

783. ———.

784. Brandeis University, Florence Heller Graduate School for Advanced Studies in Social Welfare: *Factors Affecting Selection of a Clinic Population.* Papers in Social Welfare No. 5, Waltham, Mass., 1963.

785. Lambert, C., Freeman, H.E., Morris, R.: "Public clinic care and eligibility." *Am. J. Public Health* 53: 1196–1204, 1963.

786. Freeman, H. E. and Lambert, C.: "Preventive dental behavior of urban mothers." *J. Health Soc. Behav.* 6: 141–146, 1965.

787. Klerman, L. V. and Lambert, C. Jr.: "Attitudes of private dentists toward a public dental care program." *J. Am. Dent. Assoc.* 68: 416–423, 1964.

788. Lambert, C., Jr., and Freeman, H. E.: *The Clinic Habit.* New Haven: College and University Press, 1967.

789. Cohen, L. K. and Fusillo, A. E. (Eds.): "The social sciences and dentistry's attitudes toward public dental programs for children, 1959–1968." *J. Pub. Health Dent.* 31: 60–61, 1971.

790. Quarantelli, E. L.: "The dental student image of the dentist-patient relationship." *Am. J. Public Health* 51: 1312–1319, 1961.

791. Simonds, S. K.: "The patient's perception of his problem." *Internat'l. J. Health Educ.* 6: 10–15, Jan.-Mar., 1963.

792. Goulding, P. C.: "What the public thinks of the dentist and of dental health." *J. Am. Dent. Assoc.* 70: 1211–1215, 1965.

793. Brunswick, A. F.: "Health needs of adolescents: How the adolescent sees them." *Am. J. Public Health* 59: 1730–1745, 1969.

794. Richards, N. D. and Cohen, L. K. (Eds.): *Social Sciences and Dentistry: A Critical Bibliography.* Federation Dentaire Internationale, The Hague: A. Sijthoff, 1971.

795. O'Shea, R. M. and Cohen, L. K. (Eds.): "Toward a sociology of dentistry." *The Milbank Memorial Fund Q.* 49: No. 3, Part 2, 1971.

796. Newman, J. F. and Anderson, O. W.: *Patterns of Dental Service*

Utilization in the United States: A Nationwide Social Survey. Chicago: Univ. of Chicago, Center for Health Administration Studies, 1972.

797. Suchman, E. A. and Rothman, A. A.: "The utilization of dental services." *The Milbank Mem. Fund Q.* 47: 56-63, 1969.

798. Kreisberg, L. A. and Treiman, B. R.: "Socio-economic status and the utilization of dentists services." *J. Am. College Dent.* 27: 147-165, 1960.

799. Hochstim, J. R., Athanasopoulos, D. A., and Larkins, J. H.: "Poverty area under the microscope." *Am. J. Public Health* 58: 1815-1827, 1968.

800. Bodnarchuk, A.: "Utilization of dental services by welfare recipients in a private dental office." *J. Can. Dent. Assoc.* 33: 126-130, 1967.

801. Schonfeld, H. K. and Milone, C. L.: "The utilization of dental services by families at the Hill Health Center." *Am. J. Public Health* 62: 942-952, 1972.

802. Leverett, D. H. and Jong, A.: "Variations in the use of dental care facilities by low-income white and black urban populations." *J. Am. Dent. Assoc.* 80: 137-140, 1970.

803. Nikias, M. K.: "Trends and patterns of dental care in an urban area before Medicaid." *HSMHA Health Reports* 86: 52-65, 1971.

804. Morrison, R. D., Gurley, W. B., Ragsdale, D. L., *et al.*: "Analysis of a metropolitan dental clinic population." *J. Missouri Dent. Assoc.* 45: 9-19, 1965.

805. Lotzkar, S.: "Dental care for the chronically ill, aged and homebound." *J. Am. Dent. Assoc.* 67: 71-76, 1963.

806. Kegeles, S. S., Lotzkar, S., and Andrews, L.: "Predicting the acceptance of dental care by residents of nursing homes." *J. Public Health Dent.* 26: 290-302, 1966.

807. Waldman, H. B.: "Report of a demonstration dental care program for homebound, chronically ill and aged patients." *J. Am. Dent. Assoc.* 69: 722-729, 1964.

808. American Dental Association Council on Dental Health, Council on Hospital Dental Services: "Survey of dental services." *J. Am. Dent. Assoc.* 71: 1510-1515, 1965.

809. U. S. Dept. of Health, Education, and Welfare, Public Health Service: *Report on the Dental Program of the ILWU-PMA-The first three years.* 1954. U. S. Dept. of Health, Education, and Welfare, Public Health Service, National Institutes of Health, Div. of Dental Health, 1962.

810. Smith, Q. M., Mitchell, G. E., and Lucas, G. A.: *An Experiment in Dental Prepayment-The Naismith Dental Plan.* Washington: U.S. Gov't. Print. Off., 1962.

811. Smith, Q. M., Pennell, E. H., Bothwell, R., *et al.*: *Dental Care in a Group Purchase Plan. A Survey of Attitudes and Utilization at the St. Louis Labor Health Institute.* Public Health Service Pub. No. 684, U.S. Dept. of Health, Education, and Welfare, Public Health Service. Washington: U. S. Gov't. Print. Off., 1959.

812. Zalk, M.: "Report on the North New Jersey Dental Plan for Teamster Members." *Med. Care Rev.* 24: 226-228, 1967.

813. Dept. of Health, Education, and Welfare, Public Health Service: *Comprehensive Dental Care in a Group Practice. A Study of Service and Time Requirements.* Public Health Service Pub. No. 395, Washington: U. S. Gov't. Print. Off., 1954.

814. Schoen, M. H.: "Group practice and dentistry." *Med. Care* 5: 176-183, 1967.

815. Schoen, M. H.: "Group practice and poor communities." *Am. J. Public Health* 60: 1125-1132, 1970.

816. _____

817. Genet, P. E.: "A private group practice utilizing capitation prepayment." *J. Pub. Health Dent.* 32: 40-45, 1972.

818. Simons, J. H.: "Consumer attitudes toward prepaid dentistry." *J. Am. Dent. Assoc.* 76: 673-677, 1967.

819. Avnet, H. H. and Nikias, M. K.: *Insured Dental Care.* New York Group Health Dental Insurance, Inc., 1967.

820. Nikias, M. K.: "Social class and the use of dental care under prepayment." *Med. Care* 6: 381-393, 1968.

821. Nikias, M. K.: "Prepaid dental care: Patterns of use and source of premium payment." *Am. J. Public Health* 59: 1088-1103, 1969.

822. Draker, H. L.: *A Study of Family Expenditures for Dental Care in*

New York State. Report of a study. Albany: Health Research, Inc., 1964.

823. Draker, H. L. and Allaway, N. C.: "Facts on motivation in buyers of dental care: Partial report from phase I, study of expenditures of families for dental care in the State of New York." *J. Public Health Dent.* 23: 208–221, 1963.

824. Draker, H. L., Metzner, C. A., and Allaway, N. C.: "The dentists and the services they provided for two populations: Comments on methodology of study." *J. Public Health Dent.* 25: 23–32, 1965.

825. Mitchell, G. E. and Haggard, T. M., Jr.: *The Dental Service Corporation.* Public Health Service Pub. No. 1274, U. S. Dept. of Health, Education, and Welfare, Public Health Service, Washington: U. S. Gov't. Print. Off., 1965.

826. Vidmar, G. C.: "The Dental Service Corporation. Its role in delivery of oral health services." *J. Public Health Dent.* 30: 21–37, 1970.

827. Baum, B. J.: "Medicaid and the practicing dentist." *J. Massachusetts Dent. Soc.* 18: 30–31, 1969.

828. Schonfeld, H. K.: "The quality of dental care in community programs." *J. Public Health Dent.* 27: 70–82, 1967.

829. Schonfeld, H. K., Falk, I. S., Sleeper, H. R., *et al.*: "The content of good dental care: Methodology in a formulation for clinical standards and audits, and preliminary findings." *Am. J. Public Health* 57: 1137–1146, 1967.

830. Jong, A. and Leverett, D. H.: "The operation of a community dental clinic in a health center. An evaluation." *J. Public Health Dent.* 31: 27–31, 1971.

831. Williams, A. F., Wechsler, H., and Avery, M. H.: "Motivation of dentists to expand their practice." *Med. Care* 8: 408–413, 1970.

832. Christopher, A.: "The role of computers in dentistry." *J. Am. Dent. Assoc.* 74: 720–724, 1967.

833. Pelton, W. J., Dilworth, J. B., Overstreet, C. A., *et al.*: "Comparison of computer-generated data with actual use of therapists." *J. Dent. Educ.* 37: 21–25, Feb. 1973.

PHARMACY-RELATED HEALTH
SERVICES RESEARCH

834. Furstenberg, F. F., Taback, M., Goldberg, H., *et al.*: "Prescribing an index to quality of medical care: A study of the Baltimore City Medical Care Program." *Am. J. Public Health* 43: 1299–1309, 1953.

835. Teplitsky, B.: "A survey of hospital drug detailing." *Am. Prof. Pharmacist* 21: 816–824, 1955.

836. Coleman, J. S., Katz, E., and Menzel, H.: "Diffusion of an innovation among physicians." *Sociometry* 20: 253–270, 1957.

837. Winick, C.: "The diffusion of an innovation among physicians in a large city." *Sociometry* 24: 384–396, 1961.

838. Menzel, H. and Katz, E.: Comment on Charles Winick. "The diffusion of an innovation among physicians in a large city." *Sociometry* 26: 125–127, 1963.

839. Bauer, R. A. and Wartzel, L. H.: "Doctor's choice: The physician and his sources of information about drugs." *J. Marketing Res.* 3: 40–47, 1966.

840. Ferber, R. and Wales, H. G.: *The Effectiveness of Pharmaceutical Promotion.* Urbana: Univ. of Illinois, Bu. of Economic Business Research, 1958.

841. Burkholder, D. F.: "The role of the pharmaceutical detailman in a large teaching hospital." *Am. J. Hosp. Pharm.* 20: 274–285, 1963.

842. Wilson, C. W. M., Banks, J. A., Mapes, R. E. A., *et al.*: "The assessment of prescribing: A study in operational research" in *Problems and Progress in Medical Care: Essays on Current Research.* Edited by G. McLachlan. Published for the Nuffield Provincial Hospitals Trust. London: Oxford Univ. Press, 1964, pp. 173–201.

843. Wilson, C. W. M., Banks, J. A., Mapes, R. E. A., *et al.*: "Influence of different sources of therapeutic information on prescribing by general practitioners." *Br. Med. J.* 2: 599–604, 1963.

844. Martin, J. P.: *Social Aspects of Prescribing.* London: Heinemann Ltd., 1957.

845. Wilson, C. W. M., Banks, J. A., Mapes, R. E. A., *et al.*: "Patterns

of prescribing in general practice." *Br. Med. J.* 2: 604–607, 1963.

846. Lee, J. A. H.: "Prescribing and other aspects of general practice in three towns." *Proc. R. Soc. Med.* 57: 1041–1047, 1964.

847. Lee, J. A. H., Draper, P. A., and Weatherall, M.: "Primary medical care: Prescribing in three English towns." *Milbank Mem. Fund Q.* 43: No. 2, Part 2, 285–301, 1965.

848. *Report of the Committee on Enquiry into the Relationship of the Pharmaceutical Industry with the National Health Service. 1965–1967.* London: Her Majesty's Stationery Office, 1967.

849. Muller, C.: "The study of prescribing as a technic of examining a medical care system." *Am. J. Public Health* 57: 2117–2126, 1967.

850. Cluff, L. E.: "The prescribing habits of physicians." *Hospital Practice* 2: 100–104, Sept. 1967.

851. Stolley, P. D. and Lasagna, L.: "Prescribing patterns of physicians." *J. Chronic Dis.* 22: 395–405, 1969.

852. Stolley, P. D., Becker, M. H., Lasagna, L., *et al.*: "The relationship between physician characteristics and prescribing appropriateness." *Med. Care* 10: 17–28, 1972.

853. Maronde, R. F., Burks, D., Lee, P. V., *et al.*: "Physician prescribing practices: A computer based study." *Am. J. Hosp. Pharm.* 26: 566–573, 1969.

854. Maronde, R. F., Lee, P. V., McCarron, M., *et al.*: "A study of prescribing patterns." *Med. Care* 9: 385–395, 1971.

855. Kunin, C. M. and Dierks, J. W.: "A physician-pharmacist voluntary program to improve prescription practices." *N. Engl. J. Med.* 280: 1442–1446, 1969.

856. Safren, M. A. and Chapanis, A.: "A critical incident study of hospital medication errors." Part I—*Hospitals* 34: 32–34, 57, 62, 64, and 66, May 1, 1960, and Part II—*Hospitals* 34: 53, 65, 66, and 68, May 16, 1960.

857. Muller, C. and Westheimer, R.: "Formularies and drug standards in metropolitan hospitals." *Hospitals* 40: 97–102, Jan. 16, 1966.

858. Muller, C.: "Institutional drug purchasing factors influencing drug choices by pharmacists and physicians." *Hospitals* 39: 94, 96, 98, and 100, June 16, 1965.

859. Lamy, P. P. and Flack, H. L.: "The hospital formulary system-1965." *Am. J. Hosp. Pharm.* 23: 662–672, 1966.

860. Simon, J. R., LeMay, R. P., and Tester, W. W.: "Attitudes of nurses, physicians, and pharmacists toward a unit dose drug distribution system." *Am. J. Hosp. Pharm.* 25: 239–247, 1968.

861. Durant, W. J. and Zilz, D. A.: "Wisconsin information service and medication distribution." *Am. J. Hosp. Pharm.* 24: 625–631, 1967.

862. Slater, W. E. and Hripko, J. R.: "The unit-dose system in a private hospital. Part I: Implementation." *Am. J. Hosp. Pharm.* 25: 408–417, 1968.

863. Slater, W. E. and Hripko, J. R.: "The unit-dose system in a private hospital. Part I: Implementation." *Am. J. Hosp.* 641–648, 1968.

864. Barker, K. N. and Heller, W. M.: "The development of a centralized unit-dose dispensing system. Part I. Description of the UAMC experimental system." *Am. J. Hosp. Pharm.* 20: 568–579, 1963.

865. Black, H. J. and Tester, W. W.: "Pharmacy operations utilizing the unit dose concept." *Am. J. Hosp. Pharm.* 21: 345–350, 1964.

866. Greth, P. A., Tester, W. W., and Black, H. J.: "Decentralized pharmacy operations utilizing the unit dose concept. II. Drug information services and utilization in a decentralized pharmacy substation." *Am. J. Hosp. Pharm.* 22: 558–563, 1965.

867. Burkholder, D.: "Some experiences in the establishment and operation of a drug information center." *Am. J. Hosp. Pharm.* 20: 506–513, 1963.

868. Benson, S. B. and Kabat, H. F.: "Drug information needs in the hospital environment." *Am. J. Hosp. Pharm.* 24: 263–267, 1967.

869. Bell, J. E., Grimes, B. J., Bouchard, V. E., *et al.*: "New approach to delivering drug information to the physician consultation program." *Am. J. Hosp. Pharm.* 27: 29–37, 1970.

870. Owyang, E., Miller, R. A., and Brodie, D. C.: "The pharmacist's new role in institutional patient care." *Am. J. Hosp. Pharm.* 25: 624–630, 1968.

871. "Report of Task Force on the Pharmacist's Clinical Role." *J. Am. Pharm. Assoc.* NS11: 482–485, 1971.

872. White, A. M.: "Clinical pharmacy plan for a community health center." *J. Am. Pharm. Assoc.* NS12: 207–209, 1972.

873. Drew, F. and Shapiro, A.: "Sociological determinants of drug utilization in a university hospital." *J. Chronic Dis.* 17: 983–990, 1964.

874. Greenlick, M. R. and Darsky, B. J.: "Prescription utilization by the aged." *J. Gerontology* 19: 149–156, 1964.

875. Jeffreys, M., Brotherston, J. H. F., and Cartwright, A.: "Consumption of medicines on a working-class housing estate." *Br. J. Prev. Social. Med.* 14: 64–76, 1960.

876. Brewster, A. W., Allen, S. I., and Holen, A.: "Patterns of drug use by type in a prepaid medical plan." *Public Health Reports* 79: 403–409, 1964.

877. Greenlick, M. and Saward, E.: "Impact of a reduced-charge drug benefit in a prepaid group practice plan." *Public Health Reports* 81: 938–940, 1966.

878. Slavin, M.: "Automation and the hospital pharmacist." *Am. J. Hosp. Pharm.* 19: 274–280, 1962.

879. McEvilla, J. D.: "A computerized prescription recording system." *J. Am. Pharm. Assoc.* 7: 636–638, 1967.

880. Allen, S. I., Hurd, P. S., and Dodds, A. W.: "A method of pharmacy data automation." *Am. J. Hosp. Pharm.* 21: 314–318, 1964.

881. Flack, H. L., Downs, G. E., and Lanning, L. E.: "Electronic data processing and the hospital formulary." *Am. J. Hosp. Pharm.* 24: 5–17, 1967.

882. Seibert, S., Brunjes, S., Soutter, J. C., *et al.*: "Utilization of computer equipment and techniques in prescription processing at Los Angeles County General Hospital." *Drug Intelligence* 1: 342–350, 1967.

883. Slone, D., Gaetano, L. F., Lipworth, L., *et al.*: "Computer analysis of epidemiologic data on effect of drugs on hospital patients." *Public Health Reports* 84: 39–52, 1969.

884. Preston, J. and Boisseree, V. R.: *California Medicaid (Medi-Cal). A Management and Utilization Study.* State of California Human Relations Agency, Dept. of Health Care Services, December 1970.

885. Bartel, G. J. and Fahey, J. J.: "Nursing station is home base for phone-printer system." *Mod. Hosp.* 113: 85–91 and 154, Nov. 1969.

886. Knapp, D. A., Wolf, H. H., and Rudy, T. A.: "The pharmacist as a drug advisor." *J. Am. Pharm. Assoc.* NS9: 502–505, 1969.

887. Galloway, S. P. and Eby, C. E.: "Poverty area residents look at pharmacy services." *Am. J. Public Health* 61: 2211–2222, 1971.

888. Nelson, A. A., Jr. and Watkins, C. E.: "Motivation: Why people select pharmacy as a career." *Pharmacy Times,* 37: 27–31, Nov. 1971.

889. DHEW Task Force on Prescription Drugs: *Final Report.* U.S. Dept. of Health, Education, and Welfare, Washington, Feb. 1969.

890. DHEW Task Force on Prescription Drugs: *The Drug Prescribers.* U.S. Dept. of Health, Education, and Welfare, Washington, Dec. 1968.

891. DHEW Task Force on Prescription Drugs: *The Drug Users.* U.S. Dept. of Health, Education, and Welfare, Washington, Dec. 1968.

892. DHEW Task Force on Prescription Drugs: *The Drug Makers and the Drug Distributors.* U.S. Dept. of Health, Education, and Welfare, Washington, Dec. 1968.

893. DHEW Task Force on Prescription Drugs: *Approaches to Drug Insurance Design.* U. S. Dept. of Health, Education, and Welfare, Washington, Feb. 1969.

HEALTH CARE TECHNOLOGY

894. Bush, V.: *Science the Endless Frontier. A Report to the President on a Program for Postwar Scientific Research.* Washington: National Science Foundation, 1945.

895. Bush, V.: "Science in medicine and related fields." *Med. Ann. Dist. of Col.* 22:, 1–6 and 58, 1953.

896. Lipkin, M. and Hardy, J. D.: "Mechanical correlation in differential diagnosis of hematological diseases." *J.A.M.A.* 166: 113–125, 1958.

897. Ledley, R. S. and Lusted, L. B.: "Reasoning foundations of medical diagnosis." *Science* 130: 9–21, 1959.

898. Lipkin, M., Engle, R. L., Davis, B. J., *et al.*: "Digital computer as aid to differential diagnosis—use in hematologic diseases." *Arch. Intern. Med.* 108: 56–72, 1961.

899. Caceres, C. A.: "Integration of data in diagnosis." *Circulation Research* 11: 563–568, 1962.

900. Caceres, C. A., Steinberg, C. A., Abraham, S., *et al.*: "Computer extraction of electrocardiographic parameters." *Circulation* 25: 356–362, 1962.

901. Caceres, C. A. and Abraham, S.: "Computer use in health and medical research—role for computers in heart disease control." *Am. J. Public Health* 53: 582–593, 1963.

902. Caceres, C. A.: "Electrocardiographic analysis by a computer system." *Arch. Intern. Med.* 111: 196–202, 1963.

903. Caceres, C. A., Rikli, A. E., *et al.*: *Diagnostic Computers.* Springfield, Ill.: Charles C. Thomas, 1969.

904. Horvath, W. J.: "The effect of physician bias in medical diagnosis." *Behavioral Science* 9: 334–340, 1964.

905. Cooper, J. K., McGough, T., Ostrow, B., *et al.*: "Role of a digital computer in a diagnostic center." *J.A.M.A.* 193: 911–915, 1965.

906. Dickson, J. F., III and Stark, L.: "Remote real-time computer system for medical research and diagnosis." *J.A.M.A.* 196: 967–972, 1966.

907. Lincoln, T. L. and Parker, R. D.: "Medical diagnosis using Bayes Theorem." *Health Serv. Res.* 2: 34–45, 1967.

908. Gorry, G. A. and Barnett, G. O.: "Sequential diagnosis by computer." *J.A.M.A.* 205: 849–854, 1968.

909. Gorry, G. A. and Barnett, G. O.: "Experience with a model of sequential diagnosis." *Computers and Biomed. Res.* 1: 490–507, 1968.

910. Lusted, L. B.: *Introduction to Medical Decision Making.* Springfield, Ill.: Charles C. Thomas, 1968.

911. Gleser, M. A. and Collen, M. F.: "Towards automated medical decisions." *Computers and Biomed. Res.* 5: 180–189, 1972.

912. Bishop, C. R. and Warner, H. R.: "A mathematical approach to medical diagnosis." *Computers and Biomed. Res.* 2: 486–493, 1969.

913. Warner, H. R., Rutherford, B. D., and Houtchens, B.: "A sequential Bayesean approach to history taking and diagnosis." *Computers and Biomed. Res.* 5: 256-262, 1972.

914. Warner, H. R., Olmsted, C. M., and Rutherford, B. D.: "HELP: A program for medical decision making." *Computers and Biomed. Res.* 5: 65-74, 1972.

915. Barnett, G. O.: "Computers in patient care." *N. Engl. J. Med.* 279: 1321-1327, 1968.

916. Bleich, H. L.: "The computer as a consultant." *N. Engl. J. Med.* 284: 141-146, 1971.

917. Collen, M. F., Ruben, L., Neyman, J., *et al.*: "Automated multiphasic screening and diagnosis." *Am. J. Public Health* 54: 741-750, 1964.

918. Collen, M. F., Ruben, L. and Davis, L.: "Computers in multiphasic screening" in *Computers in Biomedical Research.* Vol. I. Edited by R. W. Stacy and B. D. Waxman. New York: Academic Press, 1965, pp. 339-352.

919. Collen, M. F., Feldman, R., Siegelaub, A. B., *et al.*: "Dollar cost per positive test for automated multiphasic screening." *N. Engl. J. Med.* 283: 459-463, 1970.

920. Brodman, K. and van Woerkom, A. J.: "Computer-aided diagnostic screening for 100 common diseases." *J.A.M.A.* 197: 901-905, 1966.

921. Hochberg, H. M., Calatayud, J. B., Weihrer, A. L., *et al.*: "Automatic electrocardiogram analysis in rapid mass screening." *Arch. Environ. Health* 15: 390-398, 1967.

922. Silver, H. M., Schonfeld, E. M., Abraham, S., *et al.*: "Survey for chronic obstructive lung disease in a clinic population." *Med. Ann. Dist. of Col.* 34: 213-216, 1965.

923. *Screening in Medical Care: Reviewing the Evidence.* Published for the Nuffield Provincial Hospitals Trust. London: Oxford Univ. Press, 1968.

924. AMHTS Advisory Committee to the National Center for Health Services Research and Development: *Provisional Guidelines for Automated Multiphasic Health Testing and Services* (in 3 vols.).

     Vol. 1. *Planning and Principles*—Report No. PB195654, U.S. DHEW/HSMHA/NCHSRD, 1970.

Vol. 2. *Operational Principles*—Report No. PB196000, U.S. DHEW/HSMHA/NCHSRD, 1970.

Vol. 3. *Proceedings of the Invitational Conference on AMHTS,* DHEW Pub. No. (HSM) 72-3011, 1971.

925. Spencer, W. A. and Vallbona, C.: "Digitation of clinical and research data in serial evaluation of disease processes." *IRE Transactions on Medical Electronics* 7: 296–308, 1960.

926. Spencer, W. A. and Vallbona, C.: "Application of computers in clinical practice." *J.A.M.A.* 191: 917–921, 1965.

927. Vallbona, C.: "Preparing medical record data for computer processing." *Hospitals* 41: 113–118, May 1, 1967.

928. Beggs, S., Vallbona, C., Spencer, W. A., *et al.*: "Evaluation of a system for on-line computer scheduling of patient care activities." *Computers and Biomed. Res.* 4: 634–654, 1971.

929. Barnett, G. O. and Hofmann, P. B.: "Computer technology and patient care: Experience of a hospital research effort." *Inquiry* 5: 51–57, September 1968.

930. Greenes, R. A., Pappalardo, A. N., Marble, C. W., *et al.*: "Design and implementation of a clinical data management system." *Computers and Biomed. Res.* 2: 469–485, 1969.

931. Greenes, R. A., Barnett, G. O., Klein, S. W., *et al.*: "Recording, retrieval, and review of medical data by physician: Computer interaction." *N. Engl. J. Med.* 282: 307–315, 1970.

932. Betaque, N. E. and Gorry, G. A.: "Automating judgmental decision making for a serious medical problem." *Manage. Sci.* 17: B421–B434, 1971.

933. Weil, M. H., Shubin, H., and Rand, W.: "Experience with a digital computer for study and improved management of the critically ill." *J.A.M.A.* 198: 1011–1016, 1966.

934. Warner, H. R.: "Computer-based patient monitoring" in *Computers in Biomedical Research.* Vol. III. Edited by R. W. Stacy and B. D. Waxman. New York: Academic Press, 1969, pp. 239–251.

935. Lipmann, E. O. and Preece, J. F.: "A pilot on-line data system for general practitioners." *Computers and Biomed. Res.* 4: 390–406, 1971.

936. Lamson, B. G.: "Computer assisted data processing in laboratory medicine" in *Computers in Biomedical Research.* Vol. I.

Edited by R.W. Stacy and B. D. Waxman. New York: Academic Press, 1965, pp. 353–376.

937. Hicks, G. P., Evenson, M. A., Geishen, M. M., *et al.*: "On-line data acquisition in the clinical laboratory" in *Computers in Biomedical Research.* Vol. III. Edited by R. W. Stacy and B. D. Waxman. New York: Academic Press, 1969, pp. 15–53.

938. Hicks, G. P., Geishen, M. M., Slack, W. V., *et al.*: "Routine use of a small digital computer in the clinical laboratory." *J.A.M.A.* 196: 973–978, 1966.

939. Seligson, D.: "Clinical laboratory automation." *J. Chronic Dis.* 19: 509–517, 1966.

940. Westlake, G., McKay, D. K., Surh, P., *et al.*: "Automatic discrete sample processing." *Clin. Chem.* 15: 600–610, 1969.

941. Seligson, D.: "Observations regarding laboratory instrumentation and screening analysis." in *Multiple Laboratory Screening.* Edited by E. S. Benson and P. E. Strandjord. New York: Academic Press, 1969, pp. 87–113.

942. Seligson, D.: "Automated collection and processing of clinical laboratory data" in *Automation and Data Processing in the Clinical Laboratory.* Edited by G. M. Brittin and M. Werner. Springfield, Ill.: Charles C. Thomas, 1970, pp. 11–19.

943. Seligson, D.: "Effect of computer on precision and accuracy of laboratory data" in *Automation and Management in a Clinical Laboratory.* Edited by G. E. Westlake and J. Bennington. Baltimore: University Park Press, 1972, pp. 235–258.

944. Seligson, D. and McKay, D.: "An approach to automated data collection and processing (1130 System)" in *Clinically Oriented Documentation of Laboratory Data.* Edited by E. R. Gabrieli. New York: Academic Press, 1972, pp. 241–255.

945. Rappoport, A. E., Gennaro, W. D., and Constandse, W. J.: "Cybernetics enters the hospital laboratory." *Mod. Hosp.* 108: 107–110, Apr. 1967.

946. Rappoport, A. E., Gennaro, W. D., and Constandse, W. J.: "Computer-laboratory link is base of hospital information system." *Mod. Hosp.* 110: 94 and 101–102, Apr. 1968.

947. Rappoport, A. E.: "Punch card technic saves technologist time." *Mod. Hosp.* 111: 86–87 and 126, Dec. 1968.

948. Rappoport, A. E., Gennaro, W. D. and Constandse, W. J.: *A Clinical Laboratory Information System Achieved Through Comput-*

er-Coupled Automation. in Proceedings of 6th National ISA Biomedical Sciences Instrumentation Symposium, May 21–23, 1968, Pittsburgh, Penn. Biomedical Sciences Instrumentation, vol. 5. Plenum Press, 1969, p. 47.

949. Rappoport, A. E. and Rappoport, E. N.: "Laboratory automation." *Hospitals* 44: 116, 117, 120, and 121, August 16, 1970.

950. Lindberg, D. A. B.: *The Computer and Medical Care.* Springfield, Ill.: Charles C. Thomas, 1968.

951. *Automation and Data Processing in Pathology.* Edited by T. P. Whitehead. *J. Clin. Path. 22;* Supplement (Coll. Path.) 3, 1969.

952. Acheson, E. D.: *Medical Record Linkage.* Published for the Nuffield Provincial Hospitals Trust. London: Oxford Univ. Press, 1967.

953. Levy, R. P., Cammarn, M. R., Smith, M. J., *et al.:* "Computer handling of ambulatory clinic records." *J.A.M.A.* 190: 1033–1037, 1964.

954. Slee, V. N.: "Information systems and measurement tools." *J.A.M.A.* 196: 1063–1065, 1966.

955. Korein, J., *et al.:* "Computer processing of medical data by variable-field-length format."
    I. (With Tick, L. J., Woodbury, M. A., *et al.*) *J.A.M.A.* 186: 132–138, 1963.
    II. (With Goodgold, A. L. and Randt, C. T.)—"Progress and application to narrative documents." *J.A.M.A.* 196: 950–956, 1966.
    III. (With Bender, A. L., Rothenberg, D. *et al.,*—"Statistical analysis of narrative content." *J.A.M.A.* 196: 957–963, 1966.

956. Slack, W. V., Peckham, B. M., Van Cura, L. J., *et al.:* "A computer-based physical examination system." *J.A.M.A.* 200: 224–228, 1967.

957. Davis, L. S., Collen, M. F., Ruben, L., *et al.:* "Computer-stored medical record." *Computers and Biomed. Res.* 1: 452–468, 1968.

958. Davis, L. S.: "Prototype for future computer medical records." *Computers and Biomed. Res.* 3: 539–554, 1970.

959. Weed, L. L.: "Medical records that guide and teach." *N. Engl. J. Med.* 278: 593–600, 1968.

960. Weed, L. L.: *Medical Records, Medical Education and Patient Care: The Problem-Oriented Record as a Basic Tool.* Chicago: Press of

Case Western Reserve Univ., Distrib. by Year Book Medical Publishers, Inc., 1969.

961. Kiely, J. M., Juergens, J. L., Heisey, B. L., *et al.*: "A computer-based medical record." *J.A.M.A.* 205: 571–576, 1968.

962. Robinson, R. E., III: "Acquisition and analysis of narrative medical record data." *Computers and Biomed. Res.* 3: 495–509, 1970.

963. Warner, H. R. and Morgan, J. D.: "High density medical data management by computer." *Computers and Biomed. Res.* 3: 464–476, 1970.

964. Slack, W. V., Hicks, G. P., Reed, C. E., *et al.*: "A computer-based medical history system." *N. Engl. J. Med.* 274: 194–198, 1966.

965. Slack, W. V. and Van Cura, L. J.: "Patient reaction to computer based medical interviewing." *Computers and Biomed. Res.* 1: 527–531, 1968.

966. Slack, W. V.: "Computer-based interviewing system dealing with nonverbal behavior as well as keyboard responses." *Science* 171: 84–87, 1971.

967. Slack, W. V. and Slack, C. W.: "Patient-computer dialogue." *N. Engl. J. Med.* 286: 1304–1309, 1972.

968. Collen, M. F., Cutler, J. L., Siegelaub, A. B., *et al.*: "Reliability of a self-administered medical questionnaire." *Arch. Intern. Med.* 123: 664–681, 1969.

969. Grossman, J. H., Barnett, G. O., McGuire, M. T., *et al.*: "Evaluation of computer acquired patient histories." *J.A.M.A.* 215: 1286–1291, 1971.

970. Swedlow, D. B., Barnett, G. O., Grossman, J. H., *et al.*: "A simple programming system (Driver) for the creation and execution of an automated medical history." *Computers and Biomed. Res.* 51: 90–98, 1972.

971. Mayne, J. G., Weksel, W., and Sholtz, P. N.: "Toward automating the medical history." *Mayo Clinic Proceedings* 43: 1–25, 1968.

972. Kanner, I. F.: "Programmed medical history-taking, with or without computer." *J.A.M.A.* 207: 317–321, 1969.

973. Coombs, G. J., Murray, W. R., and Krahn, D. W.: "Automated

medical histories: Factors determining patient performance." *Computers and Biomed. Res.* 3: 178-181, 1970.

974. Gottlieb, G. L., Beers, R. F., Bernecker, C., *et al.*: "An approach to automation of medical interviews." *Computers and Biomed. Res.* 5: 99-107, 1972.

975. De Land, E. C. and Waxman, B. D.: *Hospital Information Systems.* A Rand Corporation Publication. No. P-4337, 1970.

976. Cronkhite, L. W.: "Patient location control as a first step toward a total information system." *Hospitals* 41: 107-112, May 1, 1967.

977. Cronkhite, L. W.: "Computer brings order to clinic scheduling." *Hospitals* 43: 55-57, April 16, 1969.

978. Leighton, E. and Headly, P.: "Computer analysis of length of stay." *Hosp. Prog.* 49: 67-70, April 1968.

979. Collen, M. F.: "General requirements for a medical information system (MIS)." *Computers and Biomed. Res.* 3: 393-406, 1970.

980. Terdiman, J. F.: "Mass random storage devices and their application to a medical information system (MIS)." *Computers and Biomed. Res.* 3: 528-538, 1970.

981. Van Brunt, E. E.: "The Kaiser-Permanente medical information system." *Computers and Biomed. Res.* 3: 477-487, 1970.

982. Caceres, C. A. and Barnes, D. R.: "Computerized care." *Hospitals* 43: 49-52, Dec. 1, 1969.

983. Lindberg, D. A. B.: "A statewide medical information system." *Computers and Biomed. Res.* 3: 453-463, 1970.

984. Schenthal, J. E., Sweeney, J. W., and Nettleton, W., Jr.: "Clinical application of electronic data processing apparatus."

    "I. New concepts in clinical use of the digital computer." *J.A.M.A.* 173: 6-11, 1960.
    "II. New methodology in clinical record storage." *J.A.M.A.* 178: 267-270, 1961.
    "III. System for processing of medical records." *J.A.M.A.* 186: 101-105, 1963.

985. Baruch, J. J.: "Hospital automation via computer time-sharing" in *Computers in Biomedical Research.* Vol. II. Edited by R. W.

Stacy and B. D. Waxman. New York: Academic Press, 1965, pp. 291–312.

986. Stacy, R. W. and Waxman, B. D. (Eds.): *Computers in Biomedical Research* (3 vols.). New York: Academic Press, Vol. I, 1965, Vol. II, 1965, and Vol. III, 1969.

987. Rikli, A. E., Allen, S. I., and Alexander, S. N.: "Study suggests value of shared computers." *Mod. Hosp.* 106: 100–108, May 1966.

988. O'Toole, R., Cammarn, M. R., Levy, R. P., *et al.*: "Computer handling of ambulatory clinic records: Sociological analysis of physicians' responses." *J.A.M.A.* 197: 705–709, 1966.

989. Cromwell, D. F., Brown, Q. R., and Kurzenake, R. A.: *Selected References: Automation of the Health Care Field.* DHEW/HSMHA/NCHSRD/Health Care Technology Program, Arlington, Va., 1968.

990. De Land, E. C., Stacy, R. W. and Waxman, B. D.:, "Computers and the delivery of medical care" in *Computers in Biomedical Research.* Vol. III. Edited by R. W. Stacy and B. D. Waxman. New York: Academic Press, 1969, pp. 1–14.

991. Dickson, James F., III, and Brown, J. H. U. (Eds.): *Future Goals of Engineering in Biology and Medicine.* (Esp. Section C—Health Care.) New York: Academic Press, 1969.

992. Barnett, G. O. and Greenes, R. A.: "High level programming language." *Computers and Biomed. Res.* 3: 488–494, 1970.

993. Caceres, C. A.: "Large versus small, single versus multiple computers." *Computers and Biomed. Res.* 3: 445–452, 1970.

994. Richart, R. H.: "Evaluation of a medical data system." *Computers and Biomed. Res.* 3: 415–425, 1970.

995. Slack, W. V., Van Cura, L. J., and Greist, J. H.: "Computers and doctors: Use and consequences." *Computers and Biomed. Res.* 3: 521–527, 1970.

996. Yarnall, S., Wakefield, J. S., and McGovern, R. E.: *Acquisition of the Patient Database: A Review of Design Approaches, Performance and Cost of Fifty-five Different Systems.* Seattle: Medical Computer Services Association, (Processed) 1971.

997. Karpinski, R. H. S. and Bleich, H. L.: "MISAR: A miniature information storage and retrieval system." *Computers and Biomed. Res.* 4: 655–660, 1971.

RESEARCH METHODS

998. Stewart, G. T. (Ed.): *Trends in Epidemiology, application to Health Service Research and Training.* Springfield, Ill.: Charles C. Thomas. 1972.

999. Campbell, D. T.: "Factors relevant to the validity of experiments in social settings." *Psych. Bull.* 54: 297–312, 1957.

1000. Caro, F. G. (Ed.): *Readings in Evaluation Research.* New York: The Russell Sage Foundation, 1971.

1001. Schulberg, H. C., Sheldon, A., and Baker, F.: *Program Evaluation in the Health Fields.* New York: Behavioral Publications, Inc., 1969.

1002. Hyman, H. H., Cobb, W. J., Feldman, J J , *et al.*: *Interviewing in Social Research.* Chicago: Univ. of Chicago Press, 1954.

1003. Hyman, H. H.: *Survey Design and Analysis.* Glencoe, Ill.: Free Press of Glencoe, 1955.

1004. Hyman, H. H. and Wright, C. R.: "Evaluating social action programs" in *The Uses of Sociology.* Edited by P. F. Lazarsfeld, W. H. Sewell, and H. L. Wilensky. New York: Basic Books, Inc., 1967, pp. 741–782.

1005. Freeman, H. E. and Sherwood, C. C.: "Research in large-scale intervention programs." *J. Social Issues* 21: 11–28, 1965. Reprinted in *Readings in Evaluation Research.* Edited by F. G. Caro. New York: Russell Sage Foundation, 1971, pp. 262–276.

1006. Pennell, E. H.: "The family survey as a method of studying rural health problems (Brunswick-Greensville Study No. 3)." *Public Health Reports* 50: 210–223, 1935, Reprint No. 1671.

1007. Pennell, E. H. and O'Hara, H.: "The validity of health service data gathered by the family survey method." *Public Health Reports* 53: 439–446, 1938, Reprint No. 1943.

1008. Hoffer, C. R. and Schuler, E. A.: "Measurement of health need and health care." *Am. Sociol. Rev.* 12: 719–724, 1948.

1009. Sanders, B. S.: "How good are hospital data from a household survey?" *Am. J. Public Health* 49: 1596–1606, 1959.

1010. Elinson, J. and Trussell, R. E.: "Some factors relating to degree of correspondence for diagnostic information as obtained by household interviews and clinical examinations." *Am. J. Public Health* 47: 311–321, 1957.

1011. Trussell, R. E. and Elinson, J.: *Chronic Illness in a Rural Area. The Hunterdon Study.* (Vol. 3 of the Report of the Commission on Chronic Illness.) Cambridge: Published for The Commonwealth Fund by Harvard Univ. Press, 1959.

1012. Feldman, J. J.: "The household interview survey as a technique for the collection of morbidity data." *J. Chronic Dis.* 11: 535–557, 1960.

1013. Hutchinson, G. B., Shapiro, S. and Densen, P. M: "Evaluation of a mailed questionnaire." *Am. J. Public Health* 52: 1894–1917, 1962.

1014. Solon, J. A., Sheps, C. G., Lee, S. S., *et al.*: "Patterns of medical care: Validity of interview information on use of hospital clinics." *J. Health Soc. Behav.* 3: 21–29, 1962.

1015. Haggerty, R. J.: "Family diagnosis: Research methods and their reliability for studies of the medical-social unit, the family." *Am. J. Public Health* 55: 1521–1533, 1965.

1016. Bergman, A. B. and Werner, R. J.: "Failure of children to receive penicillin by mouth." *N. Engl. J. Med.* 268: 1334–1338, 1963.

1017. Colombotos, J.: "Physicians and Medicare: A before-after study of the effects of legislation on attitudes." *Am. Sociol. Rev.* 34: 318–334, 1969.

1018. Perrow, C.: "Research in a home care program." *Am. J. Public Health* 49: 33–44, 1959.

1019. Shapiro, S., Strax, P. and Venet, L.: "Evaluation of periodic breast cancer screening with mammography." *J.A.M.A.* 195: 731–738, 1966.

1020. Shapiro, S., Strax, P., and Venet, L.: "Periodic breast cancer screening in reducing mortality from breast cancer." *J.A.M.A.* 215: 1777–1785, 1971.

1021. Kosa, J., Alpert, J. J., and Haggerty, R. J.: "On the reliability of family health information." *Social Sci. and Med.* 1: 165–181, 1967.

1022. Alpert, J. J., Kosa, J., Haggerty, R. J., *et al.*: "Attitudes and satisfactions of low-income families receiving comprehensive pediatric care." *Am. J. Public Health* 60: 499–506, 1970.

1023. Klarman, H. E.: "Economic aspects of projecting requirements for health manpower." *J. Human Resources* 4: 360–376, 1969.

1024. Yett, D. E.: "The chronic 'shortage' of nurses: A public policy dilemma" in *Empirical Studies in Health Economics*. Edited by H. E. Klarman. Baltimore: The Johns Hopkins Press, 1970, pp. 357–389.

1025. Slee, V.: "Uniform Methods of Measuring Utilization" in *National Conference on Utilization, March 2–3, 1962*. American Hospital Association, Report Series No. 2, Chicago, 1962, pp. 11–17.

1026. Hess, I., Riedel, D. C., and Fitzpatrick, T. B.: *Probability Sampling of Hospitals and Patients*. Ann Arbor: Univ. of Michigan, 1961.

1027. Fitzpatrick, T. B. and Riedel, D. C.: "Some general comments on methods of studying hospital use." *Inquiry* 1: 49–68, Jan. 1964.

1028. Anderson, O. W.: "Research in hospital use and expenditures." *J. Chronic Dis.* 17: 727–733, 1964.

1029. Mann, J.: "Technical and social difficulties in the conduct of evaluative research" in *Changing Human Behavior*. Edited by J. Mann. New York: Charles Scribner's Sons, 1965, pp. 177–189.

1030. Horvitz, D. G.: "Methodological considerations in evaluating the effectiveness of programs and benefits." *Inquiry* 2: 96–104, Sept. 1965.

1031. Packer, A. H.: "Applying cost-effectiveness concepts to the community health system." *Operations Res.* 16: 227–253, 1968.

1032. Packer, A. H. and Shellard, G. D.: "Measures of health-system effectiveness." *Operations Res.* 18: 1067–1070, 1970.

1033. Rossi, P. H.: "Evaluating social action programs." TRANSaction, Inc., New Brunswick, N. J., June 1967. Reprinted in *Readings in Evaluation Research*. Edited by F. G. Caro. New York: Russell Sage Foundation, 1971, pp. 276–281.

1034. Sanazaro, P. J.: "Seminar on research in patient care." *Med. Care* 4: 43–50, 1966.

1035. Report of the Fifty-sixth Ross Conference on Pediatric Research—*Assessing the Effectiveness of Child Health Services*. Columbus, Ohio: Ross Laboratories, 1967.

1036. Berkowitz, N. H., Malone, M. F., and Klein, M. W.: "Patient care as a criterion problem." *J. Health Soc. Behav.* 3: 171–176, 1962.

1037. Lave, J. R.: "A review of the methods used to study hospital costs." *Inquiry* 3: 57–81, May 1966.

1038. Lave, J. R. and Lave, L. B.: "Hospital cost functions." *Am. Economic Rev.* 60: 379–395, 1970.

1039. Rice, D. P.: "Measurement and application of illness costs." *Public Health Reports* 84: 95–101, 1969.

1040. Flagle, C. D., Huggins, W. H., and Roy, R. H. (Eds.): *Operations Research and Systems Engineering.* Baltimore: The Johns Hopkins Press, 1960.

1041. Flagle, C. D.: "Evaluation techniques for medical information systems." *Computers and Biomed. Res.* 3: 407–514, 1970.

1042. Bailey, N. T. J.: "Operational research" in *Medical Surveys and Clinical Trials, 2d ed.* Edited by L. J. Witts. London: Oxford Univ. Press, 1964, pp. 165–181.

1043. Horvath, W. J.: "Operations research in medical and hospital practice" in *Operations Research for Public Systems.* Edited by P.M. Morse assisted by L. W. Bacon. Cambridge: MIT Press, 1967, 127–157.

1044. van Woerkom, A. J. and Brodman, K.: "Statistics for a diagnostic model." *Biometrics* 17: 299–318, June 1961.

1045. Gorry, G. A.: "Modeling the diagnostic process." *J. Med. Educ.* 45: 293–302, 1970.

1046. Chiang, C. L.: *An Index to Health: Mathematical Models.* Series 2, No. 5, Vital and Health Statistics, U. S. Dept. of Health, Education, and Welfare, Public Health Service, 1965.

1047. Chiang, C. L.: *Introduction to Stochastic Processes in Biostatistics.* New York: John Wiley and Sons, Inc., 1968.

1048. Feldstein, M. S.: "An aggregate planning model of the health care sector." *Med. Care* 5: 369–381, 1967.

1049. Feldstein, M. S.: *Economic Analysis for Health Service Efficiency: Econometric Studies of the British National Health Service.* Amsterdam: North-Holland Publishing Co., 1967.

1050. Anderson, O. W. and Kravits, J.: *Health Services in the Chicago*

Area. A Framework for Use of Data. Univ. of Chicago, Center for Health Administration Studies, Research Series No. 26, Chicago, 1968.

1051. Acheson, E. D. (Ed.): *Record Linkage in Medicine.* Proceedings of the International Symposium, Oxford, July 1967. London: E. and S. Livingstone, Ltd., 1968.

THE EMERGING CONCEPT OF HEALTH SERVICES RESEARCH

1052. Peebles, A.: *A Survey of the Medical Facilities of Shelby County, Indiana: 1929* (CCMC Report No. 6). Washington: Committee on the Costs of Medical Care, 1930.

1053. Sinai, N. and Mills, A.: *A Survey of the Medical Facilities of Philadelphia, 1929* (CCMC Report No. 9). Chicago: Univ. of Chicago Press, 1931.

1054. Sinai, N., *et al.*: *A Survey of the Medical Facilities of San Joaquin County, California, 1929* (CCMC Report No. 12). Chicago: Univ. of Chicago Press, 1931.

1055. Peebles, A.: *A Survey of the Medical Facilities of the State of Vermont* (CCMC Report No. 13). Chicago: Univ. of Chicago Press, 1932.

1056. Guild, C. St. C. and Falk, I. S.: *Surveys of the Medical Facilities in Three Representative Southern Counties* (CCMC Report No. 23). Chicago: Univ. of Chicago Press, 1932.

1057. Falk, I. S., Klem, M. C., and Sinai, N.: *The Incidence of Illness and the Receipt and Costs of Medical Care Among Representative Families: Experience in Twelve Consecutive Months During 1928–1931* (CCMC Report No. 26). Chicago: Univ. of Chicago Press, 1933.

1058. Stern, B. J.: *American Medical Practice in the Perspectives of a Century.* New York: The Commonwealth Fund, 1945.

1059. Stern, B. J.: *Medicine in Industry.* New York: The Commonwealth Fund, 1946.

1060. Stern, B. J.: *Medical Services by Government.* New York: The Commonwealth Fund, 1946.

1061. Mott, F. D. and Roemer, M. I.: *Rural Health and Medical Care.* New York: McGraw-Hill Book Co., Inc., 1948.

1062. Sinai, N. and Anderson, O. W.: *EMIC (Emergency Maternity and Infant Care): A Study of Administrative Experience.* University of Michigan, School of Public Health, Bu. of Public Health Economics, Research Series No. 3, Ann Arbor, 1948.

1063. Weinerman, E. R.: *Social Medicine in Western Europe.* Berkeley: Univ. of California, School of Public Health, 1951.

1064. Klem, M. C., McKiever, M. F., and Lear, W. J.: *Industrial Health and Medical Programs.* Public Health Service Pub. No. 15, Federal Security Agency, Public Health Service, Washington: U. S. Gov't. Print. Off., 1950.

1065. Commission on Chronic Illness. *Chronic Illness in a Large City. The Baltimore Study,* (Vol. 4 of the Commission's Report). Cambridge: Published for The Commonwealth Fund by Harvard Univ. Press, 1957.

1066. Winter, K. E. and Metzner, C. A.: *Institutional Care for the Long-Term Patient: A Study of Hospitals and Nursing Facilities in Michigan.* University of Michigan, School of Public Health, Bu. of Public Health Economics Research Series No. 7, Ann Arbor, 1958.

1067. Sheps, C. G. and Taylor, E. E.: *Needed Research in Health and Medical Care.* Chapel Hill: The University of North Carolina Press, 1954.

1068. Harting, D., Sanders, B.S., Macgregor, G. *et al.*: *A Health Study in Kit Carson County, Colorado.* Public Health Service Pub. No. 844. USDHEW/PHS/Div. of Community Health Services. Washington: U. S. Gov't. Print. Off., 1962.

1069. Freeman, R., Sheps, C. G., Tibbitts, H. G., *et al.*: "Patient care research: Report of a symposium." *Am. J. Public Health* 53: 965–969, 1963, and *Med. Care* 1: 161–163, 1963.

1070. White, K. L. (Ed.): *Medical Care Research: Proceedings of the Symposium on Medical Care Research.* London: Pergamon Press, 1965.

1071. White, K. L.: "Problems and methods in research." *Milbank Mem. Fund Q.* 43: No. 2, Part 2, 261–265, 1965.

1072. White, K. L.: "Improved medical care statistics and the health services system." *Public Health Reports* 82: 847–854, 1967.

1073. White, K. L.: "Research in medical care and health services systems." *Med. Care* 6: 95–100, 1968.

1074. White, K. L., Williams, T. F., and Greenberg, B. G.: "The ecology of medical care." *N. Engl. J. Med.* 265: 885–892, 1961.

1075. Lerner, M.: *Hospital Use and Charges by Diagnostic Category. A Report on the Indiana Study of a Blue Cross Population in 1956.* Health Information Foundation, Research Series No. 13. New York: 1960.

1076. Lerner, M.: "Some aspects of the increase in inpatient hospital utilization and charges, 1956 to 1961, in the experience of the Indiana Blue Cross." *Blue Cross Reports* 4: 1–15, April–June 1966.

1077. Lerner, M. and Anderson, O. W.: *Health Progress in the United States, 1900–1960.* Chicago: Univ. of Chicago Press, 1963.

1078. Lerner, M. and Fitzgerald, S. W.: "A comparative study of three major forms of health care coverage: A review." *Inquiry* 2: 37–60, June 1965.

1079. Lindsey, A.: *Socialized Medicine in England and Wales: The National Health Service, 1948–1961.* Chapel Hill: Univ. of North Carolina Press, 1962.

1080. Silver, G. A.: *Family Medical Care: A Report on the Family Health Maintenance Demonstration.* Cambridge: Harvard Univ. Press, 1963.

1081. Horvath, W. J.: "British experience with operations research in the health services." *J. Chronic Dis.* 17: 779–788, 1964.

1082. Klem, M. C.: "Physician services received in an urban community in relation to health insurance coverage." *Am. J. Public Health* 55: 1699–1716, 1965.

1083. Gottlieb, S. R. and Spaulding, P. W.: "Controls within and upon the voluntary health system" in *Hospital and Medical Economics: A Study of Population, Services, Costs, Methods of Payment, and Controls.* Vol. 2. Edited by W. J. McNerney. Chicago: Hospital Research and Educational Trust, 1962, pp. 1205–1459.

1084. Charron, K. C.: *Health Services, Health Insurance, and Their Interrelationship: A Study of Selected Countries.* Ottawa: Department of National Health and Welfare, 1963.

1085. Wirick, G. C., Jr., and Barlow, R.: "The economic and social determinants of the demand for health services" in *The Eco-*

nomics of Health and Medical Care. Ann Arbor: Univ. of Michigan, 1964, pp. 95–125.

1086. Morris, R.: "Basic factors in planning for the coordination of health services." *Am. J. Public Health* 53: 248–258 and 462–472, 1963.

1087. Anderson, O. W. and Andersen, R. W.: "Patterns of use of health services" in *Handbook of Medical Sociology — 2d ed.* Edited by H. E. Freeman, S. Levine, and L. G. Reeder. Englewood Cliffs, N. J.: Prentice-Hall, Inc., 1972, pp. 386–406.

1088. Navarro, V.: "Planning personal health services. A Markovian model." *Med. Care* 7: 242–249, 1969.

1089. Navarro, V.: "Planning for the distribution of personal health services. A review of methods used." *Public Health Reports* 84: 573–581, 1969.

1090. Navarro, V.: "A systems approach to health planning." *Health Serv. Res.* 4: 96–111, 1969.

1091. Navarro, V.: "Methodology on regional planning for personal health services: A case study: Sweden." *Med. Care* 8: 386–394, 1970.

1092. Navarro, V.: "Systems analysis in the health field" in *Global Systems Dynamics, International Symposium, Charlottesville, 1969.* Edited by E. O. Attinger. Basel: Karger, 1970, pp. 287–297.

1093. Navarro, V. and Parker, R. D.: *A Mathematical Model for Health Planning: Prediction, Simulation, and Goal Seeking.* in Proceedings of 5th International Scientific Meeting of the International Epidemiological Association, 1970, pp. 163–178.

1094. Gue, R. L.: "Operations research in health and hospital administration." *Hosp. Admin.,* 10: 6–25, Fall 1965.

1095. Wirick, G. C.: "A multiple equation model of demand for health care." *Health Serv. Res.* 1: 301–346, 1966.

1096. Jelinek, R. C.: "A structural model for the patient care operation." *Health Serv. Res.* 2: 226–242, 1967.

1097. Feldstein, P. J. and Kelman, S.: "A framework for an econometric model of the medical care sector" in *Empirical Studies in Health Economics.* Edited by H. E. Klarman. Baltimore: The Johns Hopkins Press, 1970, pp. 171–190.

1098. Zemach, R.: "A model of health service utilization and resource allocation." *Operations Res.* 18: 1071–1086, 1970.

1099. Anderson, J. G.: "Causal model of a health services system." *Health Serv. Res.* 7: 23–42, 1972.

1100. Jaeger, B. J.: "Evaluating national hospital policy: A systems approach." *Health Serv. Res.* 7: 11–22, 1972.

1101. Sasuly, R. and Hopkins, C. E.: "A medical society-sponsored comprehensive medical care plan." *Med. Care* 5: 234–248, 1967.

1102. Bellin S. S., Geiger, H. J., and Gibson, C. D.: "Impact of ambulatory health care services on the demand for hospital beds." *N. Engl. J. Med.* 280: 808–812, 1969.

1103. Haggerty, R. J.: "The boundaries of health care." *The Pharos.* 35: 106–111, 1972.

1104. Hurtado, A. V., Greenlick, M. R., and Saward, E. W.: "The organization and utilization of home care and extended-care-facility services in a prepaid comprehensive group practice plan." *Med. Care* 7: 30–40, 1969.

1105. Hurtado, A. V., Greenlick, M. R., McCabe, M., *et al.*: "The utilization and cost of home care and extended care facility services in a comprehensive prepaid group practice program." *Med. Care* 10: 8–16, 1972.

1106. Curran, W. J., Stearns, B., and Kaplan, H.: "Privacy, confidentiality, and other legal considerations in the establishment of a centralized health data system." *N. Engl. J. Med.* 281: 241–248, 1969.

1107. Weinerman, E. R.: *Social Medicine in Eastern Europe.* Cambridge: Published for The Commonwealth Fund by Harvard Univ. Press, 1969.

1108. Weinerman, E. R.: "Research on comparative health service systems." *Med. Care* 9: 272–290, 1971.

1109. Roemer, M. I. and DuBois, D. M.: "Medical costs in relation to the organization of ambulatory care." *N. Engl. J. Med.* 280: 988–993, 1969.

1110. Pauly, M. V. and Drake, D. F.: "Effect of third-party methods of reimbursement on hospital performance" in *Empirical Stud-*

ies in Health Economics. Edited by H. E. Klarman. Baltimore: The Johns Hopkins Press, 1970, pp. 297–314.

1111. Stevens, R.: *American Medicine and the Public Interest.* New Haven: Yale Univ. Press, 1971.

1112. Gartside, F.: *Utilization and Costs of Services in the San Joaquin Prepayment Project.* Los Angeles: Univ. of California, 1971.

1113. Hardwick, C. P., Shuman, L., and Barnoon, S.: "Effect of participatory insurance on hospital utilization." *Health Serv. Res.* 7: 43–57, 1972.

1114. McDermott, W., Deuschle, K. W., and Barnett, C. R.: "Health care experiment at Many Farms." *Science* 175: 23–31, 1972.

1115. Kane, R. L. and Kane, R. A.: *Federal Health Care (With Reservations).* New York: Springer Publishing Co., 1972.

1116. Gibson, G.: "Explanatory models and strategies for social change in health care behavior." *Soc. Sci. and Med.* 6: 635–639, 1972.

References – Chapter II

1117. *The Milbank Memorial Fund. Current Program, Policy and Organization.* New York: The Milbank Memorial Fund, 1972.

1118. *The Commonwealth Fund. Historical Sketch, 1918-1962.* New York: The Commonwealth Fund, 1963.

1119. Dinwiddie, C.: *Child Health and the Community: An Interpretation of a Cooperative Effort in Public Health.* New York: The Commonwealth Fund, 1931.

1120. *A Chapter of Child Health: Report of the Commonwealth Fund Child Health Demonstration in Clarke County and Athens, Georgia.* New York: The Commonwealth Fund, 1928.

1121. Warner, E. F. and Smith, G.: *Children of the Covered Wagon: Report of the Commonwealth Fund Child Health Demonstration in Marion County, Oregon, 1925-1929.* New York: The Commonwealth Fund, 1930.

1122. Mustard, H. S.: *Cross-Sections of Rural Health Progress: Report of the Commonwealth Fund Child Health Demonstration in Rutherford County, Tennessee, 1924-1928.* New York: The Commonwealth Fund, 1930.

1123. *Five Years in Fargo, North Dakota: The Development of a Community Health Program.* New York: The Commonwealth Fund, 1928.

1124. Walker, W. F.: *Ten Years of Rural Health Work – Rutherford County, Tennessee, 1924-1933.* New York: The Commonwealth Fund, 1935.

1125. Southmayd, H. J. and Smith, G.: *Small Community Hospitals.* New York: The Commonwealth Fund, 1944.

1126. W. K. Kellogg Foundation: The. First Twenty-Five Years. Battle Creek, Michigan: The W. K. Kellogg Foundation, 1955.

1127. W. K. Kellogg Foundation 1971 Annual Report, Battle Creek, Michigan, 1972.

1128. W. K. Kellogg Foundation 1972 Annual Report, Battle Creek, Michigan, 1973.

1129. Shaplen, R.: Toward the Well-Being of Mankind—Fifty Years of the Rockefeller Foundation. Garden City, N. Y.: Doubleday and Co., Inc., 1964.

1130. President's Ten-Year Review and Annual Report 1971. The Rockefeller Foundation, New York, 1972.

1131. Lewis, M. O. and Bowers, P. (Eds.): The Foundation Directory. Edition 4. New York: Prepared by The Foundation Center, Distributed by the Columbia Univ. Press, 1971.

1132. Rorem, C. R.: Blue Cross Hospital Service Plans. Chicago: Hospital Service Plan Commission, American Hospital Association, 1944.

1133. American Medical Association. Report of the Commission on the Cost of Medical Care. Vol. I. General Report, Chicago, 1964. Vol. II. Professional Review Mechanisms, Chicago, 1963. Vol. III. Significant Medical Advances, Chicago, 1964. Vol. IV. Changing Patterns of Hospital Care, Chicago, 1964.

1134. Lembcke, P. A.: "Evolution of the medical audit." J.A.M.A. 199: 111–118, 1967.

1135. The American Academy of Pediatrics. Child Health Services and Pediatric Education. New York: The Commonwealth Fund, 1949.

1136. Hughes, E. C., Hughes, H. and Deutscher, I.: Twenty Thousand Nurses Tell Their Story. Philadelphia: J. B. Lippincott Co., 1958.

1137. Commission on the Survey of Dentistry in the United States. The Survey of Dentistry. Washington: American Council on Education, 1961.

1138. American Dental Association, Bureau of Economic Research and Statistics. "Survey of dental partnerships." J. Am. Dent. Assoc. 69: 529–538, 1964.

1139. American Dental Association, Council on Dental Health and

Council on Hospital Dental Service. "Survey of dental services." *J. Am. Dent. Assoc.* 71: 1510–1515, 1965.

1140. American Dental Association, Bureau of Economic Research and Statistics. "Utilization of the American Dental Association Dental Health Care Plan during 1965 and 1966." *J. Am. Dent. Assoc.* 75: 952–957, 1967.

1141. American Dental Association, Bureau of Economic Research and Statistics. "Use of the American Dental Association Dental Health Care Plan during 1966 and 1969." *J. Am. Dent. Assoc.* 81: 723–728, 1970.

1142. American Public Health Association. *A Guide to Medical Care Administration.*

Vol. I. Concepts and Principles. APHA, New York, 1965, Revised 1969. Myers, B.A.
Vol. II. Medical Care Appraisal-Quality and Utilization. APHA, New York, 1969. Donabedian, A.

1143. National Commission on Community Health Services. *Health is a Community Affair.* Cambridge: Harvard Univ. Press, 1966.

1144. Abdellah, F. G.: "State nursing surveys and community action." *Public Health Reports* 67: 554–560, 1952.

1145. USDHEW/PHS/HSMHA. *The Maternal and Child Health Service Reports on: Promoting the Health of Mothers and Children, 1970.* Rockville, Md., 1971.

1146. Merriam, I. C.: "Social Security Formulation and Health Research." *Internat. J. Health Services* 3: 59–68, 1973.

1147. The President's Commission on Heart Disease, Cancer, and Stroke. *A National Program to Conquer Heart Disease, Cancer, and Stroke, Vol. II.* Washington: U. S. Gov't. Print. Off., 1965, pp. 441–630.

1148. *Report of the National Advisory Commission on Health Manpower, Vol. I.* Washington: U. S. Gov't. Print. Off., 1967.

1149. U. S. Department of Health, Education, and Welfare. *Report of the Secretary's Advisory Committee on Hospital Effectiveness.* Washington: U. S. Gov't. Print. Off., 1968.

1150. National Advisory Commission on Health Facilities. *A Report to the President.* Washington: U. S. Gov't. Print. Off., Dec. 1968.

References — Chapter III

1151. "Proceedings of the House of Delegates, American Medical Association, April 26–30, 1920." *J.A.M.A.* 74: 1317–1328, 1920.

1152. Falk, I. S.: "The Committee on the Costs of Medical Care — Twenty-five years of progress." *Am. J. Public Health* 49: 979–982, 1958.

1153. Falk, I. S.: Personal Interview (April 24, 1972).

1154. Editorial — "The Committee on the Costs of Medical Care." *J.A.M.A.* 99: 1950–1954, 1932.

1155. Schottland, C. I.: *The Social Security Program in the United States.* New York: Appleton-Century Crofts, 1963.

1156. Hirshfield, D. S.: *The Lost Reform: The Campaign for Compulsory Health Insurance in the United States from 1932 to 1943.* Cambridge: Harvard Univ. Press, 1970.

1157. Pihlblad, C. T.: "National Health Survey: Preliminary reports." Washington: National Institute of Health and U. S. Public Health Service, 1937. *Am. J. Public Health* 28: 533–534, 1938.

1158. Atwater, R. M.: "National Health Conference — A Review." *Am. J. Public Health* 28: 1103–1113, 1938.

1159. Winslow, C-E. A.: "The public health aspects of medical care from the standpoint of public health." *Am. J. Public Health* 29: 16–24, 1939.

1160. *Proceedings of the National Health Conference, Washington, D. C., July 18, 19, 20, 1938.* Interdepartmental Committee to

Coordinate Health and Welfare Activities. Washington: U. S. Gov't. Print. Off., 1938.

1161. "Proceedings of the Special Session of the House of Delegates, American Medical Association, September 16-17, 1938." *J.A.M.A.* 111: 1191-1217, 1938.

References — Chapter V

1162. Purola, T., Kalimo, E., Sievers, K., *et al.*: *The Utilization of Medical Services and its Relationship to Morbidity, Health Resources, and Social Factors.* Helsinki: Research Institute for Social Security, 1968.

1163. Andersen, R., Smedby, B., and Anderson, O. W.: *Medical Care Use in Sweden and the United States: A Comparative Analysis of Systems and Behavior.* Univ. of Chicago, Center for Health Administration Studies, Research Series No. 27. Chicago, 1970.

1164. Patrick, D. L., Bush, J. W., and Chen, M. M.: "Toward an operational definition of health." *J. Health Soc. Behav.* 14: 6-23, 1973.

1165. de Bie, P.: "Problem-focused research" in *Main Trends of Research in the Social and Human Sciences.* Edited by R. Maheu. Paris: Mouton/UNESCO, 1970, pp. 578-644.

1166. Bice, T. W. and White, K. L.: "Cross-national comparative research on the utilization of medical services." *Med. Care* 9: 253-271, 1971.

1167. Olson, M., Jr.: "An analytic framework for social reporting and policy analysis." *The Annals* 388: 112-126, 1970.

1168. Ben-David, J.: "How to organize research in the social sciences." *Daedalus* 102: 39-51, 1973.

1169. Dubin, R.: *Theory Building.* New York: The Free Press, 1969.

1170. Eichhorn, R. L. and Wysong, J. A.: "Perspectives on policy research." *Health Serv. Res.* 7: 272-275, 1972.

References — Chapter VI

1171. *Proceedings of the White House Conference on Health, November 3 and 4, 1965, Washington, D. C.,* U. S. Department of Health, Education, and Welfare, Office of the Secretary. Washington: U. S. Gov't. Print. Off., 1967, p. 299.

1172. *President's Message on Health and Education,* H. Doc. No. 90–68, Feb. 28, 1967.

1173. *A Report to the President on Medical Care Prices by the Department of Health, Education, and Welfare,* Feb. 1967.

1174. Senate Report No. 90-724, Public Health Service Amendments, November 4, 1967 (Committee on Labor and Public Welfare).

1175. Sanazaro, P. J.: "A new Federal program: Health services research and development." *Mod. Med.,* July 26, 1971, pp. 19 ff.

1176. Sanazaro, P. J.: "Health services research and development." *Bull. N. Y. Acad. Med.* 48: 157–165, 1972.

1177. *America's Health. A Report to the Nation by the National Health Assembly. Official Report.* New York: Harper and Bros., 1949.

1178. *Building America's Health. A Report to the President by the President's Commission on the Health Needs of the Nation. Vols. I–V.* Washington: U. S. Gov't. Print. Off., 1952.

1179. *Towards a Comprehensive Health Policy for the 1970's. A White Paper.* Department of Health, Education, and Welfare. Washington: U. S. Gov't. Print. Off., May 1971.

1180. Lee, P. R. and Silver, G. A.: "Health planning — A view from the top with specific reference to the U.S.A." in *International Medical Care.* Edited by J. Fry and W. A. J. Farnsdale. Wallingford, Pa.: Washington Square East, 1972, pp. 284–315.

1181. Kissick, W. L.: "Health policy directions for the 1970's." *N. Engl. J. Med.* 282: 1343–1354, 1970.

1182. Mueller, M. S.: "Private health insurance in 1969: A review." *Social Security Bull.*, Feb. 1971, pp. 3–17.

1183. McKeown, T. A.: "A conceptual background for research and development in medicine." *J. Internat. Health Services* 3: 17–28, 1973.

1184. McEwan, E. D.: "A case for government-sponsored health care research and development in the formulation of health policy and an account of early experience of government-sponsored health care research in one jurisdiction." *J. Internat. Health Services* 3: 45–58, 1973.

1185. Kirk, R. F. H., Alter, J. D., Browne, H. E., *et al.*: "Family nurse practitioners in Eastern Kentucky." *Med. Care* 9: 160–168, 1971.

1186. Runyan, J. W., Jr., Phillips, W. E., Herring, O., *et al.*: "A program for the care of patients with chronic diseases." *J.A.M.A.* 211: 476–479, 1970.

1187. Jackson, E. B., Jr. and Seeno, E.: "The screening nurse." *Hospitals* 45: 66, 68, 71–73, June 1, 1971.

1188. "New Mexico hamlet avoids medical isolation with Family Nurse Practitioner." *J.A.M.A.* 207: 1808–1809, 1969.

1189. Sanazaro, P. J.: "Physician support personnel in the 1970's. The R&D approach to health manpower." *J.A.M.A.* 214: 98–100, 1970.

1190. Smith, R. A., Bassett, G. R., Markarian, C. A., *et al.*: "A strategy for health manpower. Reflections on an experience called MEDEX." *J.A.M.A.* 217: 1362–1367, 1971.

1191. Chow, R. K.: "Research and PRIMEX equal improved health services." *Internat. Nurs. Rev.* 19: 319–327, 1972.

1192. Lave, J. R., Lave, L. B., and Morton, T. E.: "The physician's assistant. Exploration of the concept." *Hospitals* 45: 42–50, June 1, 1971.

1193. Ballenger, M. D.: "The physician's assistant. Legal considerations." *Hospitals* 45: 58–61, June 1, 1971.

1194. Lewis, C. E.: "Acceptance of physician's assistants." *Hospitals* 45: 62–64, June 1, 1971.

1195. Andrews, P. M. and Yankauer, A.: "The pediatric nurse practitioner. Part I. Growth of the concept." *Am. J. Nurs.* 71: 504–506, 1971.

1196. Duncan, B., Smith, A. N., and Silver, H. K.: "Comparison of the physical assessment of children by pediatric nurse practitioners and pediatricians." *Am. J. Public Health* 61: 1170–1176, 1971.

1197. Dept. of Health, Education, and Welfare. *Report on Licensure and Related Health Personnel Credentialing.* Washington: U. S. Gov't. Print. Off., 1971.

1198. *Extending the Scope of Nursing Practice. A Report of the Secretary's Committee to Study Extended Roles for Nurses.* Washington: U. S. Gov't. Print. Off., Nov. 1971.

1199. Todd, M. C. and Foy, D. F.: "Current Status of the Physician's Assistant and Related Issues." *J.A.M.A.* 220: 1714–1720, 1972.

1200. Brosseau, J. D.: "MEDEX on the Northern Plains." *Health Services World* 8: 17–19, April 1973.

1201. *Reimbursing Hospitals on Inclusive Rates.* A Report prepared for the National Center for Health Services Research and Development by The Boston Consulting Group, 1970.

1202. Brown, R. E. (Ed.): *Economies of Scale in the Health Services Industry. Proceedings of an Invitational Seminar, May 10–12, 1971, Chicago.* U. S. Dept. of Health, Education, and Welfare, Health Services and Mental Health Administration, National Center for Health Services Research and Development. DHEW Pub. No. (HSM) 73-3009, 1972.

1203. Edwards, S. A. and Astolfi, A.: "Study analyzes effects of merger." *Hospitals* 47: 44–49, Feb. 16, 1973.

1204. Rosenfeld, L. S.: *Ambulatory Care: Planning and Organization.* Springfield, Va.: National Technical Information Service, U. S. Dep't. of Commerce, Report No. PB-204-925, 1971.

1205. Garfield, S.: "The delivery of medical care." *Scientific American* 222: 15–23, Apr. 1970.

1206. Lewis, C. E. and Hassanein, R. S.: "Continuing medical education: An epidemiologic evaluation." *N. Engl. J. Med.* 282: 254–259, 1970.

1207. *Experimental Medical Care Review Organization (EMCRO) Programs.* Arthur D. Little, Inc. Staff. U. S. Dept. of Health, Education, and Welfare, Health Services and Mental Health Administration, National Center for Health Services Research and Development. DHEW Pub. No. (HSM) 73-3017, 1973.

1208. *Guidelines for Hospital Care. A Quality Care Criteria Manual for Mississippi.* Mississippi State Medical Association, 1972.

1209. Gross, P. F.: "Development and implementation of health care technology: The U. S. experience." *Inquiry,* 9: 34–48, June 1972.

1210. White, K. L., Murnaghan, J. H., and Gaus, C. R.: "Technology and health care." *N. Engl. J. Med.* 287: 1223–1227, 1972.

1211. Dobrow, R. J., Fieldman, A., Clason, W. P. C., *et al.*: "Transmission of electrocardiograms from a community hospital for remote computer analysis." *Am. J. Cardiol.* 21: 687–698, 1968.

1212. *A Study of Automated Clinical Laboratory Systems.* Berkeley Scientific Laboratories, Inc., Bethesda, Maryland. Springfield, Va.: National Technical Information Service, U. S. Dep't. of Commerce, Report No. PB 204–923, 1971.

1213. Budd, M. A., Bleich, H., Sherman, H., *et al.*: *The Acquisition of Medical Histories by Questionnaire.* Springfield, Va.: National Technical Information Service, U. S. Dep't. of Commerce, Report No. PB 195–382, 1971.

1214. *Summary Report on Hospital Information Systems.* Health Care Technology Program. National Center for Health Services Research and Development. Springfield, Va.: National Technical Information Service, U. S. Dep't. of Commerce, Report No. PB 189–174, 1969.

1215. Collen, M. F. (Ed.): *Technology and Health Care Systems in the 1980's. Proceedings of a Conference, January 19–21, 1972, San Francisco, California.* U. S. Dept. of Health, Education, and Welfare, Health Services and Mental Health Administration, National Center for Health Services Research and Development, DHEW Pub. No. (HSM) 73-3016, 1973.

1216. *Uniform Hospital Discharge Data Demonstration. Final Report.* Chicago: Health Services Foundation, 1972.

1217. Murnaghan, J. H. (Ed.): "Ambulatory medical care data. Report of the conference on ambulatory medical care records." *Med. Care* 11: No. 2, Supplement, 1973.

1218. Eichhorn, R. L.: *Health Services Data System. The Family Health Survey.* Health Services Research and Training Program. Lafayette, Ind.: Purdue Univ., Undated.

1219. Oreglia, A.: *The Uses of Census Data for Health Services Planning and Management.* Health Services Research and Training Program. Lafayette, Ind.: Purdue Univ., Undated.

1220. Eichhorn, R. L.: *Health Services Data System. Ambulatory Care Data.* Health Services Research and Training Program. Lafayette, Ind.: Purdue Univ., Undated.

1221. Wilson, V. E.: "The role of health statistics in achieving effective health care systems." *Statistical Reporter* No. 73-1, pp. 1–5, July 1972.

References — Chapter VII

1222. "Papers from the Workshop on International Studies of Medical Care. Asilomar, California, Aug. 27–30, 1969." *Med. Care* 9: 193–290, 1971.

1223. Evang, K.: *Health Service, Society, and Medicine.* London: Oxford Univ. Press, 1960.

1224. Abel-Smith, B. J.: *Major Patterns of Financing and Organization of Medical Care in Countries Other than the United States. Social Policy for Health Care.* New York: The New York Academy of Medicine, 1969. pp. 13–33.

1225. Abel-Smith, B. J.: *An International Study of Health Expenditure.* WHO Public Papers No. 32, Geneva: World Health Organization, 1967.

1226. Anderson, O. W.: *Health Care: Can There be Equity? The United States, Sweden and England.* New York: John Wiley and Sons, Inc., 1972.

1227. Mechanic, D.: "Some notes on medical care systems: Contrasts in medical organization between the United States and Great Britain" in *Medical Sociology, A Selective View,* pp. 325–364. (See reference No. 611).

1228. Fry, J.: *Medicine in Three Societies.* New York: American Elsevier Publishing Co., 1970.

1229. Hogarth, J.: *The Payment of Physicians: Some European Comparisons.* New York: Pergamon Press, 1963.

1230. Roemer, M. I.: *The Organization of Medical Care Under Social Security.* Geneva International Labor Office, 1969.

1231. Peterson, O. L., Berfenstam, R., Burgess, A. M., Jr., *et al.*:

"What is value for money in medical care? Experiences in England and Wales, Sweden and the U.S.A." *Lancet* 1: 771–779, 1967.

1232. Liang, M. H., Eichling, P. S., Fine, L. J., *et al.*: "Chinese health care: Determinants of the system." *Am. J. Public Health* 63: 102–110, 1973.

1233. Litman, T. J. and Robins, L.: "Comparative analysis of health care systems — A socio-political approach." *Soc. Sci. and Med.* 5: 573–581, 1971.

1234. White, K. L. and Murnaghan, J. H.: *International Comparisons of Medical Care Utilization: A Feasibility Study.* National Center for Health Statistics, Series 2, No. 33. Washington: U. S. Gov't. Print. Off., 1969.

1235. Rabin, D. (Ed.): "International comparisons of medical care. Preliminary report of the World Health Organization/International Collaborative Study of Medical Care Utilization." *Milbank Mem. Fund Q.* 50: No. 3, Part 2, 1972.

1236. White, K. L., Andjelkovic, D., Pearson, R. J. C., *et al.*: "International comparisons of medical care utilization." *N. Engl. J. Med.* 277: 516–522, 1967.

1237. Bice, T. W. and Kalimo, E.: "Comparisons of health-related attitudes: A cross-national factor analytic study." *Soc. Sci. and Med.* 5: 283–318, 1971.

1238. Haggerty, R. J., Clark, D. W., Hofstra, R., *et al.*: "Health services research in Scandinavia." *Milbank Mem. Fund Q.* 46: 227–261, 1966.

1239. Sanazaro, P. J., Bierman, P., Connors, E. J., *et al.*: "Health services research in Great Britain." *Milbank Mem. Fund Q.* 46: 9–102, 1968.

1240. Lowe, C. R. and McKeown, T.: "The care of the chronic sick. I. Medical and nursing requirements." *Brit. J. Soc. Med.* 3: 110–126, 1949.

1241. Backett, E. M., Shaw, L. A., and Evans, J. C. G.: "Studies of a general practice. (I). Patients' needs and doctors' services; A description of method." *Proc. Roy. Soc. Med.* 46: 707–712, 1953.

1242. Morris, J. N.: *Uses of Epidemiology.* London: E. and S. Livingstone, 1957, pp. 24–34.

1243. Revans, R. W.: Sociological Review Monograph No. 5, 1962.

1244. Townsend, P.: *The Last Refuge.* London: Routledge and Kegan Paul, 1963.

1245. Abel-Smith, B. and Titmuss, R. M.: *The Cost of the National Health Service in England and Wales.* London, 1956.

1246. Medical Research Council (Great Britain): *The Application of Scientific Methods to Industrial and Service Medicine.* London: His Majesty's Stationery Office, 1951.

1247. Bailey, N. T. J.: "Queueing for medical care." *Applied Statistics* 3: 137–145, 1954.

1248. Bailey, N. T. J.: "Calculating the scale of impatient accommodation" in *Towards a Measure of Medical Care. Operational Research in the Health Services. A Symposium.* Published for the Nuffield Provincial Hospitals Trust. London: Oxford Univ. Press, 1962. pp. 55–65.

1249. *Towards a Measure of Medical Care. Operational Research in the Health Services. A Symposium.* Published for the Nuffield Provincial Hospitals Trust. London: Oxford Univ. Press, 1962.

1250. Luch, G. M., Luckman, J., and Smith, J.: *Patients, Hospitals, and Operational Research.* London: Tavistock Publications, 1971.

1251. Logan, W. P. D. and Cushion, A. A.: *Morbidity Statistics from General Practice. Volume I (General),* 1958, *Volume II (Occupation),* 1960, *Volume III (Diseases in General Practice),* 1962. General Register Office, Studies on Medical and Population Subjects No. 14. London: Her Majesty's Stationery Office.

1252. Glover, J. A.: "The incidence of tonsillectomy in school Children." *Proc. Roy. Soc. Med.* 31: 1219–1236, 1938.

1253. Morrell, D. G., Gage, H. G., and Robinson, N. A.: "Patterns of demand in general practice." *J. Roy. College General Practitioners* 19: 331–342, 1970.

1254. Rein, M: "Social class and the utilization of medical care services: A study of British experience under the National Health Service." *Hospitals* 43: 43–54, July 1, 1969.

1255. Cartwright, A. and Marshall, R.: "General practice in 1963. Its conditions, contents and satisfactions." *Med. Care* 3: 69–87, 1965.

1256. Cartwright, A.: *Patients and Their Doctors: A Study of General Practice.* New York: Atherton Press, 1967.

1257. Fry, J.: "Five years of general practice: A study in simple epidemiology." *Brit. Med. J.* 2: 1453–1457, 1957.

1258. Crombie, D. L. and Cross, K. W.: "The contribution of the nurse in general practice." *Brit. J. Prev. Soc. Med.* 11: 41–44, 1957.

1259. Cartwright, A.: *Human Relations and Habitual Care.* London: Routledge and Kegan Paul Ltd., 1964.

1260. Garrett, F. N., Lowe, C. R., and McKeown, T.: "Investigation of the medical and social needs of patients in mental hospitals." *Brit. J. Prev. Soc. Med.* 12: 23–41, 1958.

1261. Ashley, J. S. A., Howlett, A., and Morris, J. N.: "Case-fatality of hyperplasia of the prostate in two teaching and three regional board hospitals." *Lancet* 2: 1308–1311, 1971.

1262. Ferguson, T. and McPhail, A. H.: *Hospital and Community.* London: Oxford Univ. Press, 1954.

1263. Forsyth, G. and Logan, R. F. L.: *A Study of the Case-Load in the Barrow and Furness Group of Hospitals.* Published for the Nuffield Provincial Hospitals Trust. London: Oxford Univ. Press, 1960.

1264. Brotherston, J. H. F.: "The use of the hospital: Review of research in the United Kingdom." *Med. Care* 1: 142–150, 225–231, 1963.

1265. Brotherston, J. H. F.: "Medical care investigation in the Health Service." in *Towards a Measure of Medical Care. Operational Research in the Health Services. A Symposium.* Published for the Nuffield Provincial Hospitals Trust. London: Oxford Univ. Press, 1962, pp. 18–54.

1266. Holland, W. W. and Waller, J.: "Population studies in the London Borough of Lambeth." *Community Med.* 126: 153–156, 1971.

1267. Fairbairn, A. S., Wood, C. H., and Fletcher, C. M.: "Variability in answers to a questionnaire on respiratory symptoms." *Brit. J. Prev. Soc. Med.* 13: 175–193, 1959.

1268. McKeown, T.: *Medicine in Modern Society. Medical Planning*

Based on Evaluation of Medical Achievement. New York: Hafner, 1966.

1269. Cochrane, A. L.: *Effectiveness and Efficiency. Random Reflections on Health Services.* Nuffield Provincial Hospitals Trust, 1972.

1270. Nuffield Provincial Hospitals Trust. *Studies in the Functions and Designs of Hospitals.* London: Oxford Univ. Press, 1955 (Ch. 7).

1271. Knox, E. G.: "Cervical cytology: A scrutiny of the evidence." in *Problems and Progress in Medical Care. Second Series.* Edited by G. McLachlan. Published for the Nuffield Provincial Hospitals Trust. London: Oxford Univ. Press, 1966, pp. 279–309.

1272. McLachlan, G. and Shegog, R. (Eds.): *Computers in the Service of Medicine: Essays on Current Research and Applications.* Nuffield Provincial Hospitals Trust. London: Oxford Univ. Press, 1968.

1273. Downie, B. N.: *The Elderly in Scottish Hospitals 1961–1966.* Scottish Health Service Studies No. 21. Scottish Home and Health Department, 1972.

1274. Gruer, R.: *Outpatient Services in the Scottish Border Counties.* Scottish Health Service Studies No. 23. Scottish Home and Health Department, 1972.

1275. Purola, T.: *The Utilization of General Hospital Services in Finland, 1960.* Health Services Research of the National Board of Health in Finland. Vol. I, 1966.

1276. Kalimo, E.: "Medical care research in the planning of social security in Finland." *Med. Care* 9: 304–310, 1971.

1277. Häro, A. S. and Purola, T.: "Planning and health policy in Finland." *Internat. J. Health Services* 2: 23–34, 1972.

1278. Purola, T., Kalimo, E., Nyman, K., *et al.*: "National health insurance in Finland: Its impact and evaluation." *Internat. J. Health Services* 3: 69–80, 1973.

1279. Jungner, G. and Jungner, I.: "The health screening in Värmland" in *Surveillance and Early Diagnosis in General Practice.* London: Office of Health Economics, 1966.

1280. Jungner, G.: "Data processing in the clinical laboratory" in *Proceedings on Automated Data Processing in Hospitals: International Conference in Elsinore, 1966.* Stockholm: Swedish Council of Hospital Operation Rationalization, 1966. p. 235.

1281. Fritz, H., Köhler, L., and Scherstén, B.: "Assessment of subnormal urinary glucose as an indicator of bacteriuria in population studies. An investigation of 3,911 subjects between the age of 4 and 65 years." *Acta Med. Scand.* Supp. 504, 1969.

1282. Smedby, B.: "The role of the sociologist in medical care research." *Acta Socio-Medica Scand.* 3: 187-196, 1971.

1283. RUPRO 69. Summary in English. National Board of Health and Welfare, Stockholm, 1969.

1284. *The Activities of SPRI 1970-1971.* The Swedish Planning and Rationalization Institute of Health and Social Services. Stockholm, 1971.

1285. Badgley, R. F. and Wolfe, S.: *Doctors' Strike: Medical Care and Conflict in Saskatchewan.* Toronto: Macmillan Co. of Canada, Ltd., and New York: Atherton Press, Inc., 1967. pp. 102-103.

1286. Wolfe, S. and Badgley, R. F.: "The family doctor." *The Milbank Mem. Fund Q.* 50: No. 2, Part 2, 1972.

1287. Royal Commission on Health Services. 2 vols. Ottawa: Queen's Printer, 1964.

1288. Hanson, E. J.: *The Public Finance Aspects of Health Services in Canada.* Royal Commission on Health Services. Ottawa: Queen's Printer, 1963.

1289. Judek, S.: *Medical Manpower in Canada.* Royal Commission on Health Services. Ottawa: Queens Printer, 1964.

1290. McFarlane, B. A.: *Dental Manpower in Canada.* Royal Commission on Health Services. Ottawa: Queens Printer, 1965.

1291. Department of National Health and Welfare. *Provision, Distribution, and Cost of Drugs in Canada.* Royal Commission on Health Services. Ottawa: Queens Printer, 1965.

1292. Jungfer, C. C. and Last, J. M.: "Clinical performance in Australian general practice." *Med. Care* 2: 71-83, 1965.

1293. Lichtner, S. and Pflanz, M.: "Appendectomy in the Federal Republic of Germany. Epidemiology and medical care patterns." *Med. Care* 9: 311-330, 1971.

Bibliography of Bibliographies

Part A — Health Services Research Bibliographies

Aday, L. A. and Eichhorn, R. L.: *The Utilization of Health Services: Indices and Correlates — A Research Bibliography 1972.* Dept. of Health, Education, and Welfare, Health Services and Mental Health Administration, National Center for Health Services Research and Development. DHEW Pub. No. (HSM) 73-3003.

Altman, I., Anderson, A. J., and Barker, K.: *Methodology in Evaluating the Quality of Medical Care: An Annotated Selected Bibliography, 1965-1968.* Pittsburgh: Univ. of Pittsburgh Press, 1969.

Battistella, R. M. and Weil, T. P.: *Health Care Organization — Bibliography and Guide Book.* Washington: Association of University Programs in Hospital Administration, 1971.

Carmody, J.: *Ethical Issues in Health Services — A Report and Annotated Bibliography.* Washington: U. S. DHEW/PHS/HSMHA/National Center for Health Services Research and Development, Report HSRD 70-32, 1970.

Cohen, L. K.: "Bibliography — Social Sciences and Dentistry, 1955-1970" in *Toward a Sociology of Dentistry.* Edited by R. M. O'Shea and L. K. Cohen. *The Milbank Mem. Fund Q.* 49: No. 3, Part 2, 1971. pp. 171-332.

Computer Horizons, Inc.: *Health Services Research Journal Bibliography.* Prepared for the National Center for Health Services Research and Development, HSMHA/USDHEW, April 1971.

Cromwell, D. F., Brown, Q. R., and Kurzenabe, R. A.: *Selected*

References: Automation of the Health Care Field. U.S. DHEW/ HSMHA/National Center for Health Services Research and Development, Health Care Technology Program. (Processed). Oct. 1, 1968.

Edwards, S. A. and Hurst, O. R.: *Health Care System Variables. An Annotated Bibliography.* San Antonio: Health Resources Planning Unit, Texas Hospital Association and Trinity University, 1969; Supp. 1, 1970; Supp. 2, 1971.

Fischer, E. F., Jr., and Sherrick, J. C.: *Guidelines for Health Services Research and Development: Sharing, Centralization, and Consolidation of Laboratory and Diagnostic Services: Bibliography.* Health Services Research Center of the Hospital Research and Education Trust and Northwestern Univ. DHEW Pub. No. (HSM) 72-3036. Washington: U. S. Gov't. Print. Off., 1972.

Freeman, H. E. and Reeder, L. G.: "Medical Sociology: A review of the literature." *Am. Sociol. Rev.* 22: 73–81, 1957.

Gelman, A. C.: *Multiphasic Health Testing Systems: Reviews and Annotations.* U. S. Dept. of Health, Education, and Welfare, Health Services and Mental Health Administration, National Center for Health Services Research and Development, Report HSRD 71-1, 1971.

Josie, G. H.: "Research methods in public health: An annotated bibliography with special reference to Canadian problems and experience." *Canadian J. Public Health* 54: 33–42, 1963.

Lave, J. R., Lave, L. B., and Morton, T. E.: "Suggested readings on paramedics: A survey of the issues." *Hospitals* 45: 50–51, June 1, 1971.

Pearsall, M.: *Medical Behavioral Science: A Selected Bibliography of Cultural Anthropology, Social Psychology, and Sociology in Medicine.* Lexington, Ky.: Univ. of Kentucky Press, 1963.

Reilly, M. J.: *Drug Information: Literature Review of Needs, Resources, and Services.* Prepared for National Center for Health Services Research and Development. DHEW Pub. No. (HSM) 72-3013. Washington: U. S. Gov't. Print. Off., 1972.

Richards, N. D. and Cohen, L. K. (Eds.): *Social Sciences and Dentistry: A Critical Bibliography.* The Hague: Federation Dentaire Internationale, A. Sijthoff, 1971.

Rosen, G. and Wellin, E.: "A bookshelf on the social sciences and public health." *Am. J. Public Health* 49: 441–454, 1959.

Simmons, O. G.: "Social Research in Health and Medicine: A Bibliography" in *Handbook of Medical Sociology*. Edited by H. E. Freeman, S. Levine, and L. G. Reeder. Englewood Cliffs, N. J.: Prentice-Hall, Inc., 1963, pp. 523–584.

Tenney, J. B.: *The Content of Medical Practice — A Research Bibliography*. Baltimore: The Johns Hopkins Univ., School of Hygiene and Public Health, 1969.

U. S. DHEW/PHS/NIH/Division of Nursing: *Research in Nursing 1955–1968*. Public Health Service Pub. No. 1356, Revised 1969. Washington: U. S. Gov't. Print. Off., 1970.

White, P. E. and Vlasak, G. J.: *Inter-Organizational Research in Health: Bibliography (1960–1970)*. Prepared for National Center for Health Services Research and Development. DHEW Pub. No. (HSM) 72-3028. Washington: U. S. Gov't. Print. Off., 1972.

Williamson, J. W. and Tenney, J. B.: *Health Services Research Bibliography 1972–1973*. Prepared for National Center for Health Services Research and Development. DHEW Pub. No. (HSM) 72-3034. Washington: U. S. Gov't. Print. Off., 1972.

Young, M. A. C.: *Review of Research and Studies Related to Health Education Practice (1961–1966): What People Know, Believe and Do About Health*. Health Education Monographs No. 23. New York: Society of Public Health Educators, Inc., 1967.

Bibliography of Bibliographies

Part B—Other Books, Monographs, and Articles with Extensive Research Bibliographies

Abdellah, F. G. and Levine, E.: *Better Patient Care Through Nursing Research*. New York: The Macmillan Co., 1965.

Andersen, R.: *A Behavioral Model of Families' Use of Health Services*. Univ. of Chicago, Center for Health Administration Studies, Graduate School of Business, Research Series 25. Chicago, 1968.

Balfe, B. E., Peterson, K. W., and Steinwald, A. B.: *Resource Material on the Socioeconomic and Business Aspects of Medicine*. Chicago: American Medical Association, Center for Health Services R&D, 1971.

Barro, A. R.: "Survey and Evaluation of Approaches to Physician Performance Measurement." *J. Med. Educ.* 48: 1047–1093, 1973.

Barnett, G. O.: "Computers in Patient Care." *N. Engl. J. Med.* 279: 1321–1327, 1968.

Brook, R. H.: *Quality of Care: Assessment: A Comparison of Five Methods of Peer Review*. Dept. of Health Education, and Welfare, Public Health Service, Health Resources Administration, Bureau of Health Services Research and Evaluation, DHEW Pub. No. HRA-74-3100, 1973.

Budd, M. A., Bleich, H., Boyd, G. E., *et al.*: *The Acquisition of Automated Medical Histories by Questionnaire*. Dept. of Health, Education, and Welfare, Public Health Service, Health Services and Mental Health Administration, National Center for Health Services Research and Development, PB 195–832, 1970.

301

Donabedian, A.: "An evaluation of prepaid group practice." *Inquiry* 6: 3–27, Sept. 1969.

Donabedian, A.: *Medical Care Appraisal — Quality and Utilization.* (Vol. II of *A Guide to Medical Care Administration.* New York: American Public Health Association, 1969.

Georgopoulos, B. S.: *Organization Research on Health Institutions.* Ann Arbor: Institute for Social Research, Univ. of Michigan, 1972.

Mainland, D. (Ed.): *Health Services Research.* New York: Milbank Memorial Fund, 1967.

Mossey, J. and Nicholson, S.: *Non-Physician Personnel in Ambulatory Child Health Care: A Review.* Univ. of North Carolina, Health Services Research Center, Chapel Hill, 1970.

Neuhauser, D.: *The Relationship Between Administrative Activities and Hospital Performance.* Univ. of Chicago, Center for Health Administration Studies, Research Series 28. Chicago, 1971.

Reader, G. G. and Goss, M. E. W.: "Medical sociology with particular reference to the study of hospitals." *Transactions of the Fourth World Congress of Sociology,* 2: 139–152, 1959.

Reader, G. G. and Goss, M. E. W.: "The Sociology of Medicine" in *Sociology Today.* Edited by R. K. Merton, L. Broom, and L. S. Cottrell, Jr. New York: Basic Books, Inc., 1959. pp. 229–246.

Richardson, W. C.: *Ambulatory Use of Physicians' Services in Response to Illness Episodes in a Low-Income Neighborhood.* Univ. of Chicago, Center for Health Administration Studies, Research Series 29. Chicago, 1971.

Rosenfeld, L. S.: *Ambulatory Care: Planning and Organization.* Springfield, Va.: National Technical Information Service, U. S. Dep't. of Commerce, Report No. PB 204-925, 1971.

Simmons, L. W. and Wolff, H. G.: *Social Science in Medicine.* New York: Russell Sage Foundation, 1954. pp. 201–246.

Weeks, L. E. and Griffith, J. R. (Eds.): *Progressive Patient Care — An Anthology.* Ann Arbor: Univ. of Michigan, 1964.

"Bibliography on Observer Error and Variation" in *Medical Surveys and Clinical Trials. 2d. ed.* Edited by L. J. Witts. London: Oxford Univ. Press, 1964. pp. 43–45.

Index of Authors

(by page)